W9-CDO-939

Knihovně
Opatství Sv. Prokopa,
Lisle, Ill.,

Aleš Hrdlička

CHILDREN WHO RUN ON ALL FOURS

*And Other Animal-like Behaviors
in the Human Child*

Frontispiece

PLATE 1.—A group of negro children, Johannesburg, South Africa. (*Photograph donated by the Rand Daily Mail, Johannesburg.*)

CHILDREN WHO RUN ON ALL FOURS

And Other Animal-like Behaviors in the Human Child

BY

ALEŠ HRDLIČKA, M.D., Sc.D., D.Sc. Nat.

*Curator, Division of Physical Anthropology, U. S.
National Museum, Smithsonian Institution*

WHITTLESEY HOUSE

McGRAW-HILL BOOK COMPANY, INC.

NEW YORK · 1931

Copyright 1931, *by the*

McGRAW-HILL BOOK COMPANY, INC.
All rights reserved. This book, or parts thereof,
may not be reproduced in any form without
permission of the publishers.

FIRST EDITION

155.4
H873c

Published by
WHITTLESEY HOUSE
Trade Division of the
McGRAW-HILL BOOK COMPANY, INC.
370 SEVENTH AVENUE, NEW YORK

Published with the Permission of the
Secretary of the Smithsonian Institution

Printed in the United States of America by
The Maple Press Company, York, Pa.

31632

APR 20 1941 gift

RESPECTFULLY DEDICATED TO THE
AMERICAN MOTHERS AND ALL OTHERS
WHO BY THEIR PAINSTAKING AND
INTELLIGENT AID HAVE MADE THESE
STUDIES POSSIBLE

PREFACE

CHARITY should begin at home—and so should knowledge. Man is endeavoring, and properly so, to penetrate the mysteries of the outward universe, yet there is also the inner, his own, universe, to parts of which in conscious or general knowledge he is still a stranger. And one of the least known realms of this more intimate world of his is that of his infants.

Who can say that he thoroughly knows the human infant? Certainly not the doctor, who is concerned only about the child's diseases. Nor the investigator, whose scope of work is usually limited by many conditions. And certainly not the average father, who remains, more or less, but a relative to his own progeny. Nor even the mother, for at best she knows only her own child, and that only to a certain extent, according to her intelligence, instruction, and possibilities of observation.

Yet what can there be of more interest in the world than the human child? It is a wonderful unfolding living bundle of inherited endowments, physical, functional and mental, that have been accumulated through a course of developments reaching not merely to the limits of its million years of human and near-human ancestry, but still farther back of this, very much farther, to the very beginnings of organic life.

The parents see in their infant a being exclusively their own, whereas, as a matter of fact, that new being is barely a reflection of their distinctive selves. It is partly, through inheritance, a child of its grandparents, of its great-grandparents, and, in diminishing degree or part, of all of its ancestors, back to the times even when these were not yet human, and still farther back into the depths of the organic kingdom.

What wonder then that this infant manifests again and again activities, inclinations, and other characteristics, to which its parents are more or less strangers and which are not understood. They are mostly overlooked, or explained away as seems most plausible and in time generally forgotten or nearly forgotten. They are taken as so many to-be-expected and mostly immaterial peculiarities of child life. Most are misunderstood and "thought nothing of" even by the mothers. And, where striking, they are seldom reported outside of a circle of good friends. So they have passed on largely unrecorded and unstudied. What scientific attention the child has received so far was directed essentially, on one side, to its physical development and growth and, on the other, to its mental progress. The behaviors reminiscent of the far past have remained thus far almost as if they had not existed.

A detailed, intensive, prolonged, and racially generalized study of the world of the human infant will be essentially a new and, according to indications, a most promising and fascinating field of research. This work will give an inkling of its richness. Begun over thirty years ago with the observation of an Indian child running like a little animal on all fours, it has gradually brought to light a whole bevy of highly interesting manifestations that recall part after part of our prehuman background. How much more there is can hardly be suggested.

The case just referred to was so natural, striking, and unexpected that it made a deep impression on me, and since then I have been watching for such children. But new instances were scarce. I could not apply myself directly to the subject, and incidental cases came few and far between. In the course of a score of years I saw only two more such infants, one typical, the other approaching a quadruped; and I found two typical cases pictured casually in books. It seemed to me that surely other such cases must have been observed by someone and reported, but for a time I could find no reference to the matter.

Then I decided to publish my few observations. This was done in the summer of 1927. The initial report proved evidently of interest and was soon made widely known through the *Science Service*, the magazines, and the public press. And before long there began to come letters telling me of other instances of such and other curious behaviors. This led to two further papers on the subject. The matter, thanks to the public press, the *Science Service*, *Science*, the *Literary Digest*, and other magazines and media, received then a very wide attention, reaching even to Europe; and then came a whole series of new reports of cases by parents, one more absorbing than the other.

The whole subject assumed now totally unexpected proportions and, with the accumulating details, an ever increasing interest and substance. It was seen that we were confronted here with a phenomenon not as rare as has before been supposed; that this phenomenon was evidently of distinct biological significance; and that, in addition to the quadruped-like progression, there is a whole line of occasional curious manifestations in the human infant, almost unknown or known but imperfectly to science, unknown to more than a few individual mothers, and recalling or reviving ancient, prehuman habits.

With these new and broadening horizons, steps were taken to systematize the information as far as possible through regular questionnaires, and appeals were sent out to men working among primitive peoples for reports of new cases. Especial hope was had in the missionaries in such parts of the world as Africa, Melanesia, etc., for presumably they come into a rather intimate contact with the aborigines. The results of these inquiries were highly gratifying on the part of the American public, as far as this could be reached; but they proved disappointing with most of the missionaries, some of whom even resented the inquiry as a sort of obloquy to their primitive friends. The difficulties that may arise in the search for facts such as those with which we are here concerned may be illustrated by at least one of the responses. The latter came from a missionary in one of the Pacific islands. It reads:

DEAR SIR:
   Your request of April 11, for personal observations of actions, antics, etc., of native children to prove a lower animal ancestry, came to hand in due course but I was unable to give it attention at that time.
   I fear that my reply will be disappointing to you, for I could not in any way assist in strengthening the theory of man's evolution from lower animals. True, children creep and crawl and climb, but I see in those actions no proof at all of relationship with animals that habitually go on all fours or that climb trees all their lives.
   I believe fully in the Bible account of Creation as a Divine act of God, accomplished in six days, and I have not yet found anything to disprove it. Nor can those who stand by the Bible be classed as ignorant of the findings of biologists and geologists.
   I am sorry to disappoint you, but I find nothing here to report. I would not care to have my name appear in print in

connection with any work that would encourage the belief that there was not in the beginning a literal Creation.

I beg to remain,

Respectfully yours

The total effect of the efforts made to date and of the aid received, is nevertheless a highly gratifying mass of reports, reaching well into the hundreds. These reports came mainly from the mothers of the children concerned. They are faithful and precious notes, picturing all as only mothers could, and giving details that open vistas in new directions. The most cordial thanks are tendered hereby to these mothers for the service rendered; and thanks once more also to all others who helped in these studies.

In addition to the reports it was possible in a large majority of the cases to obtain photographs of the child "in action." Most of these regrettably show the child with some clothing—for the pictures were not always taken in warm weather, or for scientific purposes. Yet they teach much, and so many are here reproduced, even if there is considerable similarity in them, for this very similarity is of importance.

The first part of this volume is devoted to the tabulation and analysis of the data. The second part gives the individual reports. They are given as received, for they exceed in value anything that could have been written by an outside observer.

With all its relative wealth of information this presentation, it is felt, is but the opening chapter of the more obscure parts of the field of child behavior. It draws aside a curtain that thus far has covered a whole range of spontaneous and more or less transitory manifestations of phylogenetic significance. It now appears that just as there are in the ontogeny of the human embryo and child physical "recapitulations," so there are also those of behavioristic nature, and of their mental connections. The whole subject presents a most attractive field for further investigation.

Such investigations ought to be facilitated by one gratifying fact which comes out with conclusive clearness from the present records. This is the mass of evidence that the children showing for a shorter or longer time such reminiscent phenomena, more particularly the quadruped locomotion, are not the feeble-minded or feeble-bodied, but rather the physically as well as mentally superiors. Such manifestations, therefore, are plainly not the marks or tokens of any defectiveness, but rather of an abundance of physical and mental energy, which is further attested by the exceedingly small morbidity and mortality among such children.

It is for these reasons that I have not hesitated to give the full names of the parents, for these may be proud rather than ashamed of such fine, robust, and promising infants.

This book cannot possibly be the concluding word on the subject. Its chief object is that of a door-opener to a fresh and most interesting field of scientific inquiry. It will stimulate, it is hoped, further attention to the peculiarities of child behavior and all further reports will be gratefully received. These reports should be made wherever possible by the mother of the child, in her own wording, and with all possible details. For a guidance and uniform comprehensiveness the following items should be considered: (1) report by (name, relation to child); (2) nationality; (3) locality; (4) sex of child reported upon; (5) age of child reported upon; (6) what child is it in the family (first, second, or which); (7) health and mentality of child; (8) nature of peculiar behavior (give in your own words all possible details on the subject); (9) peculiarities of behavior that were observed in other children or members of the family. The reports as to 7, 8 and 9 should be given by the mothers as circumstantially as only they can make them.

Photos.—The most serviceable are snapshots of the child "in action," outdoors, but *without clothing*. Clothing, even a napkin, spoils the picture. Indoor photos are also valuable, though they seldom equal in interest those taken in free nature.

Most common additional peculiarities of behavior are unusual tendencies to climbing; holding to the mother; assumption of peculiar, more or less animal-like postures in sleeping; carrying things in the teeth; etc.

The more relevant parts of the letters received to date are given in full. They are genuine intimate human documents of much value. And they contain much additional matter of more or less importance to that utilized in the analytical portion of this volume. I never tire of reading the letters. They form most justifiably the bulk of this book. They are never dull or boring. And they never repeat each other, for every child is a unit of its own, with his own interesting peculiarities. Aside from their information the letters carry also some, at least, of the psychology of the informant. They collectively represent no small time or effort. I am deeply thankful for all they convey, as well as, in many cases, for their spirit, flavor, and simple honesty. I ask for more of them of the same qualities. For I shall never be willing or able to give up an earnest interest in the studies of the human infant.

ALEŠ HRDLIČKA.

WASHINGTON, D. C.,
    October, 1930.

LIST OF CONTENTS

LIST OF CONTENTS

. xvi .

LIST OF CONTENTS

LIST OF ILLUSTRATIONS

PLATES

. xix .

LIST OF ILLUSTRATIONS

PART I

HISTORICAL AND ANALYTICAL

CHILDREN WHO RUN ON ALL FOURS

HISTORICAL NOTES

THE history of the field of investigation with which we are here concerned is meager. Curiously, it appears to be a large and highly interesting corner of the realm of knowledge that to date has remained almost unexplored. When I undertook more seriously the study of the child in these lines, it seemed that certainly someone somewhere must have written on the subject with some adequacy. I am still inclined to think that in some language if not the English, there may be some communication dealing comprehensively with the all-fours and connected manifestations of the human infant. But I have not found any, and though since three years now the subject has received very wide publicity both in this part of the world and abroad, no such communication has been brought to my attention. All that I have found are incidental notes or illustrations, with few small exceptions.

A great deal of attention has been given to the mental and physical development of the child. From Rousseau in France, Charles Darwin in England, Preyer, Sigismund, and others in Germany, and Henry P. Bowditch with G. Stanley Hall in this country—not to go farther back—there are scores of books and many hundreds of articles that deal more or less intensively with the mental and physical development of the child. A majority of these deal in the main with childhood rather than infancy (if the latter term is restricted to the normal nursing period), yet the infant, too, has received considerable attention. In a series of these publications, culminating in such thoroughly scientific reports as that of Miss Shinn of California, there are detailed notes on individual infants and children from their birth onwards. In practically all the contributions to the study of the infant the authors deal also with his motor manifestations.

Time and again these accounts occupy themselves with the grasping and climbing propensities of the infant, and with his various modes of locomotion. They approach the very threshold of the complex of running on all fours, even recording or mentioning this in some instances—and then the whole matter seems to dissolve, there is nothing further.

The observations and studies here dealt with are, therefore, not only original but in a large measure pioneer in nature, which in these advanced times of human knowledge is a rare happening and privilege.

Personal Experience, and References in Literature.—My first contact with the phenomena to which this volume is devoted did not come until 1898, after eight years of considerable medical experience. And this contact was wholly accidental. In the spring of 1898 we were with Carl Lumholtz on a joint expedition among the Sierra Madre tribes of Mexico. We reached the interesting Huichol tribe, in the heart of the mountains in the State of Jalisco, and here one day we saw an Indian child running on all fours. His action was so characteristic and so unique to me that it made a deep impression. (See Fig. 22, p. 393.)

We got no details, for the mother knew but a few words of Spanish, but Lumholtz took a snapshot of the child and in 1902 published this, with a few remarks on such occurrences.[1] His note reads as follows:

Infants, in going on all fours, do not put their knees to the ground as white babies mostly do. It is a curious sight to see these youngsters before they can stand up, moving in this way almost like monkeys and very fast, but, of course, for no great distance at a time, as they like to keep near their mothers. I took instantaneous photographs of some of them, persuading the mother to make her child creep by stepping aside and calling it. At Galup railroad station, in New Mexico, I noticed a Zuñi baby going on all fours in this same way.

This Huichol child left a lasting impression on me and since then I have been watching for such cases, without however, for a long time, giving the subject special attention. But though traveling a good deal and visiting many peoples I saw none until 1925 and 1926.

In 1925 I made an extensive trip to India, Australia, and South Africa. While in Australia, I came across two publications on the natives, in each of which I found an incidental illustration of a child running on all fours.

The first book was "Across Australia" by Baldwin Spencer and F. J. Gillen.[2] There is a picture of an aboriginal child, from Arunta,

[1] In LUMHOLTZ, CARL, "Unknown Mexico," chap. II, p. 90.
[2] Fig. 71, facing p. 188, London, 1912.

Central Australia, learning to walk, showing an infant of a little over one year of age progressing typically on all fours. The authors give no data concerning the condition. The only note relating to it being that the Australian infant, "at first it toddles about on all fours." The same picture is reproduced in W. D. Hambly's, "Origins of Education among Primitive Peoples."[1] (See Fig. 24, p. 397.)

The second picture of an aboriginal Australian child progressing on all fours I found in the possession of Dr. Herbert Basedow, of Adelaide. A copy of this picture was kindly sent to me later by Dr. Basedow. It is an Australian aboriginal child from Central Australia. But there are no details. (See Fig. 25, p. 397.)

The third case of that year I saw myself in Rhodesia. I had a chance to visit a village of one of the Bantu tribes near the Victoria Falls. Here I saw a child, not much over one year of age, moving on all fours, but the feet were bent so that it moved really on the upright hands and the knees. The walk was less free and less animal-like than in some other cases, nevertheless there was the impression of a quadruped. It was moving fast, not just trying, or crawling. (See Plate V, p. 35.)

The next case was encountered, quite accidentally again, right at home.

On Oct. 26, 1926, in the evening, at the Union Station, Washington, while waiting for a train, I saw near by a young woman, evidently a poorer country woman or mountaineer, with a child on her lap. Before long the child wanted to go down and was lowered to the floor, where it promptly and without difficulty got up on all fours, and ran about thus, much like a little animal. It moved actively, though not actually running. Went thus again and again, on all fours, all limbs upright, only knees bent little forward, hands and feet applied very nearly flat to the floor. Now and then would turn and sit down, but soon be up again. Could barely yet stand alone. The whole performance was spontaneous and almost uncanny. The mother was evidently accustomed to the procedure, nevertheless did not seem to be wholly at ease when she noticed that I watched the child; enough so to prevent me from closer questioning. I found, however, that the child was a boy, fourteen months old. He looked healthy and normal. There was no chance of obtaining a picture.

[1] Opp. p. 38, London, 1926.

I then decided to take up the subject more actively. The first step was to make inquiries as to any publications on such cases. I found but little in the more strictly scientific literature, but came across two remarkable statements in the records of African explorers and observers.

One of the most able as well as sincere of amateur African students was Prof. R. L. Garner, American, who for many years carried on studies of the apes and also the natives in the region of Fernan Vaz. He was my old and esteemed friend. After he died, Jan. 22, 1920, I received at his wish many of his unpublished notes, and among these found one, written apparently many years ago, of a peculiar interest in connection with my studies. It reads as follows:

Simian Acts of African Children.—One of the most simian-like acts that I have observed in African babies and that seems to be comparatively rare in babies of the white race, while universal among the anthropoid apes, is the manner of learning to walk. Newly born African babies almost invariably have the habit or tendency of lying with the knees expanded and the legs drawn up, usually crossed, and the soles of the feet turned obliquely upward. In the early stages of walking the African baby more frequently walks on hands and feet exactly the same as the young ape, then upon its knees. I have seen as many as three negro babies at one time, all less than one year old, playing about the open plaza of a village, and every one of them moving in this ape-like fashion; and the habit usually continues until they are able to walk upright alone.

Another striking feature of very young negro children in their first attempts to walk erect is that of pressing the weight of the body on the outer or distal side of the foot, curving the inner side and grasping at the ground with their toes. This is conspicuous in almost every negro infant that I have watched, and I have observed many of them. The same tendency may be easily noticed in white children, but it is much less pronounced and disappears at a much earlier stage.

In their early efforts to walk alone the negro baby also elevates the arms and waves them as the apes do, while the white babe holds the arms below the level of the shoulder.

The second note of interest occurs in "The Last Journals of David Livingstone in Central Africa":[1]

"Manyuema children do not creep, as European children do, on their knees, but begin by putting forward one foot and using one

[1] Edited by Horace Walker, p. 381, New York, 1875.

knee. Generally a Manyuema child uses both feet and both hands, but never both knees: one Arab child did the same; he never crept, but got up on both feet, holding on till he could walk."

As to references to the subject in the more scientific literature on the child, some mentions of the all-fours phenomenon have doubtless escaped my attention and I should be grateful for references to such. But the absence in the available writings of allusions to such works or reports by others can only mean, it would seem, that nothing of importance has appeared in these connections.

The first distinct mention of the progression on all fours in infants, in what may be regarded as fairly modern study of the child, is that of B. Perez, in his well-known book on "The First Three Years of Childhood." [1] It is to this effect: "At a year old, they take kindly, moreover, to the rôle of quadruped, which they find very convenient."

In the late eighties Preyer in his also well-known "The Soul of the Child" (a number of editions) mentions the subject. In the fourth edition[2] we read of his own child that it "creeped regularly but on one knee and it learned also, only after it could walk, to move forwards on the hands and feet." Preyer regards all the methods of locomotion of the infant as essentially hereditary and instinctive,[3] not imitative; and those movements that call for the least exertion will tend to prevail.[4]

Compayré, in 1902, quotes Preyer as saying that "walking on all fours is the natural preparatory school for normal walking."[5]

[1] Published in several editions in French; in 1885 transl. into English.

[2] P. 177, Leipzig, 1895.

[3] *Ibid.*, p. 183.

[4] *"Im Ganzen zeigen die Beobachtungen über das sitzen, stehen, kriechen, rutschen, laufen, geben, springen, klettern, werfen, dass diese Bewegungen überwiegend instinctiv sind. Sie werden nicht anerzogen. Will man sie erlernt nennen, so muss man zugeben, dass sie nur zum kleinsten Theil durch Nachahmung erlernt werden, denn ein Kind, welches Niemanden rutschen, springen, klettern, werfen sieht, wird unfehlbar diese Bewegungen ausführen. Die Vorfahren des Menschen müssen dieselben vorzugsweise nützlich gefunden haben, so dass sie sich vererbten. Dabei blieben, wie es scheint, diejenigen harmonischen Bewegungen am häufigsten im Gebrauch, welche, wie die der Augenmuskeln, mit der geringsten Anstrengung am meisten leisten."*—PREYER, W., "Die Seele des Kindes," 4th ed., 462 pp., Leipzig, 1895.

[5] COMPAYRÉ, G., "Development of the Child in Later Infancy," p. 137, New York, 1902.

H. Ploss in his well-known valuable work "Das Kind"[1] refers briefly to the above work of Livingstone though from a German translation but deals with the matter in only a by-the-way manner. He himself says, in speaking of the ways in which a child begins to walk, that, as the child endeavors to reach objects of which to get hold in its efforts to raise itself, "if these are beyond its reach it will slide and crawl on all fours to reach them."[2] In connection with Livingstone's report Ploss merely remarks "so kriechen nur Einzelne bei uns" (thus creep only isolated children among us); adding that it is one of the duties of anthropology to determine the causes of the racial differences in this respect, *i.e.*, whether such differences are due to some special development of the body or rest on inborn conditions of the nervous system.

B. Sigismund,[3] and after him K. Groos,[4] just touch the matter without sufficient precision or comprehensiveness. The note, in Groos' translation, to which he does not add, is: "Soon he becomes more active, sure, and courageous, and learns to maintain his center of gravity on three supports while he lifts the fourth member for his next step forward, for at first the child raises but one limb at a time, though he soon learns to use the right hand and left foot together."

In 1899, Miss Shinn[5] reports briefly an instance of progression on all fours in the infant under her observation: "Early in the month (307th day) I had noticed a tendency to rise imperfectly to hands and feet, instead of hands and knees, in creeping fast. The tendency increased throughout the month, and on the 323d day I noticed that every time the baby started off it was on hands and feet, but that after a few steps she would drop to hands and knees. She seemed to like the movement on hands and feet better, but to be unable to keep it up as long." There is no discussion of the matter.

About the most direct and best reference to the motor manifestations in the infant, including the going on all fours, is that of Trettien, a pupil of G. Stanley Hall and written with the assistance of Hall. It does not go any deeper into the subject of running on all

---

[1] Chap. II, pp. 120–121, 2d ed.

[2] *Und wenn die Gegenstände welche das Kind zu ergreifen sucht "sich ausserhalb des Bereiches befinden, so rutscht und kriecht es auf allen Vieren zu ihnen hin."*

[3] "Kind und Welt," p. 70, 1897.

[4] "The Play of Man," p. 79, New York, 1901.

[5] SHINN, MILICENT W., "Notes on the Development of a Child," "Univ. of Calif. Studies," vol. I, nos. 3 and 4, p. 356, Berkeley, 1899.

fours than do other authors, but gives what so far are the only statistical data on the performance. His statement,[1] which deserves to be quoted somewhat in full, is as follows:

A study of 150 children (males and females equally divided), shows that 60 per cent crept while of the remaining, 30 per cent moved along by hitching, 7 per cent by rolling, 3 per cent by crawling, swimming, or some other means peculiar to the individual. Fifty per cent of the creepers moved forward on their hands and knees, moving their limbs on the opposite corners of the body together. Twenty per cent moved forward on their hands and knees but moved the limbs on the same side of the body at the same time as in pacing. Nine per cent walked on their hands and feet with the limbs on the opposite corners of the body moving together, except one little girl moved the limbs on the same side together. One little boy planted the feet out, aside of the tracks of his hands. Twelve per cent (7 males and 4 females) walked on their hands and dragged the body and legs, and 6 per cent (3 males and 2 females) crept backwards. One used his hands only in pushing the body back to the desired spot. The remaining 3 per cent had movements which were distinct from any other or combinations of other movements of creeping, such as creeping on the hands and knees, the hands alternating and the knees moving together as in jumping; creeping by the use of both arms and one leg while dragging the other leg; or by the use of only one arm and one leg.

Hermann Dekker, in his interesting "Natural History of the Child,"[2] comes near the subject; points out the ancestral reminiscences of the infant's musculature; but the category of manifestations here to be dealt with just escapes him, with one exception to be noted in its place later.

Tracy and Stimpfl[3] barely mention the on all-fours habit: "Hitherto his locomotion has been only in the form of creeping (which is performed in a great variety of ways, some children paddling straight ahead on all fours, like little quadrupeds, some hitching along in an indescribable manner on their haunches, and some going backwards, crab-fashion); . . . Sometimes a child who has learnt to walk, partially or wholly, reverts for a season to creeping, for no apparent reason."

[1] TRETTIEN, AUGUST W., "Creeping and Walking," *Amer. Jour. Psychol.*, vol. XII, no. 1, p. 31, 1900.

[2] "Naturgeschichte des Kindes," Stuttgart, 1908.

[3] TRACY, FREDERICK, and STIMPFL, JOSEPH, "The Psychology of Childhood," pp. 104–105, Boston, 1909.

There is a brief note on the all-fours manifestation in the book of Miss Tanner:[1] "A fairly large proportion use arms and hands alone, dragging the body and legs; and almost as many go on hands and feet instead of knees."

Finally in 1926, Dr. Variot,[2] of Paris, publishes a valuable communication on what he terms "prelocomotion" in the child, or modes of motion before the child walks erect. He calls attention to the scarcity of observations on this subject. He mentions a few older authors who touched upon this field more or less. The most interesting of his references is that to Peter Camper who in a memoir on the "Physical Education of Children" (1761) remarks that "it is habitual to infants to crawl on their fours like quadrupeds until they perceive that they have enough force to sustain the weight of their body, when they raise themselves and risk, little by little, to march erect."

Doctor Variot discusses briefly the crawling on the hands and knees, believing the habit is to be distinguished from that of on all fours. As to the latter he believes that it is rather rare, for he has encountered it only three times among eighty infants. In this form of progression the child runs on the palms of its hands with the fingers separated and on the toes. The infant walks like a little quadruped; "as a little bear," say the mothers. Gerdy, a distinguished anatomist and an earlier author on the infant locomotion, denied, according to Dr. Variot, the existence in the human child of running on all fours, knowing only of that on the hands and knees.

In Dr. Variot's opinion the duration of the progression on all fours varies in general from one to three months, much as with other types of prelocomotion.

Felix Regnault, who discussed Dr. Variot's communication was of the opinion that "running on all fours is very rare."

Recent Publications.—In 1927–1928 I published my initial observations, restricted in the main to the on all-fours habit of locomotion.[3]

[1] TANNER, AMY E., "The Child," p. 347, Chicago and New York, 1915.

[2] VARIOT, G., "La prélocomotion chez le jeune enfant avant la marche bipède," *Bull. et Mém. Soc. Anthrop.*, vol. VII, pp. 128–144, Paris, 1926.

[3] "Quadruped Progression in the Human Child," *Amer. Jour. Phys. Anthrop.* vol. X, no. 3, pp. 347–354, 1927; "Children on 'All Fours,'" additional reports, *ibid.*, vol. XI, no. 1, pp. 123–126, 1927; "Children Running on All Fours," *ibid.*, vol. XI, no. 2, pp. 149–185, 1928.

Since these first publications the subject received some attention from a Dr. S. Nittis of Ann Arbor. Dr. Nittis, who is a Greek by birth, wrote an interesting paper on the subject, which since has been published in one of the medical journals.[1] Dr. Nittis in his article, a copy of which he kindly sent me, uses unfortunately, what I feel convinced, are unwarranted generalizations; nevertheless he brings forth a number of items of interest, and at the same time calls attention to the prevalence of the habit in Cyprus, his birthplace, and elsewhere in Greece.

Doctor Nittis employs the terms "Quadruped Locomotion," or "Tetrapodisis." These terms are inaccurate and should not be used. They both imply *four feet*, which, of course, is erroneous. The child does not become four-footed because it walks on all fours. It walks on its hands and feet. This is a *quadruped-like* but not a quadruped locomotion. There is involved quite a distinction here.

The people of Cyprus, according to Dr. Nittis, have a special term for the walking on all fours which means "walk like a bear" (literal translation "imitates the bear"). As there are no bears on the island and there is no evidence that they ever lived there, the term probably came from the mainland. It is, Dr. Nittis says, used by almost all the Greek islanders, and in many lands about the eastern Mediterranean, among the Greeks. In Arcadia it changes to "walk like a cat"; and in Cythera it is "walk like a donkey." And he has also heard of it among other peoples. But he has not studied any case direct.

Doctor Nittis also believes that there are definite references to the habit in Greek mythology and literature. He quotes the famous riddle, "The enigma of man, propounded by the Sphinx of Thebes and solved by Œdipous." The enigma runs as follows:

"There is a thing on earth two-footed, and four-footed, and three-footed, whose tone of voice is one, and it changes its nature alone of all creatures that move creeping on the earth or in the air and sea. But when it moves supported on most feet, the swiftness of its legs is at its weakest."

Œdipus' solution of the riddle according to an unknown poet is:

"However much against thy will, hear from me, ill-winged (ill-omened) muse of the dead, the end of thy wrong-doing; man

---

[1] "Quadruped Locomotion (Tetrapodisis) among Human Children," *Jour., Mich. Med., Soc.*, vol. XXVIII, pp. 323–326, April, 1929.

it is thou didst describe, who while living on earth, is made by nature four-footed at first when a helpless babe from his mother's womb. But when he is aged bowed down by advanced years, he leans upon a staff, a third foot, resting thereon the weight of his trunk."[1]

But Dr. Nittis found nothing on the subject in English, German, or French literature; neither does he mention any Greek, Roman, or other sources with the exception of Aristotle, the quotations from whom, however, lack in clearness.

Aside from this interesting, though regrettably not rigid and critical enough, contribution, nothing further on the subject seems to have appeared in the press until the present year, when Dr. Smotlacha, of Prague, mentions the phenomenon and a case that came under his personal observation.[2]

That the subject is attracting attention of scientific men, is shown by the fact that in several cases, learned of privately by the author, the proceeding has been filmed in individual children, some of which films have been shown to scientific assemblages.

[1] This oracle was long ago cited by Gerdy in his "*Traité pratique et didactique de Physiologie*," 1829, in connection with children who moved on hands and knees.

[2] SMOTLACHA, F., "The Biological Bases of Man's Inclination to Climb, etc.," in Czech., Prague, 1930.

STATISTICAL DATA

Number of Cases.—The total number of cases of infants who ran on all fours and are dealt with in this volume, is 387. Of these 369 are whites, 18 colored (Indian, Eskimo, Negro, Australian, mestizo).

Of the 369 whites, 331 are reported with more or less detail and will constitute the backbone of this volume. On 38 of the whites, reported among the relatives of our subjects, the information is restricted to a mention of the sex, degree of relation, and the fact that they also "ran on all fours."

Considering the great amount of publicity the subject and the requests for information have received, the fact that these reached great numbers of educated people who have interest in such matters and who generally are helpfully inclined, and the time and effort that have already been given to the matter, the number of cases that it was possible to gather is rather small and indicates that the phenomenon, while not as rare as may have seemed at first, is nevertheless not frequent. Just how scarce it is can only be determined by future, intensive, direct studies on many families. At all events, the manifestation is frequent enough to deserve the qualification of a phylogenetic persistence rather than a mere reminiscence or reversion. It is evidently a diminishing continuance from the far past and not an atavism.

Race.—The disproportion between white and colored means only that the reports and not the cases are so much scarcer on the colored than they are on the whites. The indications are that the manifestation is more common among the colored, the negroes in particular, than it is among the whites. Thus only a single record has been received from an American negro. Lack of education, more or less, and racial sensitiveness, prevent or inhibit here the giving of the desired information. It will be of very considerable interest indeed to learn the racial differences in the whole category of manifestations here dealt with. To start with there is needed as complete light as possible on these conditions in the different branches of the white people. Possibly even they will show some group variation in these respects.

Sex.—Conditions as to the sex of the children who run on all fours may best be presented in the form of a table. They are as follows:

WHITES

Cases	All	Males		Females		Proportion of males to females
		Number of cases	Per cent	Number of cases	Per cent	
Reported upon more circumstantially........	331	195	58.9	136	41.1	143.4
All.................	369	216	58.5	153	41.5	141.5

The males, it is seen, predominate, in the proportion practically of 3 to 2, or as approximately 140 to 100. As the mean proportion of males to females, in the white races at large, is only about 105 to 100 at birth and slowly diminishes thereafter, the excess of males in the children who run on all fours is quite marked and must be significant. It is most likely connected with the average greater muscular strength and activity of the male child.

Nothing definite can be said on this point in connection with the colored series, the information is not sufficient.

Order of Birth.—In 257 cases of the children who ran on all fours, there is a definite record as to the numerical order of birth of the subject, and these records show interesting conditions.

ORDER OF BIRTH OF THE CHILD THAT RAN ON ALL FOURS

Order of birth	All		Males		Females	
	Number of cases	Per cent	Number of cases	Per cent	Number of cases	Per cent
1st	144	56.0	83	55.3 ⎫	61	57.0 ⎫
2d	70	27.2	40	26.7 ⎬ 82.0	30	28.0 ⎬ 85.0
3d	27	10.5	17	11.3 ⎭	10	9.3 ⎭
4th	9	3.5	4	2.7	5	4.7 ⎫ 15.0
5th	4	1.6	3	2.0 ⎬ 18.0	1	0.9 ⎭
6th	2	0.75	2	1.3	0	
7th	1	0.4	1	0.7 ⎭		
Total	257		150		107	

The above data show, first, that the predominance of the male over female walkers-on-all-fours is manifest throughout. In only one grade (fourth child) are there more girls than boys, which probably is accidental.

In the second place, it would seem that there is a decided bias in favor of the first child developing into a runner on all fours. In well over one-half of our cases the subject was the first child. But the true values are here uncertain. In a material proportion of these cases the child was the only child of the family. To determine the true conditions it would be necessary to have data on completed normal families; or at least to be able to contrast the number of the four-walkers in each category with the total number of children in that category. Neither of these is feasible with our present data or facilities. The above showing can therefore be regarded merely as suggestive and not conclusive.

In addition, the tabulation shows that, within the sex series, there is an appreciably greater tendency for the female first and second children to develop the running on all fours than for the male. Out of each 100 first and second male children 82, out of each 100 female first and second 85, appear to develop the habit.

An explanation of whatever order-of-birth differences there may exist must be looked for, it would seem, mainly in differences of muscular and nervous vigor.

Heredity.—Quadrimembral locomotion is according to all indications a functional manifestation of such a deep-set nature that its hereditary transmission can not be questioned. But inheritance and its physical or functional manifestations are two widely different matters. In the evolutionary progress of organisms, ancestral inheritances do not disappear suddenly, but rather by a gradual and, at times, very slow weakening or submergence. Such inheritances, it can readily be understood, will not manifest themselves according to the regular laws of the more active inheritances, but only on favorable occasions, when freed for a time from inhibitive factors, or when incidentally strengthened. All of us in all probability carry masked inheritances of which we know nothing for they have never in our lives, and perhaps even in those of our parents, come to a definite manifestation.

It is, therefore, not strange that the phenomenon of running on all fours in the human child does not manifest itself in a Mendelian or evidently any other regular fashion.

Moreover, the rôle of heredity in the category of cases here considered is not easily determined. In some of the cases there are strong indications that heredity does play an important part; in others there are apparently none. We are confronted here with the serious factors of imperfect knowledge and memory. Who of the readers of this does know by himself or herself just what they did in infancy; and in many cases those who could tell are either gone or have forgotten. Not seldom the family "thought nothing" of one or the other of these procedures and so there was little to fix the remembrance of it in their mind; or other children came and the memories were confused; or the reporter was shy of acknowledging some of these peculiarities and so the record is lost also.[1] Besides all of which, heredity does not always work regularly or affect all individuals.

With all their imperfections the records here gathered are instructive. They extend to 292 separate families. In 214 of these families there is a direct statement as to the occurrence of the phenomenon in other members of the immediate families and among relatives (as far as the matter among these may be ascertainable). These statements come out as follows:

OTHER CASES OF CHILDREN WHO MOVED ON ALL FOURS IN PARENTS' FAMILIES
OR AMONG RELATIVES
("As far as known")

Number of families...................... 214
No other cases known..................... in 159 or 74.3%
Other cases.............................. in 55 or 25.7%

The proportion of families, in which no other case of progression on all fours was known of, is to those, where one or more cases did appear or were learned of, as close to 3 to 1. This proportion has no special significance, for it includes brothers, sisters, parents, grandparents, uncles, aunts, and cousins.

The total number of the relations who ran also on all fours, is 77, of which 50 were brothers or sisters, and 27 all other relatives. The number of brothers and sisters is pretty reliable; that of the other relatives is doubtless unreliable.

[1] It is greatly to be wished for in these connections that the excellent habit already practiced by some mothers of keeping a detailed daily record of the child's doings be generalized as much as may be possible. Such records, with studies in their families and among friends, will eventually help to solve many problems relating to our progeny.

In no one family appears anything like a definite Mendelian picture of inheritance.

With all its imperfections the picture permits of the following conclusions:

1. The predisposition to the progression on all fours, preceding the walking erect, is, in all probability, still universal in the human infant.

2. It is a weakened but apparently still a continued inheritance from the prehuman past.

3. It manifests itself occasionally and irregularly under favorable conditions.

Age at Which Infants Walk on All Fours and Duration of the Habit

An analysis of the data at hand shows that most frequently the phenomenon manifests itself between seven and twelve months.

The earliest reported age at which the practice began, was five and one-half months in a boy, five months in a girl, while the latest beginning was at four years in a boy, fourteen months in a girl.

The average duration of the all-fours walk was approximately four months, in both sexes. The shortest more definitely reported periods of the practice were one month in a boy, two weeks in a girl; the longest, exclusive of any other locomotion, one year and two months in a boy, and nine months in a girl.

Preceding and Following Modes of Locomotion

In 47 cases (31 males, 16 females), the child is reported to have used some other method of moving about before developing that on all fours. It "crept," or "shuffled," or "hitched," etc., in some of the more ordinary (or extraordinary) ways.[1]

In various cases the baby "crawled," which often means moving on hands and knees. In some, the latter mode is specified by the reporters.

In a certain percentage of cases the baby is stated never to have crept or crawled but to have begun at once to go on all fours, though there was usually a short stage of preparation.

[1] See Section on "Curious Initial Postures and Odd Modes of Locomotion," p. 83.

In most cases, after running on all fours for a shorter or longer period, the child began spontaneously to raise itself with the help of its hands, which was gradually followed by steps and walk in the erect position. But again and again there are met with assertions that the child stood up suddenly, without any support, and soon after walked effectively.

In but a relatively few instances was the habit of on-all-fours given up suddenly and completely when the child began to walk erect. More generally they diminish in the old habit gradually, resorting to the all-fours when they need a speedier progression. And some keep on with an occasional recourse to the all-fours, from habit or pleasure, long after they learned to walk upright. This is much more the case with boys than girls, but there are exceptions.

Exact statistics on all these points are as yet impracticable.

HEALTH AND GENERAL STRENGTH

The children who become walkers on all fours, far from being any degenerates and weaklings are generally healthier and stronger than the average. There are in our records but very few exceptions to this; and the mortality of these infants appears to be exceedingly limited. It is indeed a cause for congratulation rather than for apprehension to see the appearance of such a "little bear" in the family, for it seems to be a token of health, sturdiness and life assurance. No wonder that an intelligent father says "we hoped he (the second child) would run on all fours too"—H. N. Parker.

The state of health in the children who ran on all fours is reported as follows:

State of health	Totals		Males		Females	
	Number	Per cent	Number	Per cent	Number	Per cent
Excellent, above average .	74	22.3	36	18.4	38	27.9
Good, average, normal ...	245	73.8	152	77.6	93	68.4
More or less subnormal...	13	3.9	8	4.1	5	3.7

These are certainly an extraordinary and highly gratifying showing, which could not be equaled in children at large. And the general reliability of the records must be apparent to every one who will peruse the detailed records. These data indicate better than anything else could that the running on all fours is manifested generally in the healthy and strong child. The exceptions are few in number and their study shows mostly acquired rather than inborn conditions.

To the above data may well be added a few of the more characteristic quotations:

"The child is abnormally healthy (if such a term can be used)—she has never had a sick hour in her thirteen months and a half"—Bartlett (Professor of Biology).

"She is extremely healthy"—Roach (grandfather, father, and uncle doctors).

"Has never been sick a day in his life"—Byerley, boy, eighteen months.

"She is [and has always been] perfectly healthy in every respect"—Cannon, young lady now eighteen years old.

"Ten-pound baby at birth" [female]; now past eighty-four years; walks still "a mile, more or less, every day"—Carter.

Health "excellent," "splendid," "first class," "very good"—Many.

"She has always been perfectly normal"—Child, young lady now twenty-four years old.

"Health very good; was a large fat baby; has had no children's diseases as yet"—Master Pedenboy, four years.

"At his present age, twenty months, we have a healthy, sturdy-limbed child"—Stansfield.

"Is a little overweight but healthy, strong, vigorous, and normal in all respects"—Stark, girl, past twelve months.

Strength.

"I have never seen a lad of four years with a finer physique, with greater strength . . . nor with so great a fund of apparently inexhaustible energy"—Van Cott.

"She is now eighteen months old and handles herself as well as her brother who is nearly three"—Sullivan.

"She is the strongest most athletic child I have"—A. Anderson.

"She has always been very strong, more like a boy"—Bakalyars.

"He is remarkably well developed, and quite holds his own with his two-year old brother, who is also quite a little husky"—Dr. Barondes, boy, one year old.

"She is one of the strongest persons that I have ever known. Our family doctor has told me that she is just like a sturdy little animal"—Cannon, girl, who as an infant ran on all fours, now eighteen years old.

"Exceptional muscular development"—Many.

Quotations such as the above could be multiplied greatly. There are but few exceptions—a premature child, now and then an undernourished one, a "nervous" one, or one run down temporarily by disease. The relative weakness in these few children did not however prevent the on-all-fours phenomenon from manifesting itself, showing that it is not just the exuberance of strength and spirit that leads to the habit. It is, as one of the correspondents (Jacob) justly remarks, "not *always* the most vigorous or precocious child" who will run on all fours. There are certainly also many robust children who never run thus. Yet it is plain that, in general, the all-fours habit does manifest itself preferentially in the healthy and strong children.

Strength in Hands and Arms

It is a matter of common knowledge that the human baby has an astonishing grasp in its hands and strength in its arms, and the fact has been looked upon, probably entirely justly, as a functional survival from the prehuman times when the infant had to cling to its mother while she was running or climbing. There is no wonder, therefore, that a good many of the four-runners showed so much of hand and arm strength that it was deemed worthy of a special mention in the reports on these children. But the wording of the reports makes it probable that the character is developed more in some of these children than in the average infant who does not run on all fours. Whether this is congenitally so, or results from the very practice of running on all fours, can, it seems, hardly be decided as yet, but both factors are apparently in evidence. The notes read as follows:

Miss Lear, eleven months old, "will grasp a finger of her father or me in either hand and allow herself to be lifted shoulder high."

Patricia LeSourd, eleven months, "will hold her weight on a rod for some time"; [she will also throw ball hard and] "with great accuracy."

Richard Philleo "from the first seemed possessed of unusual strength in his arms and legs."

Gordon Metcalf, "when three and one-half years old, would be lifted up by his father to a wire clothesline, where he would chin himself three or four times."

W. K.'s little girl, three and one-half years old, has "a great tenacity of grip; delights in swinging from her hands; will pull herself up to a straight bough or a horizontal bar and hang suspended by her hands, swinging and singing, at every opportunity."

Master Van Kirk, at fourteen and one-half months, "has enormous strength in his hands and arms. I can truthfully say [mother] that he can hold his own with his older brother aged four years and it is a difficult task for me to handle him myself."

Little Seaman, less than one year old was found one day "hanging over the edge of the table, his hands pressed flat against the table top, holding himself in that manner. Nothing there to grasp a hold of at all. He seemed to have an unusual strength in his fingers to hold his weight in that manner."

The Kenney boy, since reaching the age of six or seven months, "has been able to sustain his weight with his hands for long periods."

And the Ward girl, seventeen months, "hangs on like a monkey."

ENDURANCE

Not a few of the children who ran on all fours are reported as showing general exceptional endurance. This is only what was to be expected with such a robust class of children. Yet there may be more than this to some at least of these cases.

EXAMPLES

"She was very daring, got many bumps, but seldom cried; as a child she had her teeth pulled and filled but never whimpered"—Ahlberg.

"She never seems to tire"—Barker.

"Not sensitive to cuts, burns, or bruises, very seldom complaining of the average childish injuries"—Kenney's boy.

"She can stand much pain without crying"—Parker.

"He seemed capable of making considerable distances in this manner, both on the floor and ground, without it apparently tiring him"—Philleo.

PHYSICAL AND PHYSIOLOGICAL ANOMALIES. MENTAL ABNORMALITIES

A few of the mothers and fathers report some physical anomaly in the child that runs on all fours. Many say nothing. And many declare the child to be normal, free from "other peculiarities," and express themselves in other terms to that effect. Judging from these records and from the numerous photos of the infants in question, it may safely be said that the children who run on all fours are in general free of striking physical peculiarities; at least as much so, if not more, than other children. The "abnormalities" reported are as follows:

. 21 .

Darwin's tubercles—1 case.

Sixth finger—1 case.

"Ears broad at the top, with rims rounded at the top and down about one-third of the way"—1 case.

"Second and third toes on both of her feet are grown together almost to the end"—1 case.

"Great toes extra long and large compared with the rest of the foot"—1 case.

Diastemae between lower incisors—1 case.

Area of hair on back, end of spine to about one-fifth way up, lasting about 3 months after birth—1 case.

"At birth his trunk was noticeably long and thick, after the monkey type"—1 case.

"Unusually large chest and shoulders"—1 case.

"From the top of his thigh to his knee is very short and his body is long in comparison"—1 case.

"Her ears do not match"—1 case.

"She has noticeably hollow back"—1 case.

As a baby, "her breasts were full of milk and the nurse squeezed it out every day for three weeks"—Fraser.

As to *mental* or *nervous defects,* there is but one case of a somewhat serious derangement subsequent to childhood. It would, I think, be impossible to match this record among as many children that have not run on all fours.

Of strictly *anomalous* mental conditions, there are two cases of reverse reading, spelling, and writing. The Wyllie boy "spells words backward. Reads and spells backward."

And the Welker's girl "would write her name—amroN; cat was tac; dog was god; and she commenced to write from the right to the left always. I wondered if she 'saw' things hind-side-to. She is being trained out of this now, but sometimes when she is tired I notice that she does it, then erases and does it right."

The causation and meaning of such cases as these, though the phenomenon is well known, is obscure.

With these data, taken together with the many statements in the documents as to the exceptionally good physique and mentality of this class of children, it is plain that we are not confronted here by any abnormal or degenerate category of human beings, but rather by children many of whom are of exceptional normalcy and vigor both physically and mentally.

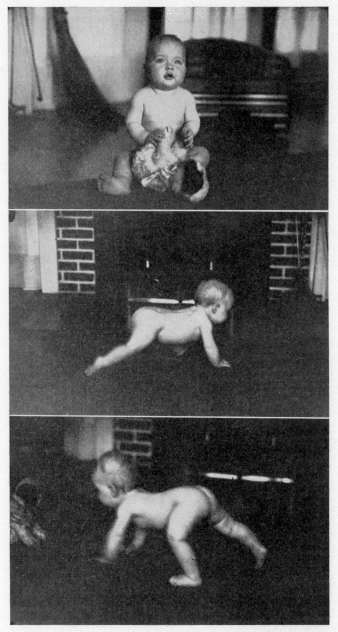

PLATE II.—Catherine McK. Barker. What finer baby? "The child behaves so as to convey the impression of naturalness and fitness, of satisfaction and pleasure."

This is not difficult to understand. The running on all fours is purely a manifestation of the muscular and the motor nervous systems. It is, however, no longer a necessity in the human infant; and unless, on the one hand, the tendency to it is sufficiently strong and, on the other, there are no effectively inhibitive conditions, it will not come to realization.

The natural tendency and impulse, though in general much weakened in man, have doubtless a range of individual variation, so that they are stronger in some children than in others. In a large majority of white children the tendency is evidently so weak already that the old habit remains dormant. In others the tendency may be somewhat greater but not strong enough to overcome a lack of muscular or nervous vigor, or the artificialities by which the child is affected (clothing, baby cages, etc.). But in the healthy and strong infant, if the tendency to running on all fours is present in some strength, it will manifest itself and run its course.

In rare instances only, the tendency is apparently strong enough even in a weaker child to overcome such handicap and thus even a subnormal child may show the peculiarity; but in such a case the manifestation is generally less perfect or durable than in the healthy children.

THE PERFORMANCE OF RUNNING ON ALL FOURS

THE general characteristics of the performance of running on all fours in the human child, once the habit is well developed, are balance, ease, speed, and endurance. The child behaves so as to convey the impression of naturalness and fitness, of satisfaction and pleasure.

BALANCE

Quite a number of the more detailed reports on the children who run on all fours remark more or less directly on the exceptional "balance" of these children. Thus:

Fig. 1.—Remarkable balance on an unstable base. Master Foy, eleven months, has climbed up into an all-fours position on the rim of his basket carriage.

The Kenney boy "possesses balance and a faculty of self-protection that are remarkable."
In the Stretch boy, the "sense of balance seems to be very keen."
The Sullivan girl has "unusually good sense of balance."
The Whitson young lady "has wonderful balance."

The Seaman little boy, "can stand on rocking-chair, rock, and balance perfectly without holding on. He very seldom falls."

And the W. K.'s most interesting little girl at seventeen months, was "more sure-footed in narrow footholds than either of her parents, and possessed an acrobatic sense of balance . . . She would, with great rapidity, climb to the arm of a chair and balance herself free handed."

Such "balance" means a high grade of normalcy of the muscular, nervous, visual, and auditory (semicircular canals) organs, and of their coordination. It is merely another indication of the exceptionally healthy status of many of these children.

SPEED

As a rule the children running on all fours do so very expeditiously, and that, soon after they started thus. There is no or only apparent clumsiness, no tumbling over one self. They run thus faster than they could creep, faster than they could walk. In cases the speed to the onlookers is "amazing." In not one case has such a child been reported to have gone slowly, and they do not tire easily.

"Walked [on all fours] with great ease and rapidity"—P. L. Smith.

"He gets around with remarkable speed"—Barondes.

"Progression very rapid"—Baud.

"Within a couple of weeks [after beginning], attained great proficiency and high speed"—G. P. B.

"Wonderful, amazing, unbelievable; she was very light and graceful and quick"—Abramowitz.

"Looks up to get her direction and then lowers her head and scampers"—Leffingwell.

"Her speed and sureness of foot were quite remarkable," and that even down and up a slope—MacLachlan.

"His rapidity and smoothness of movement, when on all fours, has been very noticeable"—Metcalf.

"She goes like a streak, pad, pad, all over the house"—Lear.

"Around the house flying"—Millisor.

"Scurried over the room with wonderful rapidity"—Mossner.

"And she could scoot"—F. Parker.

"From the first she ran quickly and confidently and ultimately acquired amazing speed. I (father) am a fast walker and she could easily outstrip me"—H. N. Parker.

"He could run so fast on all fours that people came to see him"—Ruedemann.

"Moved freely and easily" [on all fours]—Roberts.

"It was a frisky action and rapid"—Bigelow.

"It was quick and graceful"—S. B., boy.

"Could soon go so rapidly that it was difficult to catch her"—A. Bowen.

"Went like lightning"—LeNore Anderson.

"He sure could travel"—E. O. Armstrong.

"She just scampers"—J. W. Armstrong.

"Very rapidly"—Auten.

"He would run down the walk like a little dog beside me, both of us running and laughing until we were breathless"—Roberts.

"His gait suggested a bear's fat, clumsy, but surprisingly rapid gait" —Ratliff.

"She then ran about like a little race horse with hands open and head up"—Casseday.

"She almost loped like a dog when in a hurry"—Sherry.

"He used to make as much speed as a dog or a cat"—Walker.

"In one instance I ran, in a park, to catch him, and am sure he did on his all fours a gait of four and one-half miles per hour"—Chaney.

"He travels [on all fours] long distances and can run so rapidly that it is necessary for one to run in order to catch him"—Chapman.

The speed of the performance means a high nervous as well as muscular fitness and coordination, with suitable build, for the time being, of the skeleton. Such extensive fitness and coordination cannot be accidental. They can only reflect a former deeply ingrained condition. They are, while they last, the revived functions of quadruped locomotion.

GAIT

The children who run on all fours use much the same gait as do monkeys, bears, dogs, and many other animals. It is generally the gait in which the child uses one leg or arm and then the opposite arm or leg; but there are some exceptions. It is a gait that, just as with animals, is mostly difficult of precise description, and will differ in different subjects, and on occasions even in the same subject. It is a gait that is easy, effective, and in some cases quite graceful. And the child is perfectly "at home" in the whole performance, steady and well balanced, does not tire readily, and may make considerable distance. The parents' comments on the gait are not frequent, but they make an interesting reading. The photographs of the children "in action" speak for themselves.

REPORTS

Steadiness.

"When this baby was progressing on all fours on the floor, it was nearly impossible to upset him, he never seemed to get bumped and he was like a 'loaded' toy, he wouldn't tip over"—Leonard.

Gait.

"Moved as a beast does normally, and not by racking"—Stone.

"Walked like a dog on his hands and feet"—Knight.

"The feet and hands alternated, as a dog runs"—Olsen.

"Trotted around like a puppy"—Curry.

"Left foot, left hand, right foot, right hand, touching the floor at approximately equal intervals"—Shive.

"Very often she balances herself on her hands and lifts both feet off the floor, drawing them forward to progress"—J. W. Armstrong.

Body sways when running on all fours—Lowry, Terwilliger.

Kicks one or both feet up in the air (when running on all fours)—McNichol.

POSITION OF THE HEAD IN RUNNING ON ALL FOURS

The head, while the child runs on all fours, may be held at almost any angle from slight flexion toward the utmost practicable flexion backwards. The position will differ on different occasions in the same subject. But there is a tendency in each infant who runs on all fours towards the assumption of some one position which then becomes habitual and characteristic of that particular child. Thus:

Head Down.

He generally ran "head down, eyes towards the floor"—Abney.

"His head was down, *i.e.*, toward the floor"—Dr. S. R. W.

"His head is held low"—Myers.

"Looked down and not where he was going, frequently bumping his head against things"—Baxter.

"Eyes not directed forward, except to get a bearing, at times"—Hunneman, boys.

"Head sometimes down, sometimes up"—Morris, boy.

Head at Level of Body.

"Locates an object towards which he proposes to go and then travels with his head practically in line with his back, until near the object, when he lifts his head again"—Leversee.

PLATE III.—The gait of Master Chapman.

"The head was usually held in a line with the body"—Mighton, boy.

"Head held up mostly, but also at times on level with body"—Niess, boy.

"Carried his head up and back"—Leonard.

"Holds her head up to see where she is going"—Lund.

"He ran with the head up"—H. Miller.

"Her head up"—Millisor.

"Her head up and forward"—Barker.

"His face front"—Baud.

"Her head is held erect"—Bartlett.

"Heads up like a turtle"—Sefton, two boys.

"His head is held often very similar to that of a dog"—J. W. Wallace.

The Limbs in Running on All Fours

The arms in the performance are as a rule held stiff; while the lower limbs may be held stiff, but in a large majority of cases are more or less bent. Thus:

"With stiff knees and straight arms"—Mighton, boy.

"There was no intermediate movement at elbows or knees"—Stone, girl.

"Knee joints stiff"—Bartlett, girl.

"His knees were practically stiff"—Kunze.

"His legs were fully extended at the knees, being held rather stiffly"— Dr. S. R. W.

"Soles flat on the floor, hands spread out flat, legs stiff, head down"— Thompson, boy.

"Legs upright and not bent at knees"—Wood.

"There is very little flexing at the knee joint, giving a stiff-legged effect and a humping up of the hips"—Sherzer.

"Knees stiff"—Baud, boy.

"Knees extremely bent"—Baud, girl.

"Knees sometimes slightly bent, at other times straight"—Mighton, girl.

"Knees at a slight angle"—Mitchell.

"Legs only slightly flexed, left more than right"—Dr. Jones, girl.

The lower limbs are generally held well apart, sometimes markedly so. There are a number of references to this feature and it is seen on many of the photographs. There is but one note to the opposite condition.

"Legs are spread rather widely apart"—Metcalf.

"The legs are kept near together"—Swasey, boy.

The Hands in Running on All Fours

The large anthropoid apes (gorilla, chimpanzee, orang), in running on all fours, go on the knuckles of their hands; the gibbons when walking on the ground generally use the feet only, balancing themselves with the arms held nearly horizontal and partly flexed; the baboons and monkeys all run on the flat of their hands. The difference may be connected with the size of the fingers, which in the great apes are relatively enormous, and with the fact that in these apes the fingers are powerful, grasping organs which implies extraordinary development of their flexor muscles and ligaments.

The human infant, in locomotion on all fours, holds the hands generally open and applies to the ground or floor either the whole flat of the hand, or less commonly, just that of the fingers. In some instances, however, the hand is more or less flexed. Use of the dorsal parts of the fingers or of the knuckles by the human child, is intimated in several of the cases.

As the position of the hands was one of the points directly inquired into, there are many answers on the subject. A selection of these will be quite sufficient. There are some interesting collateral features.

Hands Flat.
"His hands are flat to the floor with fingers outspread"—Metcalf.
"His hands spread flat on the floor"—Abney.
"Hands fully open"—Barker, girl; Bliss, girl; etc.
"Hands with outstretched fingers flat on the floor"—Bourne, girl.
"She held her hands open while running"—Bowen.
"The palm of the hand flat"—P. H. B., boy.
"He placed his hands flat on the ground or floor"—Brooks.
"Hands perfectly flat and toes and hands inward"—Sherry, girl.
"Applied his entire hands to the floor . . . his hands ordinarily showed a tendency to turn in, *i.e.*, the lines of the middle fingers would meet ahead" [if prolonged]—Sherzer.
"The hands flat and quite apart"—Swasey, boy.

On Fingers.
Ran on tips of fingers and balls of feet—Nagle, boy.
"All at once she started on finger tips and toes"—Fraser.

Hands More or Less Closed.

"Hands were usually wide open, walking on the palms; however, sometimes he was noticed to walk with the fingers clenched, putting the weight on the knuckles"—Mighton, boy.

"Holds her hands partly closed while running" [on all fours]—Bergner.

"He ran with the end joints of his fingers bent back and under"—Rees.

"While running on all fours his hands were partly closed in gripping position and actually gripped the ground, so that his nails were often broken and full of dirt after an hour of running in this way"—P. L. Smith.

"The hands were partly closed"—Abramowitz.

"Hands usually half closed"—Barondes.

"He kept his hands partly closed"—Baxter.

"The hands were clubbed" [while running on all fours]; "the thumb being grasped in the palm of the hand"—Molloy, Negro-Indian mestizo.

"He would use his hands either clenched, or else spread half open"—Knight.

"Katharine at one time used to go about on the backs of her hands, instead of on the palms" [when carrying about toys, in one or both hands]—Wells.

SLAPPING WITH HANDS WHILE RUNNING ON ALL FOURS

Some of the children when running on all fours feel "so good" or exuberant that they slap the floor with their hands. And, of course, they enjoy doing it still more if noticed and wondered at, for vanity is a very early faculty. There are several nice reports on this habit:

Her hands when running on all fours "were placed flat on the floor and she slapped them down with force enough to be heard over most of the house"—Frick.

The younger boy "sometimes seems to stretch the fingers out and spank the hands down hard"—Hunneman.

She "loved to bring her hand to the floor with a smack"—H. N. Parker.

"As an accompaniment to this habit the child used to slap the floor with his hands when proceeding rapidly"—Storer.

Had attention been called to this trait there would probably have been additional reports.

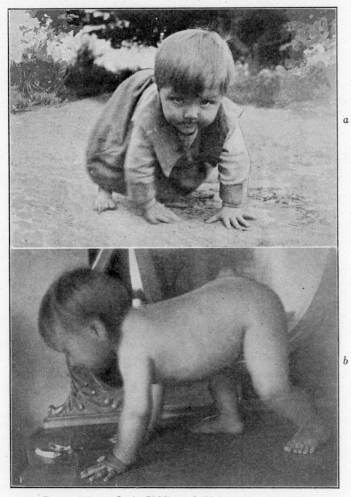

a

b

PLATE IV.—*a*. Susie Giddinge. *b*. Holmes boy (*W. K.*).

The Feet in Running on All Fours

The feet, while the child runs on all fours, in most instances are applied flat to the ground; but there are children that use only the ball of the foot and rare cases that use only the toes. The same child in going slowly may use the whole flat of the foot, but while running rapidly it will employ only the ball. The use of the feet flat, as that of the hands, implies naturally quite a difference in the conformation of the joints, etc., of these infants from those of the ordinary adult.

Examples

"Her feet were flat on the floor"—Keller.

"His feet are flat on the floor"—Myers.

"The whole surface of the foot touched the floor, the feet spread widely to allow the legs to swing well forward"—Van Cott.

"Feet flat on the soles unless in hurry, when going on toes"—Ratliff.

Tendency to put body weight on the outside of feet—Leffingwell, and some others.

"Runs on the balls of the feet with toes widely spread"—Metcalf.

On his toes, when on all fours, "was never known to put his heels down"—Stretch.

"Her feet raised on the toes"—W. K.

Imperfect Running on All Fours

Many more infants, apparently, than will run on all fours, *i.e.*, on hands and feet, run on hands and knees; so that while the perfect all-fours method is scarce that on hands and knees may be termed fairly common. Yet the latter mode, there are proofs, is substantially identical with the former. If we designate the running on all fours as 1, and that on hands and knees as 2, then we may say that 1 may, and often does, follow 2; that 2 and 1 may alternate; and that, even, 2 may follow 1. In addition to which, the two may be combined in the same infant, who then runs on both arms, one foot, and one knee. There are in our series examples of all these cases. Furthermore, one form may occur in one or more members of a family and either of the others in another; and the essentials of all are quite similar, except that the children running typically on all fours as a class are evidently sturdier and more interesting, the hands-and-knees merging more with the average.

· 34 ·

PLATE V.—Negro pickaninnies running on hands and knees. *a*. Belgian Congo.
b. Congo. *c*. Near Victoria Falls.

A typical hands-and-knees position may well be seen in the Goldberg and Zambezi children (Plate V). As to the "both hands, one foot, and one knee" there are a number of notes. Thus:

"Our second child, a girl, crept in a somewhat similar manner [to that of the first child who ran on all fours], using her right hand and right foot, and left hand and left knee. After some time she changed to both knees, before learning to walk at fourteen months"—Lovell.

"His oldest brother and an uncle [of a boy who ran typically on all fours] used an intermediate form, employing both hands and one foot with the other leg bent under, and assisting somewhat with the locomotion by pushing from the knee"—Magill.

a   b

FIG. 2.—Progress "on threes" (both hands, one foot, one knee). *a*. Miss Affleck. *b*. Miss E. J. Wyant.

"At eight months he would roll from one end of a room to the other; at nine he was beginning to creep, but always went backward. Then, one day, he suddenly, without practice, began creeping forward. After about three weeks of this, at the age of ten and one-half months, he began to creep with one leg and walk with the other, *i.e.*, he put his weight on his right knee and his left foot. It was a funny, awkward gait, which soon, when he learned to use both feet instead of only one, developed into exactly the walk you describe, resembling it in every detail"—Evans.

"When Jeremy started to crawl at seven months he used his whole body, pushing backward on his abdomen and digging in with toes and hands but not raising his body. During the eighth month he began raising one knee, creeping with hands, one foot, and one knee, a sort of hitch; went forward, backward, and sideways. This continued for about two weeks. Then he began walking on hands and feet"—P. L. Smith.

"At the age of seven and one-half months, after weeks of attempts to progress by means of swimming motions executed on her stomach with hips and shoulders in the air, she raised herself onto her hands and knees . . . At eight months and one week she rolled from a position flat on her back to her stomach and then was sitting up . . . At eight months and three weeks began to go on one knee and one foot. Before nine months she had taken a step or two with both feet and both hands on the ground"—Scott.

"Although he could run quite rapidly this way, he did so only when he was on the lawn. When in the house he used a different method. In the house he would keep his left leg doubled back under, so that whenever he wished to stop and sit up he could do so without difficulty. His right foot he placed on the floor after the manner of walking on all fours and his manner of locomotion could more properly be described as walking on 'all threes'"—Patton.

"He started to crawl on hands and knees when nine months old. Before long he began using his feet part time. When crawling on the rug, he uses his knees, but on the polished floor he goes up on his feet. He is a normal baby; weighed 10 pounds at birth"—Day.

"He did not walk until eighteen months old, and a month or so [his mother thinks about two months] before that he took to creeping on his hands and knees, in normal posture, abandoning the 'palms-and-soles' method"—Ganong.

RUNNING ON ALL FOURS IN ITS VARIATIONS

Walking Backwards, Sideways, Etc., in Children Who Run on All Fours

IN general, the children traveling on all fours proceed straight forward to whatever object they want to go. But there are little ones that sometimes show an exceptional form of progression before or after they have assumed the all-fours position.

This "crab-walking" or "craw-fishing" seems to be a peculiar complex of early locomotion that is more common than might have been expected. It has been noticed repeatedly in literature and some attempts have been made at its explanation. The true understanding of it awaits further studies. *References:*

Baldwin's[1] *girl:* "At first most of these movements were the reverse of the natural walking movements, being oftenest such as would carry the child backward"; [and a week later:] "Fine activity in walking reflex—good alternations, but more backwards than forwards . . . It is easy to see that this backward alternation might be due to some accident of stimulation or discharge when the reflex was first called out; a tendency which early efforts at creeping would soon correct. Yet in H.'s case it was so marked that for a period she preferred to creep backward. Two other cases of this have been verbally reported to me; but I am not sure of the conditions under which one of them was observed. The second exact observation I owe to Professor Cattell."

Shinn:[2] "On the first day of the month, among sundry indefinite movements, several steps of 'crawfishing' were taken—a sort of retrograde creeping, pushing backward with the hands. Apparently there was no intention of getting anywhere by this, only a disposition to movement. On the second day the baby backed away from me when she wished to come to me, scolding with disappointment

---

[1] Baldwin, James Mark, "Mental Development in the Child and the Race," 496 pp., New York and London, 1895.

[2] Shinn, Milicent W., "Notes on the Development of a Child," "Univ. of Calif. Studies," vol. I, nos. 3 and 4, pp. 340–341, Berkeley, 1899.

all the time. At other times she would back into the wall, to her own displeasure, and scold vigorously, all the time pushing back against the obstacle like a little engine unable to reverse itself . . . In a day or two the baby's action in this 'crawfishing' became quite free, and she would move some distance, 'half creeping, half wriggling' [thirty-sixth week]."

"Sometimes the child crawls backward like a crab, even when there is nothing before him which he wishes to shun."[1]

Tanner:[2] "Of the babies Trettien watched, 6 per cent crept backward at first. Both Miss Shinn and Mrs. Hall record this peculiarity. It is due to the fact that the baby's arms are stronger than his legs and are predisposed to push instead of to pull, so that until he has learned to coordinate his movements he pushes himself away from the object he wants, instead of toward it. Much to his amazement and displeasure he finds it moving away instead of approaching him."

Children at times will progress backward in either crawling or on all fours; while others will proceed sideways. As no defects were reported in any of these cases the infants were presumably normal; yet it would be desirable to examine such cases, particularly those of sidling motion, in detail, both physically and as to their eyes and other sensory organs, for possible asymmetries or irregularities. However, both the backward and the side motions are frequent in puppies and other young animals, particularly when in a playful mood.

The backward and sideways forms are of nearly equal frequency, with the backward apparently slightly more common. In most if not all cases, backward motion has antedated the running on all fours, though it may also accompany the latter. There are seven especially well-defined cases in the records, as follows:

"At nine months he was beginning to creep, but always went backward"—Evans.

"At seven and one-half months she raised herself onto her hands and knees; as her knees presently slipped out from under her she moved backwards, retrogressing about a yard in several repetitions of this operation." [At eight months] "she was crawling backwards for some distance"—Scott.

[1] Groos, K., "Die Spiele des Menschen," 1899; Eng. trans., after Sigismond, p. 174.
[2] Tanner, Amy Eliza, "The Child," p. 346, Chicago and New York, 1915.

At about seven months "we would put her on the floor and we tried to teach her to crawl. But instead of going forward, she would back up" —Hill.

At about six months he began crawling on his hands and knees "and at first crawled backward"—Huffaker.

"She began creeping backward on March 17 [six months twenty-four days old]. This method was used until May 14"—H. K. Jones.

"He goes backwards on all fours quite a bit just now"—Becker.

When on all fours she "always 'backed up' when anything was to be reached in back of her instead of turning around [like a bear cub] . . . " —Sherry.

Just what is involved in these retrograde manifestations is not fully clear. Doubtless, at the moment they develop, they are either compulsive, or easier than a forward locomotion. This is probably due to structural conditions of the lower limbs; yet there may also be some mental or nervous element, the same as is behind similar manifestations in young animals.

The side motions appear to be limited to the more advanced period, where the children already run on all fours. It may be manifested in an infant that has also crawled or run backward. There are four nice examples in the records, *viz.:*

When on all fours, "he usually went straight to the object desired, but sometimes he approached it with a funny sidling motion, such as sometimes employed by puppies"—Crooks.

"Backed up"; in the eleventh month "began to 'scuttle' sideways on all fours"; [also] "she would 'reverse' rather than turn around, as I have seen cub bears do, to reach an article back of her . . . also walked [on all fours] sideways, sometimes wheeling with incredible rapidity"— Sherry.

While running on all fours "he has shown a peculiar tendency to veer off to one side with his hips while his head was being steered to its goal, as though his steps were not equally spaced"—Sherzer.

"His general course is partially sideways, rather than directly forward"—Worcester.

It would seem that in such cases as that of the Crooks and also probably the Sherry baby, the cause of the side motion is essentially mental—he is pretending; while in the other two the cause was more probably an asymmetry of either the lower limbs or their muscles.

Sleeping on "All Fours"

The human infant is but seldom a free agent. From birth on, it has to conform mostly to what the mother and other women in the family think is best for it, the means toward which ends range in the United States from all sorts of restraining clothes, shoes, and

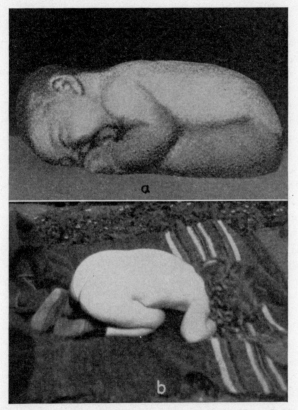

Fig. 3.—Sleeping "on all fours." *a.* A new-born infant. (*After Dekker.*) *b.* A three and one-half year girl (*W. K.*).

appliances, from innumerable "mustn'ts" and "musts" to little spankings, and in the Old World, as well as among the Indians, etc., to the binding of the poor little one in a roll of swaddling clothes or on a cradle board. Thus many incipient manifestations of the baby are cut short or inhibited and both the baby as well as the grownups are the losers.

But, now and then, a baby escapes more or less the thraldom of the adults and then it does all sorts of interesting things. One of these is the sleeping, more or less, on contracted all fours, like the rabbit and some other mammals.

The posture the little one assumes in this particular gratification of its instincts, seems to the adults a decidedly unnatural one or, at least, most uncomfortable, but the baby persists in it and is apparently never happier than in its indulgence. It certainly sleeps thus soundly and enjoyably.

The practice of sleeping on contracted all fours, or rather on the knees, stomach, and elbows, would probably be rather common if the little ones in general had their own way. It certainly is not very uncommon in those who run on all fours. Yet the practice is not much better known than the latter phenomenon. I have found references to but no adequate account of it. Dr. Louis Robinson, as quoted by Buckman, "has pointed out that as soon as children are able to shift for themselves in bed, they go to sleep on their stomachs with their limbs curled up under them; and he has rightly traced this to quadrupedal ancestors."[1] There are a few even simpler references to the fact; and a characteristic figure of a child in this position appears in Dekker's "Naturgeschichte des Kindes."[2] The figure is here reproduced. The author speaks only of small infants. He regards the posture as quite natural and as "a continuation of an earlier habit," though he does not explain what he means by this. He compares a child in this position to a folded pocket knife (Fig. 3).[3]

The fact is that the position of the child that sleeps with its limbs drawn up and folded under the body, is close to that of the fetus *in utero*. But the fetus does not repose on its front. It lies, folded or curled up, generally more or less on its back or side, only incidentally if ever on its front; and its incompletely developed limbs are not generally in the regular knee-elbow position as they are in the infant which sleeps on all fours. It seems that the method

[1] BUCKMAN, S. S., "Babies and Monkeys," *Pop. Sci. Monthly*, vol. XLVI, p. 377, 1894–1895.

[2] P. 48, 1903.

[3] *Die Beine sind zu sonderbaren Kunststückchen geschickt: sie können sich der Länge nach an den Leib legen, dass das Kind aussieht wie ein zusammengeklapptes Taschenmesser (Abb. 22). Für gewöhnlich liegt es mit an den Leib gezogenen Beinen und über der Brust gekreuzten Armen. Es ist die von früherher gewöhnte Lage.*

of sleeping on folded all fours and the front, though favored by the child's similar position *in utero,* may at the root be a survival of prehuman habits of sleeping. The folded limbs and the front position serve both to protect and to keep warm the abdominal organs; and the not yet fully human development of the limbs, together with the inborn proclivity towards the posture, result in its manifestation. But there is a need here of further precise observations.

The habit once assumed tends to persist more or less into childhood. It seems to be a definite complex apart from the common habit of drawing up one's knees in sleep, which latter may well be a continuation of the intra-uterine habit, or of the habit of sitting posture while awake and which persists in many people throughout life. It is associated now and then with additional interesting behaviors.

EXAMPLES

"As a baby, I preferred to sleep with my mother holding me in her arms faced toward her, with my head on her breast, and resting on my knees and 'haunches' much as a monkey holds its young; slept this way until nearly two years of age"—LeNore Anderson.

"She has always slept on her stomach since a tiny baby, moving her head from side to side for a change of air, has both arms down flat at her side, sometimes with her knees drawn up to her chest"—J. W. Armstrong, twenty months.

"Slept on knees, hands doubled under, up to age of four or five, not consistently, but for days or weeks at a time"—W. W. Bacon.

"Often both my girls [three and four] sleep hunched on all fours"— Bakalyars.

"She always sleeps on her stomach with her knees drawn up under her, and hands and arms stretched out above her head"—Barker, ten months.

"He always sleeps on his elbows and knees, his back up in the air and his head turned to one side"—Barondes, one year.

"Generally slept with arms raised above head; still does. Would not stay covered as a baby, climbed up out of them and then crouched down on arms and legs on top of the covers . . . The other day he said, 'I wish I could curl up like Brownie [dog] or Kitty when I go to sleep'" —Bevis, now seven years.

"Up to a few months ago she would often go to sleep lying on her stomach, with her knees bent forward beneath her, but this has not been noticed but once recently"—Harper, two years.

"She is now nearly three and a half years old . . . she still sleeps often on her elbows and knees, head on hands"—W. K.

"Our first boy, who is now four years old, when he was a baby used to sleep in a kneeling down position, with his face resting on the pillow"—Knight.

"He sleeps on his face with his knees up"—Leonard, two years, three months.

"Little girl cousin slept on her face with her knees under her chest"—Leonard.

"Slept on knees and chest, rather like the attitude of a Moslem at prayer"—Mason, boy.

"I must have slept curled up because they told me that they would have to bury me in a cheese box if I died in my sleep"—May, girl.

"Slept with knees up often"—Sherry, girl.

"All the children slept most of the time on their stomachs. Katharine sometimes drew her knees up under her and slept that way, looking for all the world like a little rabbit"—Wells.

Sleeping on stomach, hands and feet folded under the body—Many.

An isolated case is that of the Becker boy who, "since a year old, sleeps on hands and knees or with knees drawn up under him, at one end of bed. Before year old always slept on back."

Recourse to All Fours When in Hurry or from Enjoyment, after Walking Erect

Many of these children continue more or less to run on all fours for varying periods after they have learned to walk on two. In a large majority of cases the reason for this, as observed by the parents, is the desire or a temporary need of making more speed. In some cases the child resorts to the method, and that occasionally until well up in childhood, from pure preference or enjoyment.

Preference of Fours Method.

"He is just taking his first steps now [one year], but much prefers to run around like a little bear"—Barondes.

"When he gets in a hurry he still goes on all fours at fifteen months"—Leonard.

"When in a hurry—up and on all fours and go like the wind"—Talbot.

"He often started to walk on two feet and, finding that method too slow, went on all fours"—Wyllie.

"Even now, when he walks, will resort to the swifter, surer method of the animal, particularly if he is fleeing from danger"—Mitchell.

"At fourteen months he still makes use of the method [on all fours] to insure speed and safe footing, apparently"—Leversee.

"Always fell back to all fours when tired or in a hurry"—Talbot.

Resorts to all fours [after learning to walk] "when vexed over something"—J. W. Smith.

"Now at three and one-half years when she wants a real hilarious time she says, 'Mama, let's play bear' and this means a chase with her on all fours"—Talbot.

"Used to run on all fours between school hours just for enjoyment"—Nagle.

The facts shown by the above quotations, which could be greatly multiplied, are of importance. They show that frequently the ancestral animal method is both easier and more effective, than the later and at that period of life as yet imperfect mode of walking erect. The all-fours method is evidently a method in the direction of least resistance, and hence greater effectiveness as well as enjoyment. Enjoyment of the method is in reality general, at whatever age it is indulged in. Its sources are the ease of the motion and the speed acquired. There is also an element of vanity in some of these little ones, they like to show off and be admired. But where the parents discourage the practice, the children will resort to all fours when they believe nobody sees them, showing that there is a purely personal gratification in the procedure.

Running on All Fours in Dreams

These cases are of peculiar interest. They show a participation in the manifestation of the deeper brain activities. There are three of these instances reported, but the experience may be more frequent.

The first of these reports is that of Mr. Gage. He says: "I have had several times dreams, generally nightmares, in which when pursued I was forced to run on my hands and feet in order to escape. In all of these dreams I realized that this was undignified and felt humiliated at being compelled to resort to it, and yet I knew that I could run on all fours faster than on two feet." He does not know whether he ran on all fours as a child.

The second very interesting account is that of my friend Dr. Thone, whose sister, and probably whose mother, ran in childhood on all fours and who also did so himself in infancy. He told me of some peculiar dreams which he describes thus:

In my dream I find myself fleeing in terror from some unknown pursuer, running as fast as I am able, bending my body somewhat forward. My arms must be a good deal longer than normal, although if this is the case I have never taken notice of it. At any rate, in my haste and anxiety to get away I find myself frequently placing my hands on the ground and vaulting forward on them, very much as I have seen long-armed apes do in running about the floors of their cages. This terrified flight of which I dream usually takes .place through a rather open woodland, and sometimes on the side of a hill. But whether I am running up hill or down, I assist my feet with my hands.

The third case is that of May E. May who says:

Dreaming if I wanted to get away from some terrible indefinable menace which has always beset me asleep and often awake, I took to all fours. If in my dreams tonight I was beset by this threat I would get down and run on my hands and feet, but I do not run as animals do; my arms do more of the work than my legs. I pull myself forward in an unexplainable way, and several times in my life when running to catch a car or hastening to keep an appointment I have had a momentary impulse to get down on all fours.

BELATED RUNNING ON ALL FOURS

In rare cases the tendency to run on all fours does not manifest itself until after the child has commenced to walk erect. In a way these cases are particularly instructive, showing that there is a distinct and separate proneness to the all-fours method and that this is not merely a prelude and means toward the erect position.

There are three good, well-authenticated examples of such delayed manifestation. Professor Worcester's boy "started walking at about thirteen months, and between fifteen and sixteen months, after his walking habit was quite well developed, he took to running on all fours." While in the case of Master Stone, he "crept like other children, but at the age of three or four in his play, indoors or outdoors, he ran, of his own will, on all fours."

Frank Thone was a normal creeper as a baby; but he says "I do recall that as a child of seven or eight I used to 'go quadruped' as a stunt to amuse my younger cousins, and used to carry them on my back in that way." His family history as well as some of his own (see "Dreams") makes it more than probable that this was not mere play or imitation.

PROLONGATION OF THE HABIT

In some cases the running on all fours becomes so ingrained, or so liked, that it is more or less persisted in until late in childhood; and for reasons not as yet well studied, it may be met with even in adult life.

The Hinton boy "is five years old now, and he has been going on all fours from the time he was eight months old"; he walks erect since he was fourteen months old, but for speed resorted after that to the all-fours, and "even now, when he plays 'wild animal,' it's down on hands and feet."

"A great-nephew of my wife, an unusually active, agile child and very bright mentally. He visited us when he was about six years of age and it was wonderfully interesting to see him walk, trot, and gallop as the dog does. Apparently with as much ease as walking on his feet alone, or with as much ease as a dog."—C. S. Miller.

The Gaddas boy walked alone on two at twelve months, "but still ran on all fours for greater speed. Continued on all fours in decreasing amount up to 15 months or more, and still does it very easily at the age of ten years."

Nagle, who always could easily run on all fours eventually commercialized his ability and performs "the cat" most effectively to date, at thirty-one.

Dr. Walter Hough remembers "a colored boy about twenty years old, named 'Snap' Dorsey, who could run on all fours as readily as a dog. He was a livery-stable attendant at Morgantown, West Virginia, about 1870. He was proud of his skill as it gave him notice, which the negro at that period craved very much. Snap ran races with boys in the livery-stable yard and so far as I know always won. As I remember, he ran with head up. His strength and activity were phenomenal."

Mrs. Thone, now fifty-five, "practiced quadrupedism ever since she was a child . . . and is still able to do it. She does not know whether she was a naturally quadruped infant."

And Miss Frazer, Indian teacher, reports the following case which, unfortunately, could not be traced further: "We have a very strange and interesting case of an old Indian man, known as 'the Creeper.' He is now about seventy and is an Indian medicine man. He is deformed, *i.e.*, his lower leg is very short. The distance between his knee and foot is about six or eight inches. He runs around like a bear, his head upheld and walking on the palms of his hands. Sometimes the Indians call him 'the Bear.' "

These records make it plain that, rarely, the ability of and inclination to the running on all fours is much prolonged beyond infancy, and may remain if exercised more or less late into life. It is quite probable that in the latter cases structural factors and possibly even injuries or other pathological factors and conditions may play an important contributing rôle.

EFFECTS OF THE ALL-FOURS HABIT ON WALKING UPRIGHT

The most common effect of the all-fours method of progression appears to be more or less of a delay in walking erect.

"He was slow to begin to walk upright because the other way was so quick and easy"—Roberts.

This seems to tell the story for many of these children. They are quite satisfied with their easy and rapid on-all-fours, and were they left to their own devices and not influenced by other examples, they might possibly keep on, on hands and feet, for a longer time, if not indefinitely. It would be interesting to experiment in this line, to see how near some humans, at least, may in reality still be to quadrupeds.

Nevertheless there is evidence that the erect habit also has already a considerable force, so that probably the majority of even these infants would sooner or later start on walking erect though they were not prompted to do so by word or example. And there are instances of children who, notwithstanding the all-fours habit, do walk normally or even early.

There are in our records a number of references to the delay in walking occasioned by the quadruped progression. Thus, with the Treidel girl—"She finally got so that she was running on all fours without making any attempt at walking erect."

"She just seemed not to find walking necessary"—Bowen.
"She did not seem interested in learning to walk"—Burchard.
The speed with which he could thus get about on all fours "was a reason, we thought, why he delayed walking so long . . . he did not walk until eighteen months old"—Ganong.

"She is seventeen and one-half months old and won't attempt to walk upright unless someone leads her," though running much faster than the average child can on all fours—E. B. Jones.

"It seemed to me that he did not acquire skill in walking as rapidly as children who used the two-legged method entirely"—E. K. W.

"I feel sure that the oldest child could have walked much sooner than he did (at sixteen months) but it was possible for him to get about with such ease and rapidity on all fours that he evidently did not see the necessity of adopting any other method of locomotion"—R. M. Kirby-Smith.

Another interesting expression of the delay in the start to walk erect is the frequent suddenness and full-fledgedness of such a start. The generally robust child keeps on running on all fours until one day, suddenly, without trials and unaided, it rises to a standing position in the middle of the floor, soon after which it begins to walk. The function has evidently been delayed until the child is quite ready for the upright posture and progression. The following few quotations will show how some of these children behaved. In some of them, where walking erect was adopted in good time, the generally very good physical condition and strength may have been responsible for the lack of a period of preparation.

"After he began to walk [fourteenth month] he seemed very sure of himself"—Auten.

After she started to walk [twelve and one-half months] "in a week she could walk as good as a child that had walked a year"—Bahl.

"She was over fourteen months old before she took her first steps unsupported; however, she became at once very steady on her feet"—Burchard.

Ran on fours until one year old; "all at once she stood up alone and walked from then on"—Cornell.

"She did not walk upright until she was twelve and one-half months of age, but when she started to walk she never faltered or wobbled"—Coeyman.

Walked upright when thirteen and one-half months old; "she could walk nearly as good when she began as she can now"—Cumberworth.

"Two days after a year old he raised right up in the middle of the room and walked upright from then on"—Daugherty.

Ran "bear-fashion, until he pulled himself upright to a standing position in the middle of the floor without holding on to anything at the age of about 11 months"—Fritts.

"She walked in an upright position at thirteen months; she apparently had no difficulty for she walked off immediately when she discovered she could step"—Green.

"She continued running on all fours until the day before her first birthday when suddenly she picked herself up, stood erect and proceeded to walk without any support whatever"—Lund.

"When he started to walk [at eleven months] he simply raised himself from the floor and started out with a great deal of confidence, going a few steps at a time"—Van Kirk.

Running on All Fours and Bow-leggedness

The lower limbs of the infant are generally longer than the upper. In some cases they are relatively longer than in others, and in all the difference increases with age. As a result the body in the all-fours position, if the legs are held straight, slopes more or less down towards the front, which is a disturbance of balance and thereby a disadvantage. This disadvantage the child tries to overcome by spreading its lower limbs and (or) by bending the knees. But these aids are not perfect and have some disadvantages of their own. Thus it happens that in many cases there develops, evidently, more or less of a tension outwards on the lower limbs, and this tension appears occasionally to cause moderate bow-leggedness. Such bow-leggedness has no connection with rickets and generally disappears without any treatment after the child walks erect. Yet there may be instances where some trace of it is left.

Examples

John Henry Gahm, seventeen months, "when he stands up is very bow-legged; his knees being about six and one-half inches apart and his feet about five inches apart."

Master Jefferson, who started walking on all fours at about a year, was not allowed to get up on his feet as early as he wanted to "due to bowed legs."

W. K.'s very remarkable little girl "in walking on all fours treads upon the outer rim of the foot and grips the ground with her toes. This gives her a decided pigeon-toed and bow-legged appearance, although in rest her legs are normally straight."

Master Laurence, "when he started to walk upright [after a period of running on all fours], was a bit bow-legged, but soon outgrew that."

Little Miss Roach who until recently was a four-walker, "is slightly bow-legged." While Master Downes "when he first started to walk at fifteen months [after running on all fours] was very bow-legged indeed."

Finally, in Mrs. Treidel's family, where both the mother and her little daughter ran on all fours before walking; in the words of the mother, "my legs below my knees are not perfectly straight and I toe in slightly. Her legs are shaped exactly like mine and she walks just as I do."

These and other reports concerning all healthy strong children without any suggestion of rickets, indicate that the all-fours progression does in some cases at least favor the development of slight to moderate bow-leggedness; but in nearly all cases this rights itself spontaneously after the child learns to walk erect and needs to cause therefore no serious apprehension on the part of the parents.

MENTALITY OF THE CHILDREN WHO RUN ON
ALL FOURS

AFTER we have learned that a certain proportion of human infants will for a shorter or longer period run on all fours; decided that this is, in all probability, a remnant of the pre-human past; and found that physically such children are as a class above rather than below the average, the most insistent next question is, naturally, "What about their mentality?"

Mentality is a great and intricate complex, however, even in an infant, and its evaluation is much more difficult than that of physique. But the little child has not yet learned how to dissemble and so, to its mother at least, it gives plenty of indications of its brain workings, both in general and in special manifestations. And most mothers are intently observant of their own babies, though they may lack in experience and discrimination and are prone to extol the good qualities of their own little idols.

Notwithstanding all this, those who will read the precious documents gathered in this volume cannot but be impressed with the evident sincerity of the reporters, both mothers and fathers, and with the consequent value of the reports, even as to the mentalities of the children concerned. Moreover, time and again, there are or were other children in the family, even twins, with whom the "runner on all fours" could be contrasted. And the overwhelming testimony, supported in many instances by school and college records, is that, as a rule, the children who showed this peculiarity are not only normal to decidedly above average physically, but also mentally. They show, it is true, various other quaint behaviors, but they are in general mentally strong and often markedly bright children, leaders among their brothers and sisters, leaders in schools.

Being healthy they too are mostly of a good, happy disposition:

"She is mentally very keen and of a very sunny disposition"—Roach.
"He was a gay and jolly baby, and so proud of his athletic prowess"—Roberts.

"Is very good natured"—Seaman, boy.

"Has a perfect disposition"—Barker, girl.

"Disposition lovable"—Treidel, girl.

"Of happy disposition"—Sevringhaus, boy.

"Sunny, thoughtful"—Sims, boy.

"He is a very happy child and always has been"—E. C. Smith.

"If there is anything out of the ordinary about this kid it is the way she dances around on her toes, claps her hands, etc., as an expression of delight"—Stenger; girl, two years five months.

"He has been an extremely happy and lively baby"—Versfelt.

"She is unusually good-natured. She laughed where most babies cried—she even laughed when she fell and hurt herself"—Whitson; girl, twenty-eight months.

"Extremely good-natured and affectionate"—Leonard, boy.

And such quotations could be multiplied. In some cases, however, there are interesting peculiarities of disposition. The following show lack of fear and unusual strength of character:

"As a child was recklessly daring . . . never afraid of animals or bugs, dead or alive"—Ahlberg, girl.

"He is afraid of nothing at all"—Berney; boy, fourteen and one-half months.

"Most determined, cannot be moved by compulsion or punishment" —LeSourd; girl, eleven months.

"Independent, won't let me do anything for her that she can do herself"—Whitson; girl, two years four months.

"Her memory and tenacity of an idea is remarkable, also persistence" —F. Parker; girl, thirteen months.

"Had a high temper; contented, not nervous, very active, strong willed"—Sherry; girl, now fifteen years, controlled.

Has high temper—"boisterous and tempestuous"—W. K.; girl, three and one-half years old.

Normally destructive [without anger]—Casseday, girl.

In one case, that of the E. C. W. boy, now eight years the willfulness of the child has gone evidently beyond the normal bounds.

A few cases only show a sensitive or nervous disposition:

She is "very quick and rather nervous"—Abramowitz.

Always nervous, a poor sleeper—Young, boy.

"Nervous and high strung to a high degree"—Younger, boy.

"He seemed excessively shy, never would say anything"—Rees, boy.

"Is very sensitive about being laughed at, as was his older brother" [also four-walker]—Abercrombie, boy.

Some of these cases may be those of quite normal but unusually self-conscious children; while others are in all probability due to disturbances of health, connected perhaps with the digestive and eliminative organs.

Aside of all this there are more or less odd dispositions:

"Is precocious, sensitive, and extremely affectionate"—Walter, boy.
"Likes to play by herself"—F. Parker, girl.
"Does not mix easily with other children"—Pedenboy, boy.

Contrasted with which is the A. N. Bowen boy, one year two weeks old, who is a "regular cyclone; not still one moment."

MENTAL ABILITIES

A large majority of the children who run on all fours are decidedly bright children, which is in accord with their above-average health and strength. There are great many statements to this effect which, even if presumed to be a bit biased, have nevertheless plainly substantial value.

EXAMPLES

"He is very bright and normal in every way except trying to act like a little bear"—Leonard.

Above average in his school work, finishing highest in his room—Albers.

Is now, at nineteen, "a Senior in Radcliffe College"—G. P. B.

"Does some of the motor and mechanical tests of children older than he"—P. L. Smith.

"Exceptionally bright," [always]—Bakalyars, girl.

Showed "early interest [two and one-half years] in letters and numbers as well as to what promises to be real mechanical genius"—Baud, boy.

"His intelligence is at least average"—Beebe.

"The child is very smart"—Berney, boy.

"She is a very bright child"—Bliss.

"The child has been precocious both physically and mentally"—Bowen.

"He is very bright, quick to learn"—Brooks.

At one year—"he seems to his admiring adult relatives the brightest child there ever was"—Buchanan.

"She seems somewhat advanced in both physical and mental development (not only in our prejudiced eyes, but by comparison with standards)"—Burchard.

"Every day we are marveling at the way he develops," [both physically and mentally]—Byerley.

"She graduated at the head of her class at high school this year with the highest mark for the four years; there were 178 in her class"—Cannon.

"At four years had mentality of seven-year child" [by actual test]—Wood, boy.

And there could be pages of such quotations, with a moderate number of "just normal" and but very rare instances of subnormal or abnormal.

ENJOYMENT OF THE ALL-FOURS PROGRESSION BY THE CHILDREN

There are many indications that the children running on all fours enjoy the procedure. The enjoyment is mostly subconscious and is the exhilaration of easy coordinate motions and progression; but soon the liking and pleasure become more sensible or rational. The little being is in his element. He is discharging his energies in a natural and pleasurable way, and reaching or galloping or running away, as he wants to. He is the master of his environment in this for him just then all-important direction. No wonder that he "seems very happy running about that way"—Lason; or that the parents "have never seen anyone enjoy locomotion as she did [on the fours]"—H. N. Parker. Nagle, as a boy, was "knocked all about the house" for his habit of running on all fours, besides being laughed at; "but kept on because he liked it."

LOOKING BACKWARD BETWEEN FEET WHEN ON ALL FOURS

The sound human baby is a bundle of mental qualities at which one never ceases to be astonished. One of the earliest of these qualities is curiosity, another secretiveness, while still another, somewhat later, is humor. It is the first and last that probably, together with convenience, are most involved when a tot running on all fours stops for a moment and looks at things or people through the space between its legs. The occurrence doubtless is not infrequent, but only a few of the parents thought it worth while for separate mention. The following two describe the procedure sufficiently:

Molly Harper, fourteen months, "while 'bear-walking,' lowered her head and looked back between her legs at a child behind her" [from a diary kept by her mother].

As to Miss Maslen, nineteen months, "she will put her hands and feet flat on the ground with her fingers wide open and she will sometimes put her head on the ground and try to see behind her."

Actions such as these are naturally of no special importance, but they enrich our notions of infant behavior.

LIKES AND DISLIKES

Our detail documents contain notes on various likes and dislikes of the children who run on all fours. Some of these are quite ordinary, others peculiar. Some may have none, others a strong connection with what is behind the all-fours manifestation.

These likes and dislikes may be motor, sensory, or mental, or of a complex motor-mental or sensory and mental nature.

EXAMPLES

Motor.

"She is very fond of rough-house playing"—Parker; girl, thirteen months.

"She is very limber and enjoys rough handling"—Schlenk; girl, fifteen months.

Showed a "strong dislike of being held in one's lap," even before he had finished nursing—Bevis.

Sensory-mental.

"As early as three months she seemed to like colors, like blue and lilac, but screamed in terror when a relative clad in mourning came to see her. She showed a most intense dislike for people with grey hair as early as five months"—Casseday.

"When her dad put a new pair of pretty beaded moccasins on her feet and held them up for her to see she yelled and would not be pacified until her pink ones were put back on her feet"—Fraser.

"Has distaste for clothing; apt to appear anywhere, at any time with no clothing on; but she has a passion for self-adornment—a fluffy dress, a string of gaudy wooden beads, or the contents of a bottle of mercurochrome all rank alike"—W. K.; girl, three and one-half years.

"Does not mind when she slips and fills her ears, eyes, and nose full of water. Part fish, I think"—Miss Bourne, nine months.

Preference of Raw Food.

"He always liked raw vegetables, and cares very little for meat"—Olsen.

"In appetite she prefers raw fruits and vegetables to the cooked sorts. She will spurn sweet puddings or rusk and milk for a handful of shelled peas or bit of banana"—W. K.; girl, one year five and one-half months.

In many cases the parents whose attention was not specially directed to this subject have doubtless not reported on the likes and dislikes of these children; but there were probably not many striking cases or they would have been mentioned. Here as in many other lines there opens a field for new interesting researches. Just what of these manifestations belongs and what does not belong to the syndrome that in locomotion is marked by the running on all fours, must for the present remain uncertain. That some of these manifestations have a distinct animal flavor is, I think, quite apparent.

Music, Rhythm

When does the infant begin to appreciate music, and what kind of music? We know but very little on this subject. In general we are often painfully conscious of their love of loud and not particularly concordant noises, the propensity for which lasts not seldom, especially with boys, well into adolescence. It is also known that in rare cases there appears a genuine inclination to music in early childhood, perhaps as early as the first and certainly as early as the third year. But in a large majority of infants there seems to be little if any "ear" for the more advanced or what could be called the more intellectual forms of music. In place of this there is apparently a generalized responsiveness to rhythm. This responsiveness is discharged through corresponding rhythmic movements of the limbs and body that plainly are pleasurable. Rhythm could be defined as motor music. It is an earlier form and one appreciable even by various animals. The modern jazz, aside from its degenerate cacophonies, is merely a reversion in or from music.

A study of children in these respects will doubtless be very revealing. The subject has already attracted scientific attention, but is in need of a systematic study on large numbers and by modern methods. Edwin A. Kirkpatrick[1] discusses it as follows:

The universal tendency to rhythm in action may be considered under the head of instinctive tendencies, though it is really an organic and automatic tendency even more fundamental than an instinct.

[1] In "Fundamentals of Child Study," p. 233, New York, 1917.

Rhythm is a marked feature in physical phenomena as well as in plant and animal life. In man, all bodily processes are rhythmic, and all repeated movement tends to take a rhythmic form. It is not surprising, therefore, that consciousness is rhythmic. There are rhythms of attention, activity is followed by rest, and one emotional extreme is succeeded by its opposite. Consciousness even makes rhythmic what is objectively without rhythm, as when continuous and uniform beats of a metronome are heard as rhythmic beats.

The more instinctive form of the rhythmic tendency is shown in the impulse to produce rhythmic movements and sounds, and to appreciate or respond in a particular way when such rhythms are produced by others. Both of these tendencies are manifested in the first few months of infancy.

The records on the children who run on all fours contain no reference to a real musical appreciation. Of the few notes there are on rhythm, two are rather interesting:

The Roberts boy "is very fond of dance music and jazz. The W. K.'s girl "has very good sense of rhythm," dancing spontaneously "to accented rhythm and jazz."

To which may perhaps be added the case of the Thompson boy, who shakes things violently [crib, fence of his enclosure, high chair]—"always with a rhythmical motion."

INVENTIVENESS

Two of our records show a remarkable inventiveness in direct connection with the running on all fours. In some of these infants the arms are, relatively to the lower limbs, shorter than in others, which when the child is on its hands and feet would disturb the balance of the body. To overcome this the children adopt usually one or the other or both of two expedients, which are a spreading of the "hind" limbs, or bending the knees. But in these two cases the child adopted an artificial means for the lengthening of its arms. Thus, Nagle used to take wooden blocks in his hands, which both raised his arms a bit and permitted him to imitate the sound of a running horse. In this case the imitation was probably the main motive. But with the two Brown boys, twins, in about their eleventh month, the case was different. "They had some aluminum cups with which they played and within a short time after they began walking this way [on all fours], they began taking an aluminum cup in each hand to lengthen their arms to nearly the length of their legs and it was common for three months after that for them to find two aluminum cups and walk around on all fours."[1]

A somewhat related case is that of the little Casseday girl who learned the placing of her hands, while on all fours, on a piece of paper and slide them, propelling herself with her feet. "During the time she was running on all fours she found a magazine cover of very slick paper. She discovered she could make a great deal of speed by resting her hands on the paper and using her legs only. I assure you it was a good show."

These, it is plain, are interesting glimpses of a psychological nature that only incidentally are connected with the propensity to four-footedness.

HUMAN MIMICRY

Aside and apparently separate from the tendency to imitate animals, some of the children of our group manifested a marked human mimicry. None of these subjects imitated animals and none of those who imitated animals were reported as also good human mimics, which suggests that the two manifestations are quite different. The cases are reported as follows:

"He seems very imitative of both sounds and actions"—Master Graves, fifteen months.

"Mimicking, in both words and actions, is one of her most pronounced characteristics"—Harper; girl, two years one month.

"Very imitative, a good mimic"—Paul; boy, now fourteen years old.

It is not known how frequent these qualities are in children who have not run on all fours; but the above records convey little if any suggestion of anything unusual.

The subject of imitation in the child has received considerable attention. Those interested may be referred especially to Kilpatrick's, "Fundamentals of Child Study," pages 163–171, New York, 1917.

RUNNING ON ALL FOURS THROUGH IMITATION

As a rule the infants who run on all fours develop that method of locomotion spontaneously. The testimony to this effect is overwhelming. The most convincing cases perhaps are those of the

[1] Prof. F. E. Brown, Ames College.

Freeman and the Welker twins, one of which in each case ran on all fours while the other never did; such as that of the two Shive boys, the older of which developed the habit: "His brother, two years younger, even with the monkey-like example of John constantly before him, never attempted quadruped walking"; and such as that of the Metcalf boy, whose "case is not one of imitation, but rather one of instinct," for "there were no household pets and no examples."

But there are well-known instances where older children will endeavor to run on all fours in play, in willful imitation of a dog, etc., and there are reported in our records a few cases where a child who had never run on all fours tried to imitate one who did. As in play so here the attempts are generally more or less clumsy and lead seldom to a habit; where they do, and even in other cases, these "imitators" may well have been masked or imperfect four-runners. More common are cases where a child imitates other animal behaviors and which will be dealt with separately.

EXAMPLES

"He can go much faster than his three-year old sister who sometimes imitates his gait because she thinks it so amusing"—Fritts.

"No other child in the family progressed in this way excepting a cousin of the same age who sometimes did it in imitation"—Green.

"The older child [little girl] learned to run on all fours from the baby and both still do so chiefly for amusement"—Schlenk.

PECULIARITIES OF SPEECH

Some of the infants who ran on all fours have shown, aside from their general mental stamp, certain peculiarities in one or another special direction. These are individual idiosyncrasies which in some cases may merely be curious family traits, while in others their origin and significance are not understood. Some appear to connect with prehuman practices. Several kinds manifest themselves in connection with speech. They may be subdivided as follows:

Precocity.—The Bacon girl began to talk—"three words upon recognizing the object, at six months; at one year she used forty words easily."

The Baud boy was "punctilious of speech from the very beginning."

Retardation.—On the other hand some more of these children showed a retardation in talking.

Little Miss Ward, though nineteen months old and finely developed, and "although she is very alert and responsive, does not talk much yet."

The Wyant's girl "was very slow at getting started to talk." And there could be quoted several other examples.

Language of Their Own.—Some babies develop more or less a "language" of their own. Thus the very interesting Miss Casseday "developed a language of her own of which I [the mother] understood only a few words; however, when I asked her to repeat she always repeated the same sounds . . . At two and one-half years she could put but few words into sentences . . . Now [five years eight months] she has a vocabulary much beyond her years."

And Miss Wyant, "along about fifteen to sixteen months she started to jabber fast, long stories with all the intonations of conversation yet no intelligible word"; but, "shortly after she was eighteen months old she began to talk and her progress was nothing short of remarkable."

Slowness in Reading.—There are several records indicating that some of these infants who ran on all fours, when arriving at the school age, show but little inclination towards reading or books, though otherwise quite normal and with good abilities.

An especially interesting case of this nature is that of Master Bevis who, though at six and one-half he has finished the second grade, "has no interest in reading, although he excels in spelling and has an unusual vocabulary and real feeling for language. His vision is perfect. This lack of interest in reading is peculiar because his father and I, both college trained, read a great deal"—Mrs. Bevis.

The second interesting case is that of Master Sims who while, according to his mother's report, "is an extremely normal child, sunny, thoughtful, and without any other peculiarities, is very slow at books, though very intuitive and observant. Oldest and youngest children much quicker than he."

Animal-like Sounds in Place of Talk.—Occasionally one encounters in the documents here gathered a mention of an infant who ran on all fours, and who, before and even for some time after learning to speak, used animal-like sounds. As these were otherwise all normal children the peculiarity deserves attention. The detailed reports, four in number, read as follows:

"Her first call to me [mother] was a natural bleat like a lamb 'mam'; I can hear it yet"—Fraser.

The Leonard boy, fifteen months, "instead of talking squeals most expressively. He can say words when he wants to but he insists on making his wants known by different kinds of squealing."

The Stutler boy, two years old, "says some words quite plainly but makes many queer sounds."

And the Thompson boy, fifteen and one-half months, when shaking things, "always with a rhythmical motion, often emits peculiar cries during this proceeding, rather like a monkey in his cage."

All this opens another vista for interesting research.

Phobias

There are many peculiar phobias in childhood. They range from acquired and subsequently more or less eradicable fears to seemingly innate, deep-set conditions that will last until they run out their period and often persist throughout life. Direct or indirect heredity, with strong frights and other affects in infancy, play here their parts.

But a few "phobias" are given in our records. As there was no particular inquiry on this subject it did not receive full attention. But considering the painstaking reports of many of the parents it may be assumed that had there been striking instances of such "peculiarities" they would have been mentioned.

As it is there are less than half a dozen of such notes and they are of no serious nature. The Baxter boy "is afraid of tortoise-shell-rimmed glasses and of anyone wearing them, but does not seem to mind any other kind." Master Seaman is "afraid of feathers or small chickens."

Abnormal Tastes and Idiosyncrasies

Abnormal tastes and idiosyncrasies involving taste have no recognizable connection with the animal-like manifestations in children that form the subject of this volume. But they occur now and then in such children, as they do in others. A painstaking inquiry into this particular matter would, I feel confident, find another unexplored and surprisingly rich nook. I am tempted to say in fact, on the basis of my medical as well as other experience, that there is probably no child, as there is no grown individual, in whom something could not be found in these directions. But such striking cases as those to be mentioned here are not common.

I have learned now of three cases where an apparently healthy child ate soap, and of two where it ate dirt. One of the subjects did both, the dirt eating following the soap. Two of the soap eaters, both male children, are cases outside of those reported here and one of these does, while the other did not (so far as known), run on all fours. The cases included in these records are a girl who ran on all fours; whose mother tells us: "When a year old she started to eat soap every time she could find any and seemed to enjoy it though she would be sick afterwards. At fourteen months until eighteen months she would run away to go out into the orchard to eat dirt, carefully selecting it and then eating with evident relish" (would not eat candy or cake).

The other case is that of a brother of a boy who walked on all fours but who himself did not. "He ate dirt until he was four or five years old."

A most unusual case finally, reported here, is that of a four-walking little girl in whose case "all milks poisoned her."—I. S. B.

These more severe cases I believe to be connected with some hidden partial peculiarities of the central nervous system. Such peculiarities may be of hereditary nature, or may be conditioned indirectly through the digestive organs.

BANGING THE HEAD

Some of the showings of the all-fours children are hard to classify, hard to understand. One of these, reported in three cases, is that of banging the head. None of these children apparently are neurotic. Perhaps the phenomenon is a variety of muscular discharge without much meaning; though it is more probable that there are definite, and that possibly not always physiological, causes for these peculiar manifestations. The reports are as follows:

During an ill spell he formed "a habit of banging his head against the end of his bed, hard enough to cause a discolored bruise . . . still persists in this habit, especially when sleepy, angry, or disturbed in any way"—Thompson.

"To express anger or joy or tense excitement he hits his head on the floor or the wall or whatever is handy"—Younger.

Winifred, one of the trio of four-walkers of Mrs. Wells, used to have peculiar waking spells. "The first came when she was nine or ten months old and lasted about two months, if I remember aright.

Every night about 12 o'clock she woke and laughed, peal after peal of laughter, till about 2 o'clock, when she grew fretful and hungry, was fed and went to sleep again. When she was about two, I think it was, she had another period of wakefulness at night. She did not laugh then, but kept up a kind of rhythmical 'mmm-mmm-mmm' until she went to sleep again. Still later she used to beat her head up and down on the pillow. These things lasted for a while, then stopped for a period, to begin again later and again stop."

Thumb Sucking

There are a few mentions in our reports of thumb sucking. Just what this habit means is still uncertain, except that it is connected with the general mammalian sucking instinct. The subject has received more or less attention by medical men and dentists. It is perhaps best dealt with by J. Thomson:[1]

The habit assumes different forms, according to the object sucked. In some cases the mouth and tongue are the only parts used. The child shuts his mouth and moves his tongue to and fro sucking the inside of the lips and cheeks. Sometimes the lips are parted and the tongue is partially protruded during the act, and then it is called "sucking the tongue." In other cases a part of the body outside of the mouth is sucked, commonly the thumb or one or more of the fingers of either hand; less frequently the back of the hand or a part of the arm, or even the big toe. In a third class some foreign body is chosen to suck—the mouthpiece of a baby's bottle, the corner of a sheet or night-dress, or a kneaded-up piece of bread.

Generally the children take the same thing every time to suck, but rarely one meets with a child who will change, *e.g.*, from one finger to another or from the tongue to the arm, and so on.

Very often the cases are simple, that is to say, the sucking of one of the above mentioned objects constitutes the whole habit, but not rarely we meet with cases which have become complicated in an interesting way. The complications arise from the child's discovering that by practicing some other little action with the free hand or hands at the same time that he is sucking he can heighten the pleasure derived from it.

Thomson considers this and related habits as "infantile dissipations."

[1] "On Some Curious Habits in Children," *Child Study Monthly*, vol. II, pp. 93–94, 1896.

There are a number of brief incidental references to thumb sucking in our records. They need not be quoted separately. A rather interesting case, however, is that of the Thompson boy who "sucked his thumb from six months to one year . . . stopped entirely all at once."

OTHER ANIMAL-LIKE MANIFESTATIONS

CLIMBING

THE most frequent accompanying animal-like manifestation among the children who develop running on all fours, is climbing. It is also about the best known of the class of phenomena here considered. There are comparatively numerous references to it in the literature on children, though few go into any details. The exceptions are the communications of Buckman, Trettien, Westenhöfer, and especially the most recent treatise on the whole subject of climbing by Prof. F. Smotlacha of Prague.

Dr. Buckman[1] says, "Nowhere is a stage of a former arboreal life, with its consequent climbing instinct, manifested more conspicuously than in the insane desire of an infant to climb upstairs. As soon as crawling is an accomplishment the climbing of stairs is attempted. Remain on the level and crawl about rooms the child will not; it must make for the nearest stairs to climb with loud crows of delight. Tumbles and consequent bruises have no effect on the child's climbing instinct."

For Trettien,[2]

Climbing is one of the early impulses of children. Indeed, some of them manifest this desire as soon as they begin to creep. The desire to climb seems to arise in a desire to explore every available spot and practice every known movement. As arms and hands precede the legs in functional development, children may be seen pulling their bodies up alongside a chair, a table leg or other object even before their legs are able to bear the weight of the body. An observer says of a little girl ten months old—"this child could climb upon chairs, upon the table and upon the refrigerator before she could walk. She had several falls, but nothing would stop this desire to climb until she learned to walk, then it seemed to pass away." There is a desire in the child to get up higher. This impulse leads it not only to draw the body into a standing position but

[1] BUCKMAN, S. S., "Babies and Monkeys," *Pop. Sci. Monthly*, vol. XLVI, p. 378, 1894–1895.

[2] TRETTIEN, AUGUST W., "Creeping and Walking," *Amer. Jour. Psychol.*, vol. XII, no. 1, pp. 34–35, 1900.

also to get to the top of every attainable object. In the case cited, the desire to climb was inhibited by the ability to walk. This is not common in children, as the ability to walk simply opens a wider range for their activity and thus favors it by an increased muscular vigor. Fear of high places or of falling is not at all common in the first acts of climbing. It is only after they have had several calamitous experiences that fear in some case may restrain this activity. As the child grows in strength, the skill it acquires as a climber is quite remarkable at times, from chairs, tables and other furniture to fences, gates, ladders, and trees.

Trettien has also an interesting paragraph on infants climbing stairs:

In going up and down stairs, of the different ways employed the most common is creeping, in which the child goes up on its hands and knees, or hands and feet; in coming down it will creep backwards, putting down its feet first on the next lower step. A child, in both ascending and descending a flight of stairs, will often turn to see how far up it has gone. Another manner of climbing stairs is that of creeping up and then turn and sit down on the step and slide down to the next one below, using the hands to steady the body. Some children go up stairs by drawing themselves up alongside of the banister with their hands, and step up with their feet. This is a more mature method and is only employed by those children who have already learned to walk. An exception to the general manner is found in a little boy who went down stairs head foremost. He put his hands on the step and then let the body slide down after him.

Dr. Westenhöfer's publication[1] was not seen, but has been utilized by the most recent author on the subject, Dr. Smotlacha.[2] The latter author gives many interesting illustrations of both infants and older subjects showing progress in climbing, grasping, balance, and other motor manifestations. Among his illustrations there are several figures that show a child walking up a tree instead of shinning; there are interesting illustrations showing infants and children climbing up on ladders and otherwise. Besides which there is a mention of one case and an illustration of one case (Fig. 67) of an infant running on all fours. Dr. Smotlacha, who was already acquainted with our publications on the children running

[1] WESTENHÖFER, M., "Über die Klettermethoden der Naturvölker und über die Stellung der grossen Zehe," *Arch. Frauenk. und Konstitutionsforsch.*, vol. XIII, Heft 5, 1927.
[2] SMOTLACHA, F., "Biologické Základy Záliby Člověka ve Šplhu a Visu," 211 pp., Praha, 1930.

on all fours, refers these phenomena correctly to the biological inheritance of the infant.

Climbing is a complex, coordinated, objective action. The human infant has no business to climb. He has no need, no object, no advantage in doing it, except so far as it is connected with the need and pleasure of muscular activity. He falls again and again and suffers for it, even to breaking his bones. If he, and just as well she, persist in climbing, on anything and everything climbable, and that from long before their actions are directed by any reason, then the manifestation can only be an expression, it would seem, of something that was decidedly of use, that was an inherent and extensive function in times earlier human or prehuman. The elementary tendency of many of these infants, who already are manifesting in a pronounced way another important prehuman affinity towards climbing, cannot be regarded as other than reminiscent of the far past. It is one of the strongest of the numerous connecting links of man of today with man of early times and with the Primate stock from which he ascended.

In some instances these climbing tendencies of the human infant and child "bear-walkers" are especially noteworthy. Some of these children when a little older do not shin but "walk" up the trees, as do the Australians, the negrillos, some other primitive humans, and the apes.

The subject is of such interest that an extended number of quotations will be permissible.

Climbing Up and Down the Stairs.

"Long before she was able to walk on her feet she went up and down stairs on all fours"—Affleck.

"Ran on all fours up and down a flight of eight stone steps without a railing, with me holding my breath"—Ahlberg, girl.

"Before she was a year old she went up stairs and backward down stairs on all fours"—G. P. B.

[As a baby] "had a strong liking for going up and down stairs on all fours"; [when less than a year old would climb 208 steps from canal to home] "and go clear to the top on his all-fours seeming to get quite a 'kick' out of it"—Pace.

Began to climb steep stairs at ten months, "climbs everything possible to climb"—Morris.

"Climbed stairs incessantly and came down backward, always on all fours"—Sherry.

. 68 .

PLATE VI.—Miss K-S., eleven years old; can still, when she is so inclined, run on all fours; and climbs by "walking up the trees."

Climbing on Chairs, Tables, Etc.

"Was always fond of climbing," [even against definite commands;] "at about twelve I had scarlet fever and during my delirium had to be held in bed because I would attempt to climb the side of the wall"— LeNore Anderson.

At twenty-two months "climbs everywhere, surely and without mishap. A four-foot wire fence was put around his play yard when he was eighteen months old to keep him in bounds, but he straightway climbed over it. A cherry tree in the yard is a favorite climbing object now and a step-ladder is one of his most desired pieces of play equipment"—Auten.

"At fifteen months began to climb and will climb as high as she can get, though very careful not to fall"—Bahl.

Climbs stairs, chairs, tables—Becker, boy, thirteen months.

"He is now starting to climb on chairs, tables, etc."—Berney.

"Showed a strong desire to climb with his arms while his feet were still helpless, had to watch him constantly; when he was put in a baby pen he would not play with his toys but tried to pull himself over the fence by his arms"—Bevis.

"He has always had a marked desire and ability to climb"; persists, notwithstanding three fractures acquired in connection—Dixon.

"He has a great tendency to want to climb up everything"—Foy, eleven months.

"She climbs like a squirrel; ladders, trees, and fences are her favorite playgrounds"—W. K., three and one-half years.

"She has a habit of climbing through chair rounds, steps, in fact anything she can"—Keller, one year.

"When he was nineteen months old I found him one day on the roof of a two-story unfinished building; to get there he had to climb a ladder leaning against the eaves"—Kenney.

"She climbs like a squirrel"—Lear, ten months.

"Climbs upon chairs, then to tables and other heights; hauls himself up much in the manner of a seal"—Leversee, one year two weeks.

"He shows an unusual interest and ability in climbing"—Magill, one year five months.

"At two years of age he would climb 10-foot ladders by himself"— Metcalf.

"The most active child I have ever seen, accomplishing feats in climbing that were phenomenal"—C. S. Miller; boy, six years.

"Likes to do all sorts of gymnastics, to climb and to jump"—Mossner; girl, six years eight months.

"He climbs on everything he sees"—Seaman; boy, about one year.

"He climbs everywhere even out of his high chair, and he is not quite two years old"—Stretch.

"Climbs everything like a boy"—Roach; girl, seventeen months.

"She climbed stairs almost at once, on all fours, and no slope but held its fascination for her exploring habits; she endeavored to climb vertically but was too heavy to get very far"—Sherry.

"Both of them are forever climbing"—Sullivan, 1st and 3d child, the latter a girl, twenty-two months, who ran on all fours; middle child not climbing, "always afraid of falling."

"She can climb up anything, never falls down"—Ward; girl, one year, seven months.

"I would often find them on the piano, table, or any piece of furniture in the house, even before they could walk"—Whisler; boy and girl, both runners on all fours.

Climbing in Ape-like Manner.

"I was teaching country school in Indiana. One of my pupils was a little girl of six years. (As I remember it, her age was given me as six, but I suspect she was a little under six.) One day at intermission I looked out and saw her climbing a small tree perhaps four or five inches in diameter. She was going up in the manner of the Australian natives, with hands grasping the trunk (or rather hooked back of it, as the trunk was too large to grasp) and with the soles of her bare feet pressed straight against the trunk as if she were walking up it. When I saw her she was up nearly 10 feet. As she was a rather "chubby" little girl with comparatively short legs, she greatly resembled a little bear as she climbed. She seemed to go up without great difficulty and would probably have gone higher if I had not brought her down to avoid a possible fall. She climbed with her body well out from the tree trunk, with legs not much flexed."—Geo. E. Davis, teacher.

"The youngest child, a girl, was (and she is!) extremely active. She climbed steps, ladders, bars on doors, chairs, anything in fact, before she made any effort to walk. She has gone up small trees and posts by literally walking up them ever since she was a small child . . .

"My husband said, on reading your last note, tell him 'the child climbs a tree as the Filipinos go up coconut trees'; but thinking a picture better than all descriptions I am enclosing two I took of her as she climbed a tree"—M. K.-S.; girl, between ten and eleven years now, a former runner on all fours.

"Sometimes climbs trees with hands and toes instead of 'shinnying'" —Paull; boy, now fourteen years, former runner on all fours.

No Fear of Height

It is not well known how much of or how often such fear is present in infancy. The indications are that on the whole it is less, perhaps much less developed or common than in later conscious and more experienced life. As children grow, however, they in general become more cautious—with some exceptions. A few such exceptions are reported among the children who used to and may still occasionally run on all fours. The lack of fear of heights is certainly associated with good balance, but there is present in addition, it would seem, a psychic factor of importance—possibly the negative factor of a lack of inhibition. There are two specially striking reports:

Dr. Dixon's seven-year-old boy is a great climber, "in spite of three fractures acquired in this sport; he is still unafraid and only two weeks ago I learned from his brother that he has been walking an eight-inch cement guard rail, 100 feet long and about 60 feet from the street below."

While W. K.'s daughter, at seventeen months, had "no fear of height" and would run in an escapade "along a narrow stone coping on the brink of a deep brook traversing the place"; and at three and one-half has still "no fear of high places, and has frequently electrified us by teetering on the edge of a chasm with no more concern than if she was on a street curb." [In travel in Mexico and Southwest.]

In such cases one is strongly reminded of the fearlessness and sure-footedness of the other Primates.

THE MOUTH USED FOR CARRYING

Not a few of the children who run on all fours use their mouth during this period more or less as do animals. The hands are busy, but that is evidently not the main reason. It may be merely a factor that favors these manifestations, which seem strongly in most if not all these cases to be of atavistic character. The records may well be allowed to speak for themselves:

Albers boy: "Another peculiar thing was the manner in which he used his mouth for picking up articles and carrying them while on all fours, causing the neighbors to exclaim that he looked 'just like a dog.'"

Casseday girl: "In many respects she was like a chicken, very carefully going over every inch of the floor searching for the tiniest particles to put into her mouth. Everything she could find went into her mouth."

Cunio boy: "When younger would pick up doll in mouth and carry same in mouth. Will try to 'lap up' water from ground."

Fordney boy: "Once in running on all fours he picked up an apple with his teeth."

G. H. Green girl: "When wishing to take any of her toys with her she would put the articles in her mouth and proceed on all fours. At times she would carry her 'sack' doll in this manner letting it dangle as a cat would its kitten."

Harris girl: "The funniest thing to us was when running on fours she carried all her toys by holding them in her teeth."

Keller girl: "She is also in habit of carrying objects in her mouth. If anything was dropped on the floor such as crumbs and she saw them, she ate them up with mouth instead of first picking them up with hands. One time I spilled some water on the floor and she lay down and drank it up from the floor."

Leonard boy: "Liked to carry toys or most anything in his mouth . . . When he has a little piece of ice and it makes his hands cold he lays it on the floor, sits down and picks it up off the floor with his mouth."

Van Kirk boy: "And sometimes he would run around this way with something in his mouth."

And the boy reported by Mrs. Rees, "would run about on all fours with a large bone in his mouth."

Prehensile Hands, Toes and Feet

In the method of using its hands, in the words of Buckman,[1]

the baby shows to the full its descent from arboreal ancestors. When it wishes to take hold of anything, like a glass or a flowerpot, it does not, like an adult, put the hand around it, or even put the thumb inside to use as a lever. On the contrary, it places all the fingers inside, makes no use of the thumb, and clasps the rim of the flowerpot between the fingers and the palm of the hand. This is exactly the action which would be acquired from arboreal ancestors; in going from bough to bough they would take their hands palms first, and would strike from above downward, grasping the bough with the fingers. Such is the action of an infant picking up a cup. So little use have some monkeys made of the thumb that abortion has resulted; and in the most arboreal species of monkeys known, the fingers have grown together because the whole hand was used merely as a grasping-hook. It is probably from our ancestors' excessive use of the hands in bough-grasping that our babies inherit a certain inability to move the fingers with freedom, or to extend the hand, especially if the least degree cold. The power to extend the fingers perfectly straight is oftentimes not obtained by children at six or seven years of age.

[1] BUCKMAN, S. S., "Babies and Monkeys," *Pop. Sci. Monthly*, vol. XLVI, p. 375, 1894–1895.

As to the toes, probably all barefoot-walking people, whites included, develop with practice more or less of prehensility, so that they are able to pick up from the ground various articles. This is particularly true of individuals used to bearing burdens, where a bending down of the body would be difficult. The ability has been observed by many travelers, and others, among the Australians, Africans, some American Indians, etc. It has been noticed again and again in white peasants and especially in individuals born without or who have lost their arms. Such persons have been shown in circuses and they have in instances acquired astonishing dexterity with the toes. There have been even toe artists.

The subject has received fair attention in literature but much remains to be learned in this direction. There is a nice paragraph on the subject in Dr. Buckman's "Babies and Monkeys."[1] He says:

Considering how little an adult can move his or her toes, the power of movement of these organs by an infant is something remarkable, and it points to some ancestral environment of very different character from that which surrounds man at the present day. The big toe the infant can project at an angle from the next toe, and the space between the big toe and the next is really the remnant of a space similar to that seen between our thumb and fore-finger, when the toe was used for grasping like a thumb, and was opposable . . . The big toe further reveals its former thumb-like use in the fact that it and the thumb are the only two of the digits in which the last joint can be bent at will and independently of moving others. This can readily be exemplified in the thumb; the baby is fond of showing its power in this direction with its big toe. Further, a baby can move any of its toes independently, and it can move them one from another so as to make a "v" between any of them. As it grows older it loses this power.

Another valuable contribution to the subject is that by Trettien.[2] It reads:

Often the great toe is found to be far separated from the other toes, with the tendency to oppose it to the sole of the foot . . . It is a very frequent occurrence to use the feet as hands in seizing objects and carrying them forward to the hands and mouth, the storehouse of all captured prizes. Several instances from observers will illustrate this.

[1] *Op. cit.*
[2] TRETTIEN, AUGUST W., "Creeping and Walking," *Amer. Jour. Psychol.*, vol. XII, no. 1, p. 18, 1900.

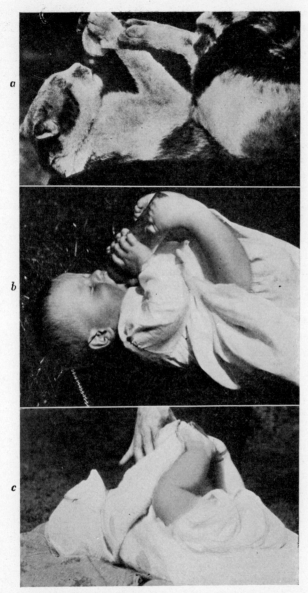

PLATE VII.—Prehensile feet. Hands, feet, and a milk-bottle: *a*. Cat. *b*. Washington, D. C., boy (*by R. Bache*). *c*. Engelmann baby.

One speaks of the spontaneous movements of the opening and closing of the toes, similar to the movements of the fingers, when the child was awake and asleep. Another states that the toes would seize and hold a pencil or other object of proper size and hold it so tight that it was difficult to remove it, or it would seize and hold the edge of its shirt as if it were using its fingers. Another child would work its way toward the foot of its couch until its feet touched the perpendicular round sticks at the foot of the crib, the foot would then attempt to grasp the sticks, finding them too large for its grasp it would move its foot from one to the other until it came to the central wire which it could encircle and this it seized and held firmly. Another observer states a peculiar tendency in a child seven months old,—if the child saw an object she wanted, which could not be reached with her hands she would reach for it with her foot, if successful, she pulled it along with her foot until it was near enough to reach it with her hand.

The human toes and feet are therefore still far from being wholly and permanently "denaturalized."

The appearance in the human infant of their prehensility, in which sometimes the feet and the whole lower limbs participate, represents evidently one of the clearest connections of man with the prehuman past; and where such instances are spontaneous and pronounced they may safely, it would seem, be relegated to the realm of atavisms.

RECORDS

"At seven he delights in using his toes as fingers"—Bevis.

"Has very high arched foot with prehensile toes; can grasp anything and walk with objects grasped with the toes"—Dunham, boy.

"My baby six months old catches hold of his bottle or anything else handed to him with both his feet and hands, the feet usually get it first" —Engelmann.

"Used his feet to draw towards him things that he wanted . . . He would work objects closer by use of a foot, and then would often grasp them between his feet. Once I saw him place a cup between his feet, and then, lying on his back, swing it back and forth through the air"— Ganong.

"Uses hands or feet, interchangeably, for picking up and holding objects. She will hold her bottle between her clenched toes in order to play with toys while drinking, or hold the bottle in her hands and pick up toys with her feet. She can pick up a safety pin or a marble with the toes of one foot"—W. K. (See Figs. 11–14, pp. 237–239.)

"She often uses her feet to reach for things"—Lear.

"He also is able to hold all sorts of articles with his feet, respectively his toes, and is capable of grasping objects with his toes as well as he is with his fingers"—Schmidt.

"During the period of walking on his all fours he used to amuse us greatly by climbing up the corner of his pen; but instead of, perhaps, wrapping his legs around the rungs, he used to wrap his toes and feet. At that time his grandmother remarked that she had never believed in. Darwinism until Sonny came"—Stretch.

"The boy could hang from anything he would get a toe-hold on before he could walk"—Sullivan.

"She started using her feet just like hands, would pick up a talcum powder box or a rubber doll with her two feet and place it in her hands . . . Neither my husband nor I have ever had much faith in this 'monkey business,' at least not any more than thinking people are forced to have in spite of religion; but to watch her juggle those toys with her feet and further stunts of swinging on her rope would almost convince anyone"—Talbot.

FONDNESS OF ANIMALS

Probably all normal little children are more or less fond of animals, more particularly dogs and cats. The boy's heartless torturing age manifests itself later.

But there are not many cases such as the W. K.'s little four-runner who shows "a marked characteristic in her fearlessness of animals . . . snakes, lizards, toads, dogs, cats, worms—and, until a recent unfortunate experience, giant roaches and centipedes—are to her animated playthings to be taken into the bosom of the family."

The Mossner girl has shown much liking for animals, especially dogs and horses; and will now [six and one-half years] "draw dogs in all possible postures."

For little Miss Lear, "the one and only toy that has so far brought real joy to this youngster is a most life-like stuffed monkey."

Nagle, to his present adult age and from pure inclination, will pick up stray dogs, attend to them and then place them with good people.

And there are a number of other cases of interest in this connection in the records.

IMITATION OF ANIMALS

The above cases connect with unconscious to semiconscious *imitation of animals*. The little Welker girl imitates a cat; also, "she seems to have an obsession to be a dog. I have sat concealed sometimes when she has played by herself and I have felt that she has acted out a complete 'dog party.' Imitates barks of five dogs perfectly; dogs to her are real folk."

FIG. 4.—Fondness of animals. Master Kenney, twenty-four months.

Nagle used to imitate dogs and horses. Used to put wooden blocks under and in his hands and imitate on all fours horse's trot and gallop, in gait and noise.

The Ganfield boy, four years eight months, "has been impersonating a bear. He is 'Billy Bear,' not only during just a part of his play time, but practically all the time, and has been 'Billy Bear' for well over a year, perhaps during all of this period when he has been using all fours as a means of locomotion" [began the practice when just a little past three years of age].

The little cousin of M. R. Langley, now four years of age, "today was 'making believe' he was a cat, and was running about on all fours, but not as naturally and easily as when he was a baby."

The Engelmann boy, sixteen months, can bend at the waist and, keeping the knees stiff, licks the contents of a dish on the floor in front of his feet. His mother thinks he is imitating the puppy as it is the dog's dish.

Mrs. Woods reports, "one day I found the baby with the dog's ball and immediately, mindful of germs, took it out of his mouth, when he growled at me just as the dog did in play"; and "he imitated every move of the dog."

Mr. Bristol, visiting an isolated farm found near the gate a "boy, about four, noticed lying in shallow mud hole, beside a dog and a pig. As the boy heard the noise I was making trying to open the gate, he aroused himself, raised himself on knees and hands, and to my consternation barked at me in perfect imitation of the racket the dog was putting up; after which he grunted like a pig."

While Mrs. Rees reports a boy of about five years who "went about out-of-doors on all fours, at times imitating the dogs in lifting his leg quite expertly at the trees and bushes in simulation of urinating."

Here we have approached phenomena that, though more or less aroused accidentally or under peculiar conditions, and realized more or less through imitation, seem nevertheless to have a deeper, far-away foundation. A curious fact is the very marked preponderance among the more striking imitators, of male infants.

Various imitations of animals are, of course, not confined to the children who run on all fours. They are quite common among children at large, though seldom carried out faithfully or to any extreme. Strong contributing causes toward such imitation are isolation of the child with want of human playmates, and a close association with animal-like toys and especially with pet animals themselves.

The prevalence among children's toys of those that represent animals, is the result of a general recognition of the fondness of little children for animals; though such toys also act not infrequently as the objects of the child's cruelty to animals, and in some cases aid in arousing animal imitation.

Miscellaneous Other Animal-like Manifestations

Aside from those already dealt with there are various animal-like manifestations in the children who run on all fours, decidedly more it would seem than in other children; and some of them are exceedingly interesting. Most of them connect plainly with animal behavior, particularly such as found in the apes.

The W. K.'s three and one-half-year-old girl bunches all coverings over her head, large or small; also, tucks bright-colored cloths or rags under chin and keeps them there; and she has had a passion for hoarding large stones carefully, making a cache of them.

The Casseday girl, as early as her ninth month, "delighted to drag torn papers, cushions, shawls, etc., into a little cage formed by a gate-leg table when closed; she amused herself for long periods in this way."

And she was very destructive—"everything she could lay hands on was destroyed; toys, books, paper, music." Further, the same little girl "since she was one month old she scratches gently on her pillow as she is going to sleep. She has a tiny pillow which to this day [six years] she takes to bed and cuddles in her arms and scratches on. If she wakes up in the night I hear this gentle scratching until she goes to sleep again."

The Barker little girl "always indicates sleepiness by scratching behind the ear."

The W. K.'s little Miss, "as an infant in arms would curve her fingers and scratch if her wishes were not immediately understood and obeyed."

She can also "clap the soles of her feet together to make noise as in hand clapping."

Mrs. Th., now fifty-five and who has "practiced quadrupedism since she was a child, can turn her feet inward and set their soles (plantar surfaces) against each other."

Nagle was so quick at jumping that for fun he would catch birds that way.

The Morris little boy has a "tendency when playing with any object to get up on all fours and circle around it, moving his hands hardly at all, but making the circle entirely with his feet."

Olsen's boy has "always smelled of any article given him, and the trait was not outgrown till he was about fourteen years old."

Little Miss Wyant "is handy with her hands but clumsy with her feet."

Master Wolf "seems very responsive to the sense of touch—feels silks and satins, enjoys creeping on a deep turkish rug, etc."

The Kenney boy shows "unusually good hearing."

The Dunham boy likes to curl legs around supports when sitting.

Master Graves runs to a corner or under table "just like an animal."

The Flindt boy used to throw himself out of chairs with hands outstretched, like a cat.

The little son of Mr. Van Cott has been seen repeatedly "raising himself up from the floor in the middle of the room, unaided by any support, much as I have observed bears to do, looking about, swaying, and then dropping back on all fours to travel again."

Esther Bower, "from the time she could sit up in arms, would hold her arms and hands as a dog does in 'begging,' hands dropping. She did this until she was about eleven or twelve months old."

The association of these manifestations in the same child with running on all fours, is certainly suggestive of atavistic causation.

COMPARISONS BY PARENTS OF CHILDREN WHO RUN ON ALL FOURS TO ANIMALS

In many cases, in fact generally, the parents of the child who runs on all fours or does some other stunt belonging to this class, recognize themselves the animal-like nature of the procedure, and call the child fondly "our little bear," "our doggie," etc. Most commonly and in the order named the little one is likened to a bear, a doggie, a pup, a monkey, a turtle, a spider.

"Like a bear after beginning to walk upright"—Knight.

"Rolling back on the hind to sit up, just like a bear cub"—Hunneman.

"We called him our little bear which greatly pleased him"—Lason.

"Honey Bear"—Pace.

"The little grizzly bear"—Ratliff.

"My small brown bear"—Sims.

"He looked just like a small bear"—Sims.

"I, too, had a little bear"—Treidel.

"Propels himself around like a cub bear"—Van Kirk.

"Walked very much like a bear when he uses all fours"—S. B., boy.

"Kicking like a dog with his feet"—J. F. Budke.

"Wonderfully interesting to see him walk, trot, and gallop as the dog does"—C. S. Miller.

Ran on all fours "with as much ease as a dog"—C. S. Miller.

"Ran just like a puppy"—Pedenboy.

"Similar to a bow-legged bull pup"—Abercrombie.

"Going like a dog or a monkey"—Niess.

"I could not describe the performance more accurately than just by saying he moves exactly as a monkey does"—J. W. Smith.

"You will no doubt think I have a little monkey, for sure, only he really doesn't look like one"—Stretch.

"Hangs on like a monkey"—Ward.

Manner of running. She "scampered all over the yard looking like a puppy or a big spider"—A. Anderson.

"I thought it amusing to see him run like a big spider, or perhaps it was like a monkey"—Wyllie.

"Looked like a big white bug making its way over the floor"—Osborne.

"We used to compare the performance to the gait of a turtle"—Sefton.

"Head held up like a turtle"—Bourne, girl.

"Ran everywhere as quickly as a kitten"—Rex (child Rayley).

"Kangaroo style"—F. Parker.

"Walked like a mule," on all fours—Beebe.

"Some called her a coon"—Cannon.

"Reminds one of a little animal"—Mellor.

"Looking for all the world like an animal"—Van Dorn.

"The neighbors must have wondered what kind of a little animal I had"—Treidel.

"Friends thought it queer that I 'ran about like an animal'"—LeNore Anderson.

SPECIAL NOTES ON THE COLORED CHILDREN WHO RAN ON ALL FOURS

The records on the colored children are regrettably very deficient. Such a child is mostly seen by accident and there is no mother who could give, in the language that the observer could understand, the desired details. There are, nevertheless, two or three points of special interest in these records, to which may be added several notes and letters of a more general nature. (See frontispiece; Figs. 26, 27; and detailed reports, pp. 398–401.)

Hands.

"The hands were clubbed, the thumb being grasped in the palm of the hand"—Molloy, Negro-Indian infant boy.

Characterization.

"Walking like cows"—Stam, Kenya negroes.

Duration.

"Some of the children are 'incurable'"—Stam, Kenya negroes.

Animal-like Behavior.

"Another striking feature of very young negro children in their first attempts to walk erect is that of pressing the weight of the body on the outer or distal side of the foot, curving the inner side and grasping at the ground with their toes. This is conspicuous in almost every negro infant that I have watched, and I have observed many of them"—Garner.

"In their earlier efforts to walk alone the negro baby also elevates the arms and waves them as apes do, while the white babe holds the arms below the level of the shoulder"—Garner.

CURIOUS INITIAL POSTURES, AND ODD MODES OF LOCOMOTION

POSTURE IN NEW-BORN

THE new-born and very young infant if left to itself tends, in many cases, it seems, to assume a characteristic posture which reminds one very much of a little animal lying on its back.

There is a very good note on the subject among the unpublished writings of my old friend Professor Garner. It reads as follows: "Newly born African babies almost invariably have the habit or tendency of lying with the knees expanded and the legs drawn up, usually crossed, and the soles of the feet turned obliquely upward." A very good illustration of such an infant, except as to turned-up feet, may be seen in the Johannesburg group (Pl. I, frontispiece).

Much the same posture, with feet more or less inverted may be seen not infrequently in young white infants. In fact, it is probably the prevalent posture of early infancy in all races; but more observations on this point are required.

The posture resembles on one hand the usual posture of the child *in utero*, while on the other it is like that of animals when turned on their back. Possibly both the habit of the child itself while in the womb and the older prehuman habits of posture are causative.

This early posture has apparently nothing to do with the development of the progression on all fours in later months. It is alluded to more or less clearly in various publications on the new-born child and young infant and may here and there be seen in the illustrations of such infants.

ROLLING

The first attempts at locomotion of the human babies embrace apparently a whole series of interesting performances. Some, perhaps a majority, of these are more or less indefinite and irregular; but some are or soon become quite coordinated and crystallized into a definite form of progression.

One of the best defined of such forms is "rolling." It occasionally develops in a child that subsequently will run on all fours, but occurs also in others. There is probably but little, if any, connection between the two manifestations.

There are a few references to this mode of progression in literature but no detailed study. Trettien[1] speaks of it as follows:

Rolling is an occasional form of child locomotion. Seven per cent of the whole number observed rolled over and over until they arrived at the place desired. One peculiarity in this rather exceptional manner appears in the apparent deliberation of the child just before setting out as if to decide just what and how to do it, but after several attempts he becomes very proficient in its movements.

The procedure will best be described by our reporters:

"My mother has told me that I never crawled [her little son ran on all fours] but lay down and rolled over and over in any direction to reach the place I wished to go to"—Miss Crooks.

"My oldest boy when about eight or nine months old, progressed by irregular rolling and sliding motions"—Danforth.

"As an infant it was never safe to leave him sleeping on a bed unprotected by some kind of a fence, as he would awake quietly and roll off, for the sake of the excitement"—Gaddas.

"She rolled over and over on the floor when five and one-half months old"—Green.

"My first mode of locomotion which I used for some time, was rolling"—Mr. Schoonover.

And there are a few other mentions of the peculiarity.

"SWIMMING"

Some infants develop what looks like swimming motions. Just what these mean it is difficult to say. Swimming is natural to very many mammals and was, of course, universal in their terrestrial and aquatic predecessors. In general such a natural ability seems to be lost in man or almost so, but there are probably exceptions, and it is not impossible that in infancy, here and there, there may be manifested a reminiscence of more or less remote ancestral conditions in this respect. But nothing can be positive before such cases are properly studied. There is no more than a few casual

[1] TRETTIEN, AUGUST W., "Creeping and Walking," *Amer. Jour. Psychol.* vol. XII, no. 1, p 33, 1900.

mentions on the subject in literature. The reports in our series are certainly suggestive:

The Olsen baby, "when a few weeks old, if placed on his stomach in the bath basin or tub, moved arms and legs in a perfect swimming manner, and he enjoyed it so much that he screamed when we took him out. The neighbors used to come in to watch him—it was quite a sight."

"Has been flopping over on her tummy since the age of five months. Her first crawling motion was flat on the stomach and she pulled herself forward with her arms as if she was swimming"—Millisor.

"She never crept as most children do, but began moving about by wriggling on her stomach and moving her arm like one swimming"—H. N. Parker.

Little Miss Scott, "at the age of seven and one-half months, after weeks of attempts to progress by means of swimming motions executed on her stomach with hips and shoulders in the air."

While with master Woods, "his first movements were in a flat swimming position with much arm movement."

Some of these cases are doubtless more significant than others, and surely not all instances of such behavior have been reported. The great need in these and other more complex cases are detailed, painstaking records by intelligent mothers and fathers.

SQUATTING

A not infrequent concomitant habit to that of running on all fours, is squatting.

Squatting to the infant must in general be much easier than it is to the adult who has not become used to it through practice. It was also in all probability the general method in human antiquity, as it is to date, among many primitive peoples and among most of the Asiatics. Its spontaneous appearance in an infant suggests therefore some inherited reminiscence. Also, perhaps, its manifestations, when closely examined into, will be found to be more frequent than would seem from our few incidental mentions. It may or may not be more frequent among the children who show also the phenomenon of running on all fours, than in others—there are no means of comparison. There are but a few references to the subject in literature. Buckman[1] says: "Children are very fond of 'sitting on their heels,' in the same manner as a dog when it begs."

[1] *Op cit.,* p. 379.

EXAMPLES

The Younger boy, fourteen months, "sits on his haunches like a frog."

A boy of sixteen months, reported by Mrs. Engelmann, "has a peculiar habit of sitting on the floor with his legs doubled back close to the body."

Little Miss Ketcham, now [1928] three years old, "to rest squatted instead of sitting on the floor. She continues to squat when playing, and keeps that position for long periods while playing in the sand."

Richard J. Laurence, at time of report four years old, when he started to walk upright, and since, "when he played on the floor, he would squat, sit on his heels, Indian-fashion, and move around without rising to his feet."

Fig. 5.—Miss Ketcham. From on all fours to squatting.

Also the little Fräulein reported by Herr Mossner "six years eight months old, sits with preference in a squatting position, as shown in the accompanying picture."

BOUNCING

There are two specific reports on this form of behavior. As both occurred in strong and at that time healthy children the practice is perhaps only a form of discharge of the pent-up energy.

"He frequently wakes, in a darkened room, and bounces up and down in his crib, sometimes as long as two hours"—A. N. Bowen; boy, one year two weeks.

"When on the floor, where she spent most of her waking hours after she was four or five months old (doctor's advice), she frequently flopped over on her stomach, threw up her head, raised her hands and feet off the ground and bounced"—Wells.

And a similar diagnosis is probably justifiable in the case that follows:

"Before she could creep or stand up she used to turn somersaults in her 'keep'"—Whitson.

Walking on Tip-toes

A curious coincidence in some of the children who walk on all fours is walking on tip-toes. Some walk thus already when in the all-fours phase, some when they begin to walk erect.

Examples

Joan Lund, eleven months, runs on all fours "on her toes, knees bent, feet set well apart."

Robert and Paul McNichol both ran on all fours "on tip-toes, knees straight so that their buttocks were much higher than their shoulders."

The little girl visitor of Mrs. Shive, eleven and one-half months old, "prefers to stand and walk on tip-toes; there is no deformity of her feet and she can place her foot on the floor with no discomfort, but will go around and around the play pen on tip-toe very rapidly, and it is only when tired enough to sit down will she drop her entire foot to the floor."

The two girls of Mrs. Bacon, two years ten months and thirteen and one-half months old, "both, when coming out of the all-fours habit showed a tendency to stand on toes or heels instead of flat on feet."

The Wallace boy, two years eleven months, "walked on his tip-toes almost all of the time until he wore shoes in the winter, and even then tried to at times . . . When allowed he will still 'tip-toe' at times."

Miss Stenger, two years five months, "dances about on her toes."

And the Stretch boy, nineteen months old, "used to get down on his hands and toes. Was never known to put his heels down," [both during his running on all fours and later.] "He seemed exceptionally steady on his feet in spite of the fact that he walked on his tip-toes until very recently . . . When he first began to walk, he walked on his toes, holding his hands parallel with his head for balance. He still shows a tendency to walk on his toes and his instep and foot are very well developed."

Just what the peculiarity of this using of tip-toes means, is not clear. If the habit developed only after a period on all fours the tendency would be to attribute it to a condition of the child's muscles induced by the use of the foreparts of the feet while on the fours. Possibly this, after all, is the right explanation, while the occasional earlier origin of the habit may lay in some peculiarity in the anatomy or dimensions of the child's lower limbs. There is in this case no prehuman parallelism.

Occasional Peculiar Modes of Locomotion

Some of the children who run on all fours, have shown at times other peculiar modes of progression. This may have been before or after the all-fours method developed. Thus, little Miss Ward "tries, whether she succeeds or not, to go either up or down stairs with one foot after the other."

Master Knight "used to move about the bed by clapping with both hands his belly, at the same time that he supported his bended body on his head and feet, and when he clapped his belly he would jump in the direction of his head, thus moving about the bed."

The interesting little Miss Casseday, after she was six months old and after she learned how to sit up, but before she started on all fours, "moved herself about without moving; she merely jiggled herself up and down and after a while seldom failed to arrive at the piano with her little feet wedged underneath."

For Master Worcester, usually the all-four "motion is semi-sideways, though hand and foot on the same side moving together; sometimes, however, he pushes his two hands forward and then brings his feet up to them."

Miss Bower before developing the all-four method, would "sit on the floor and instead of creeping would 'hitch,' using her heels as one would oars in a boat, and she would go so fast!" And similarly with Margaret Thone, who when a baby and before as well as during the time she ran on all fours, the "usual method of progression was to assume a sitting posture and then hitch herself forward with her heels."

These curious behaviors would seem to have little if any connection with the all-four method. Such and other oddities doubtless happen also in other children. They are of interest mostly as so many varieties of expression of the instincts of motion.

Cases of Special Interest

To the student of the human infant, and to the observant intelligent mother, all the documents here gathered must be of absorbing interest. But there are cases that are richer or more peculiar than others. Of such there is a whole series, and most of them are admirably reported. It may be useful to enumerate these cases. They are Anderson, LeNore; Auten; Baxter; Bevis; Kenney, W. K.; Knight, William; Keller; Lear; Leonard; Mossner; Nagle; Olsen; Parker, H. N.; Roberts; Stretch; Sherry; Thone; Treidel; Talbot; Thompson; Van Kirk; Ward; Welker; Whitson; Worcester; Wyllie; Wyant.

COMMENTS ON THE CAUSES OF THE ANIMAL-LIKE MANIFESTATIONS IN THE HUMAN CHILD

THIS volume is devoted to a whole class of hitherto but very imperfectly known manifestations displayed by the human child, but resembling closely corresponding behaviors in the apes and other mammals. These manifestations develop in normal, strong children, yet not in all such children. They are more or less transient in character, and are neither attended nor followed by anything harmful. What are the causes of these manifestations? Why do they occur in some and not in other children? And what does it all mean, to the child, to the parents, to humankind in general?

These questions have already received attention in connection with the separate sections of the analysis. The essential, moreover, cannot as yet be fully answered. But some sound deductions are possible. A brief summary of what may be said follows:

ACCIDENTAL CAUSES

The manifestations here dealt with are according to all indications not *accidental*.

It is true that a concrete walk, or irritating grass, may in some cases be the ultimate, determining factor, influencing a child to rise from the more common hands-and-knees to the rarer hands-and-feet position. But it has been shown that the former method is just a weaker mode of the latter. Such a child needed but a little exciting factor to show what instinctively it was inclined to do. There is no report of any case where high or rough grass or a cement paving would have produced a regular four-walker from a child that did not previously use the hands-and-knees method.

The same is true of the desire of the child for effective motion. That desire is present more or less in all healthy infants, but it does not evidently lead them to run on all fours except where there are present adequate structural and central nervous conditions.

Neither are apparently child's strength, vigor, liveliness alone responsible for any of the animal-like manifestations of the human infant, for a large majority of children possessing such qualities show little if any of such peculiarities.

It seems safe to conclude, therefore, that accidental factors may at best play but the part of the "last camel's straw" where the ground is ready, but that alone they are not capable of inducing any of the phenomena here considered.

IMITATION

Many children certainly are imitative. They will imitate other children, grownups, and also animals. But from the study of the cases it does not appear that imitativeness alone would be sufficient to produce any of the more lasting and more characteristic animal-like manifestations in the infant. Where, nevertheless, some such peculiarities develop apparently through imitation there is a strong reason to believe that here again the ground was prepared, the conditions were there, and the imitation acted merely as a lighted match to so much inflammatory material. In other words, the imitation factor may doubtless be the wakening cause of some of these animal-like behaviors, but it is probably at no time the whole cause. It is but rational to conclude that the child acts as a rule in accordance with and not against its organic as well as mental inclinations.

HEREDITY

This factor has already been dealt with (p. 15). The conclusion is that the manifestation is apparently still one of a continued inheritance from the past, which however is already masked or more or less inhibited in a large majority of human infants.

PHYLOGENETIC CONTINUANCE; ATAVISM

The human infant is no being apart. He is a direct continuation of his parents, just as these were of their parents, and so on to the earliest humans, who in turn were a direct product of forms prehuman. And in geological and paleontological time it is not so long ago that the human connected directly with prehuman stages. As a result of this, there are in the human body, bones, blood, brain, in human functions, and even in human mentality, innumerable remnants or reminiscences of the far past. We still have hair and beard; in many humans there is still remaining more or less of the old animal obliquity of the eyes; we still have the canine teeth, which occasionally show sufficient prominence over the rest of the denture to be called "dog teeth." There are still on all our fingers as well as toes the nails, a modification of the original claws; we still have under our skin the old ear muscles that were needed in some of our far-away animal predecessors for the movements of their ears, and there are under the skin of the neck remains of the platysma muscle, which was used in the animal past for shaking the skin and thus freeing it from flies; there are at different periods of our development as individuals traces of long-lost gills, tail, and other structures; our essential functions are so much like those of many animals, that we are actually using animal digestives and extracts for supplementing the occasional want of such substances in our system; and on closer analysis it is readily appreciated that many of our nervous and even mental reactions and actions are of a far-away, prehuman origin.

With all this it is not strange, indeed, that the human infant will show now and then running on all fours or some other animal-like manifestation. The wonder is that in the majority of human children these have already been more or less covered and replaced by those of more recent acquisition.

It is very doubtful in fact whether we are justified even in regarding such habits as that on all fours, or the tendency to climbing, or prehensility of toes, as "atavisms." More strictly they are but a continuation of prehuman practices; a continuance that has already become weakened and irregular, but which has not been preceded as in the case of true atavisms by any period during which the manifestation appeared to be completely eliminated.

BRIEF SUMMARY AND CONCLUSIONS

THE documents collected in this volume show that there is a whole category of animal-like behaviors that with lesser or greater rarity appear in human children.

These manifestations, according to all indications, are not connected with any weakness or degeneracy in the child, but occur predominantly in physically and mentally healthy, strong, and even exceptional children.

These peculiarities of behavior are for the most part limited to the first eighteen months of the child's life; but in instances they persist into further childhood and even to later into life.

The most marked of these manifestations is the running on all fours, in much the same manner as seen in most animals. Other manifestations are climbing, carrying in mouth, using the toes and feet as fingers and hands, various imitations of household animals, and different minor performances.

The running on all fours appears to be merely a full manifestation of the same instinct which is shown by many other children in the ordinary "crawling," i.e., progressing on the hands and knees.

The habit develops mostly spontaneously, but its appearance may be favored by various conditions. It extends over a period ranging from a few weeks to several months before the child learns how to walk erect; but is frequently resorted to for "speed" even after the child walks on twos.

The habit of walking on all fours is more frequent in boys than in girls, and appears to be more common in the first child of the family than in others.

The habit is in no way harmful to the child, it is in fact rather beneficial. The children manifestating it, with infrequent exceptions are marked by low morbidity and very low mortality.

None of the other animal-like manifestations in the child appear to be of any pathognomonic significance. They are temporary reminiscences of and connections with man's ancestral past. They do not appear to prejudice in the least the further normal development of the child both physically and mentally.

The realization and study of these phenomena constitute substantial further evidence of our derivation from forms prehuman.

It seems just to conclude that just as the human child before birth recapitulates, more or less, various phases of its physical ancestry, so the child after birth recapitulates and uses for a time various phases of its prehuman ancestral behavior.

BIBLIOGRAPHY

(The works here cited, while giving but little or nothing on the children running on all fours which is the main subject of this volume, give nevertheless many interesting observations or notes on other practices of the child.)

ALLEN, GRANT: "The Colour Sense; Its Origin and Development; an Essay in Comparative Psychology," 282 pp., Boston, 1879.

BALDWIN, JAMES MARK: "Origin of Right- and Left-Handedness," *Science*, vol. XVI, pp. 247–248, 1890.

———: "Mental Development in the Child and the Race," 1895.

BALLARD, PHILIP BOSWOOD: "Obliviscence and Reminiscence," *Brit. Jour. Psychol.*, monthly supp., 82 pp., vol. I, no. 2, 1913.

BINET, ALFRED and VICTOR HENRI: "De la suggestibilité naturelle chez les enfants," Revue philos., vol. XXXVIII, pp. 337–347, 1894.

BOURKE, JOHN G.: "Scatologic Rites of All Nations," 496 pp., Washington, D. C., 1891.

BUCHNER, MARTIN: "Die Entwicklung der Gemütsbewegungen im ersten Lebensjahre," 19 pp., Langensalza, 1909.

BUCKMAN, S. S.: "Babies and Monkeys," *Nineteenth Century*, London, vol. XXXVI, pp. 727–743, 1894; also, *Pop. Sci. Monthly*, vol. XLVI, pp. 371–388, 1894.

CHAILLE: "Infants, Their Chronological Progress," New Orleans Med. and Surg. Jour., June, 1886.

CHAMBERLAIN, A. F.: "The Child: A Study in the Evolution of Man," 498 pp., New York, 1900.

COMPAYRÉ, GABRIEL: "L'évolution intellectuelle et morale de l'enfant," 371 pp., Paris, 1893.

———: "Development of the Child in Later Infancy, 300 pp., New York, 1902.

DEKKER, HERMANN: "Naturgeschichte des Kindes," Stuttgart, 1908.

DEWEY, JOHN: "Psychology of Infant Language," *Psychol. Rev.*, vol. I, pp. 63–66, 1894.

DIX, KURT WALTER: "Körperliche und geistige Entwicklung eines Kindes," vol. I: "Instinktbewegungen"; vol. II: "Die Sinne"; vol. III: "Vorstellen und Handeln," 79, 176, 148 pp., Leipzig, 1911–1914.

GARBINI, A.: "Evoluzione della voce nella infanzia," 53 pp., Verona, 1892.

———: "Evoluzione del senso cromatico nei bambini," *Arch. per l'Antrop.*, vol. XXIV, pp. 71–98, 1894.

———: "Evoluzione del senso olfattivo nella infanzia," *Arch. per l'Antrop.*, vol. XXVI, pp. 239–286, 1896.

GRANT, JAMES RICHARD: "A Child's Vocabulary and Its Growth," *Ped. Sem.*, vol. XXII, pp. 183–203, 1915.

GUTZMANN, H.: "Des Kindes Sprache und Sprachfehler," 1894.

HALL, G. STANLEY: "A Study of Fears," *Am. Jour. Psychol.*, vol. VIII, no. 2, pp. 147–249, 1897.

HALL, MRS. WINFIELD S.: "The First 500 Days of a Child's Life," *Child Study Monthly*, vol. II, pp. 330–342, 394–407, 458–473, 522–537, 586–608, 1896–1897.

KIRKPATRICK, E. A.: "Fundamentals of Child Study." A discussion of instincts and other factors in human development with practical applications, 380 pp., New York, 1917.

KUSSMAUL, ADOLPH: "Untersuchungen über das Seelenleben des neugeborenen Menschen," 40 pp., Leipzig, 1859.

LOMBROSO, PAOLA: "Saggi di psicologia del bambino," 284 pp., Torino, 1894.

MATEER, FLORENCE: "Child Behavior," 238 pp., Boston, 1918.

MORGAN, C. L.: "Swimming Instinct," *Nature*, vol. LXIV, p. 208, 1901.

————: "Instinct and Experience," 299 pp., London, 1912.

PARMELEE, MAURICE F.: "The Science of Human Behavior," Biol. and Psychol. Foundations, 443 pp., New York, 1913.

PEREZ, B.: "Les trois premières années de l'enfant," Paris, several editions; 5th ed., 1892.

PLOSS, H.: "Das Kind in Brauch und Sitte der Völker," Leipzig, 1882, and several subsequent editions.

————: "Das kleine Kind," 120 pp., Leipzig, 1881.

PREYER, W.: "Die Seele des Kindes," 4th ed., Leipzig, 1895.

QUANTZ, J. O.: "Dendro-Psychoses," *Amer. Jour. Psychol.*, vol. IX, pp. 449–506, 1898.

ROBINSON, L.: "Darwinism in the Nursery," *Nineteenth Century*, London, vol. XXX, pp. 831–842, 1891.

SHINN, MILICENT W.: "Notes on the Development of a Child," pts. I and II, "Univ. of Calif. Studies," pp. 1–178, Berkeley, Calif., 1893.

————: "Notes on the Development of a Child," pts. III and IV, "Univ. of Calif. Studies," pp. 179–424, Berkeley, Calif., 1899.

————: "The Development of the Senses in the First Three Years of Life," "Univ. of Calif. Public. in Ed.," vol. IV, 258 pp., 1907.

SIGISMUND, B.: "Kind und Welt," 1856; later edition, 1897.

SIKORSKIJ, IVAN A.: "Die Seele des Kindes nebst kurzem Grundriss der weiteren psychischen Evolution," 80 pp., Leipzig, 1902.

SMOTLACHA, F.: "Biologické Základy Záliby Člověka ve Šplhu a Visu," ("Biological Basis of Inclination in Man towards Climbing and Suspension"), 211 pp., Praha, 1930.

SULLY, JAMES: "Studies of Childhood," 527 pp., London and New York, 1903.

TANNER, AMY E.: "The Child, His Thinking, Feeling and Doing," 534 pp., New York, 1915.

THOMSON, JOHN: "On Some Curious Habits in Children," *Child Study Monthly*, vol. II, no. 2, pp. 88–98, 1896.

TRACY, F.: "The Psychology of Childhood," 219 pp., Boston, 1909.

TRETTIEN, AUGUST W.: "Creeping and Walking," *Amer. Jour. Psychol.*, vol. XII, no. 1, pp. 1–57, 1900.

VIERORDT, KARL: "Physiologie des Kindesalters," "Gerhardt's Handbuch der Kinderkrankheiten," vol. I.

VARIOT, G.: "La prélocomotion chez le jeune enfant avant la marche bipède," *Bull. et Mém. Soc. Anthrop.*, vol. VII, pp. 128–144, Paris, 1926.

WESTENHÖFER, M.: "Über die Klettermethoden de Naturvölker und über die Stellung der grossen Zehe," *Arch. Frauenk. und Konstitutionsforsch.*, vol. XIII, Heft 5, 1927.

PART II

THE INDIVIDUAL REPORTS

Reports of this nature made by the scientist, or any other outsider, would probably make dull reading. The letters that follow, written for the most part by the mothers of the children, are original documents of absorbing interest; for each report embodies not only faithful information about the child but also more or less of the psychology of both the child and the mother, in addition to which it generally carries more or less of the flavor of the quaint situation. Not one of the messages bears any material signs of exaggeration. The only shade of optimism that may possibly exist in some of the estimates is as to the especial brightness of the children, but even here the testimony is too uniform not to be based on a general reality.

The letters are given in alphabetical order.

WHITE CHILDREN

First letter of L. L. A.:

October 9, 1927

I read with interest of your article on infants walking on all fours.

I realized my child was unusual in this respect but was hardly enough of an egoist to realize he was so much so; I merely thanked the gods that, by running on all fours, he did not get the knees of his stockings so dirty.

He started on all fours when he was about ten months of age and started walking at fifteen months, though for about four months after that he walked on all fours, when in a hurry. He never crawled as ordinary babies do, and people invariably laughed when they saw him going around appearing very much similar to a bow-legged bull pup. He always sat up and refused to move until the attent of the laughter was away from him.

Knowing no better I attributed his peculiar method of locomotion to never having been around a baby who crawled in the regulation manner. He was always with his sister who is two years his senior. [She never walked on all fours.] He is normal in every other respect. We are of the white race, Nordic to be explicit.

Sincerely,
MRS. L. L. ABERCROMBIE,
Seattle, Wash.

Second letter:

December 10, 1928

DEAR SIR:

Perhaps you remember my writing to you a little over a year ago in regard to my little boy traveling on all fours rather than creeping normally.

I thought you might be interested in learning that my younger son also has adopted the "all-fours" method.

He was a premature baby and has been very backward about everything. He made no effort to move about until he was a little over a year old. He traveled on his hands and knees for about three weeks and then adopted the other method. He is now nearly fifteen months old and has not as yet tried to walk. He is very sensitive about being laughed at, as was his older brother.

I hope this may be of some interest to you.

Very sincerely,

Mrs. L. L. Abercrombie.

March 10, 1928

Enclosed find clipping from the *Literary Digest*.

Barney Hobbs, Jr., 15 months, boy baby of Mr. and Mrs. Hobbs, often runs on all fours quite fast, with hands spread flat on floor, head down, eyes toward floor. Father native Georgian, mother native Alabama.

Respectfully,

Jno. T. Abney,

Columbus, Ga.

October 24, 1928

Dear Sir:

My anthropology instructor told us that you were interested in facts concerning children who run about on all fours instead of crawling. Therefore I am sending you this data concerning a cousin of mine, Miss Zamist, now eleven years old. The facts, according to her mother, are as follows:

American, born of Jewish parentage.

Female.

Second child in numerical order.

In normal health and robustness.

The phenomenon has not been observed in any other member of the family.

The child began to run on all fours at about seven months and continued to about eleven months.

She would have her fingers on the floor and her toes, and run about very quickly with her back sticking straight up. She was very light and quick, rarely coming down on her whole foot or hand.

The hand was partly closed, but she used her fingers alone very often. She held her head up at times, or else looked straight ahead. The child was very graceful.

The child still is very quick and rather nervous. She is eleven, and very graceful in dancing, walking, etc. At birth she had a sixth finger attached to the small finger of her right hand. It has been removed. The family, as a whole, is of quick nervous temperament.

> Very truly yours,
> MARY ABRAMOWITZ,
> Brooklyn, N. Y.

March 19, 1928

DEAR DOCTOR:

Our daughter at the age of about six months got up on all fours and from that time until she walked at the age of 13 months she propelled herself on her hands and feet, becoming very skillful and making wonderful speed. She never crept or hunched and long before she was able to walk on her feet she went up and down stairs on all fours. She put her hands on the floor open and held her head as high as she could, so as to be able to see where she was going. Gradually she found that she could get from one place to another on her feet alone and when she discovered this, she walked, except that whenever she approached a danger zone in the shape of an obstruction on the floor, she would drop to all fours until she got past it.

She is now six and a half years old and seems to be entirely normal.

Details:

Race and nationality—Scotch, Scotch and Irish descent.

Sex—Female.

What child in numerical order?—First of mother, second of father.

Health and robustness—100%.

Has the phenomenon been observed in any other child of the same parents or among relatives?—No.

At what age begun, etc.?—From 9 months until she walked at 13 months.

Add description, etc.—see below.

Position of hands, etc.—See photo.

Details as to any other peculiarity of behavior of the child, or any other children in family.—Normal, healthy, intelligent, speaks French fluently—now age 6½. Perhaps a little above the average in intelligence. Age of parents—father, 51—mother, 39.

Very truly yours,
BENJAMIN F. AFFLECK,
Chicago, Ill.

June 20, 1928

My daughter Maurine—an only child—walked on all fours, then moved around the room holding on to low pieces of furniture, then balanced and stood alone. Took five steps alone Aug. 20, 1911.

Was born Sept. 22, 1910, weighed eight and one-fourth pounds, height eighteen inches. She was very daring, got many bumps but seldom cried. Ran on all fours up and down a flight of eight stone steps without a railing—with me holding my breath. This she would do time and again when I was not watching. Fond of animals and birds. Never timid.

Pulled her first two teeth when five and a half by having me tie a thread around the tooth then she tied the thread to a doorknob and banged the door shut. A few days after she pulled the second tooth the same way. I do not know where she got the idea; as a child she had teeth pulled and filled but never whimpered. She has been outdoors, rain or shine, every day since she was born. Has never been sick enough to have a doctor and was absent only one-half day in her four years of High School. She graduated on June 16, this year.

I have jotted down this and more in her baby book. The date when all her baby teeth came, her height, weight, etc. I never lost one night, of sleep on her account until she was vaccinated when four and one-half years old. She was then sick with a high fever for two days. Her face broke out in small pimples and this every summer for three or four years. Her skin was without a blemish before that.

Details:

Joan Maurine Ahlberg. Born in U. S. A. Her father born in Sweden; her mother here.

Female, first and only child.

Eighteen years old September 22; never had a doctor; good health.

Do not know of any other case of walking on all fours in the family or among relatives.

Ran on fours a couple of weeks; first steps Aug. 20, 1911. Born Sept. 22, 1910.

Practiced raising herself up and balancing without assistance, on her feet.

When on all fours ran head up, fingers touching floor, feet flat on floor.

Never afraid of animals or bugs, dead or alive; in the kindergarten, caught a mouse in a cupboard, by the tail. The children and teacher screaming. As a child was recklessly daring. Very fond of animals. Long dark hair when born.

> Yours very truly,
> MRS. ESTHER AHLBERG,
> Moline, Ill.

July 2, 1928

DEAR SIR:

We are enclosing a snapshot of our son, Robert (now eleven years of age), taken at the age of one year and showing his only method of locomotion from the age of one year to the age of eighteen months. He never crept as other children and at the age of eighteen months began walking upright as any normal child, reverting to "all fours" when in any hurry, and it was amazing what speed he could make in this manner. Another peculiar thing was the manner in which he used his mouth for picking up articles and carrying them while on all fours, causing the neighbors to exclaim that he looked "just like a dog." (See Plate IX, p. 163.)

Robert has been a normal boy in every way except, possibly, a little above normal in his school work, finishing this past term with an average of 96%—the highest in his room.

> MR. AND MRS. FRED ALBERS,
> Salt Lake City, Utah.

DEAR SIR:

In reply to yours of March 15 I would say that I do not know much about my walking on "all fours" except that I have heard my mother say that I was the only one of her four children, all girls, to walk in that manner. She said that I did not creep as children usually do but went on "all fours" for a short time and then got up and walked.

I was the second of the four girls in the family. I have always been in first rate health and very robust. I am nearly fifty years of age and have eleven children, seven boys and four girls, all in good health. I think one of my own children walked in this manner but do not remember which one. Thru my father's mother I am descended from Thomas Rogers who came over in the *Mayflower*, 1620. My father was descended directly from Thomas Munson who came to Hartford, Conn., and served in the Pequot war. He came from England. They trace their ancestry to the Danes who came to England in the 10th century.

Yours truly,
Mrs. H. L. Allen,
Leominster, Mass.

First Letter:

July 16, 1928

Dear Dr. Hrdlička:

Reading in the *Literary Digest* that you are interested in children that walked on "all fours," I shall tell you about one of mine that got around that way.

I have four children and she was the third, always a strong, healthy baby, eight years old now; more athletically inclined than any of the others—perfectly normal in every way, but particularly well built and stocky (more so than the others).

I kept a "Baby Book" for her, so know exactly what she did by referring to it.

When I put her on the floor at 5½ months she crawled up on her hands and knees as an ordinary child but as the days grew warmer I brought her out of doors, taking off shirt and dresses, leaving on just a diaper and it was then that she got up on her hands and feet, drawing her knees and stomach away from the ground, and scampered all over the yard looking like a puppy or a big spider. I thought it was a splendid way to get about for it kept her cleaner and she could go so much faster and without as much danger of getting hurt.

After she once found she could get around that way she never went back to the baby crawl even if she came into the house when there was no grass or had clothes on. And even after she learned to walk at ten months in rather a tottering fashion sometimes— if she was in a particular hurry, she would drop down into that position and rush off.

At six months and three weeks she pulled herself up into a standing position by holding on to the crib. At seven and a half months she could almost run along the side of her bed, of course holding on to the top.

Mrs. Arthur Anderson
Webster Groves, Mo.

Second letter:

Yes, I shall be glad to give you any additional information that I can.

I have two boys one 13 yrs., another 10 yrs.; then the little girl who got around on all fours for awhile, aged 8½ yrs. now; another girl, 7 yrs.; four altogether, 2 boys and 2 girls.

I have a picture of her scooting over the grass that way but it is the only one I have; I would be glad to send it if you would be good enough to return it to me; you understand. Her "hind legs" were not straight up in the air but bent at the knees and her whole body lifted up.

She is the strongest most athletic child I have, turning cartwheels and enjoying anything that brings her muscles into play, mentally she gets average grades at school and is in a class of children her own age. She did not navigate around on all fours until we put her out of doors; crawled as a normal child does in the house for some little while before that.

It might be interesting to find that out if the outdoors had anything to do with her assuming that habit and if I had some more children I surely would experiment.

Mrs. Arthur Anderson.

My Dear Dr. Hrdlička:

In a recent number of the *Literary Digest* I read a very interesting article entitled "The Baby That Walks Like a Bear need not Alarm its Mother." I thought that you might be interested to know that I used to walk the same way. I have heard my mother mention it many times and she says that I "went like lightning." I began to do this at the age of nine months and continued until about the age of eighteen months, being very reluctant to walk on my feet alone.

What you say about good health of the child in connection with this kind of "creeping" seems quite applicable to me. I am now twenty-one years of age and seem to have better than average health. The only diseases I have had were mumps, measles, and scarlet fever. I had scarlet fever when I was twelve and have not spent a single day in bed since. Although I lead a very sedentary life and have never "gone in" for athletics, I seem to have exceptional muscular development and am very strong. Considering my grades in school, I would say that my mental ability was average, with no unusual capacity, with the possible exception of a very good memory.

I have a second half-cousin, now about a year and three months old who also "walked" on her hands and feet.

> Very truly yours,
> MISS LENORE ANDERSON,
> Jamestown, N. Y.

Additional information:

Report by—LeNore Anderson, the subject; American.

Parents—American.

Birthplace—Jamestown, N. Y.

Sex of subject—Female.

Age—twenty-one.

First and only child.

Health always exceptional, very strong, average mentality, unusual memory.

Instead of creeping in the usual fashion, I ran about on my hands and feet and did so very rapidly. Refused to walk until 18 months, but began talking at nine months, very plainly and distinctly.

Other cases in family—see first letter [second half-cousin, girl].

Friends thought it queer that I "ran about like an animal" rather than creeping.

Additional peculiarities: Always was fond of climbing, and would even defy definite commands not to climb through windows, etc., when I was as old as nine years. At about twelve I had scarlet fever and during my delirium had to be held in bed because I would attempt to climb the side of the wall, talk about being up on the top of the doors, etc.

As a baby, I preferred to sleep with my Mother holding me in her arms faced toward her, with my head on her breast, and resting on my knees and "haunches" much as a monkey holds its young. Slept this way until nearly two years of age.

LeNore Anderson.

June 28, 1928

My first boy who is now twenty-two years of age started going on all fours when he was seven months old, and I tell you he sure could travel. He soon climbed up to chairs and at the age of nine months could run alone every place. When I spoke to my mother-in-law about this, she said that was just the way his father had traveled.

My son has a baby boy almost two years of age and he traveled just as his father and grandfather did on all fours and walked at about the age of nine months. I have also had two girls and another boy that traveled on all fours and all walked before they were a year old.

Yours truly,
Mrs. E. O. Armstrong,
Walnut, Ia.

First letter:

October 6, 1928

Dear Sir:

Some time ago I read in the San Diego *Union* an article concerning the research you are making of children who go about on all fours. My baby girl—just past a year old—has been running that way since she was six months old. She plants her feet firmly on the floor and slaps the palms of her hands on the floor and just scampers.

She is superior mentally and physically. She sleeps on her stomach with her knees drawn up. Very often she balances herself on her hands and lifts both feet off the floor, drawing them forward to progress.

I am very much interested in your research work and will appreciate any information you may give me.

Respectfully,

MRS. J. W. ARMSTRONG,

Carlsbad, Calif.

Second letter:

May 24, 1929

DEAR SIR:

I have intended writing for some time, sending you the pictures which I now enclose, and adding the observations I have made concerning our little girl.

She is now twenty months old. She walked upright three days before she was a year old, but even now when she is in a hurry or wants to get away from something real fast she drops down on all fours and just scuttles away—for all the world like a little bear, and she certainly can go fast.

FIG. 6.—A California miss enjoying herself on all fours. (Miss Armstrong.)

She showed a very early tendency to climb and before she was thirteen months old would climb in and out of her bed which is about eighteen inches high. When she was fifteen months old she climbed up and down stairs by putting her hands on one step and pulling one foot up then pulling the other foot up to the step above, never using one step for both feet, as most children do, and as you see by the picture enclosed she comes down the same way—she was wonderfully sure footed as she has never fallen yet.

She has never progressed any other way but on all fours and started in at the age of six months. She has always slept on her

PLATE VIII.—Down and up stairs on all fours. Little Miss Armstrong.

stomach, since a tiny baby, moving her head from side to side for a change of air and has both arms down flat at her sides. Sometimes drawing her knees up to her chest.

She is healthy as can be, chubby and robust looking. Has a marvelous disposition, is always happy and is showing decided musical tendencies. She is very logical in her manner of doing things, has a wonderful memory, is quite orderly, and seldom has to be told to do or not to do a thing more than once. People who have had more to do with babies than I have ever had, tell me she is quite remarkable and unusually bright.

She is our first baby, and her father and I were both well past our youth, both of us in our early forties when she came. We are of the Caucasian race—her father Canadian and I am American. So far as we know there are no other children in either of our immediate families who have run on all fours.

One peculiar thing I have noticed about her foot is that the great toe stands quite a distance from the other toes, although they do not look at all deformed.

She has a wonderful sense of balance. I have seen her turn around in rhythm to the music over the radio for fifteen or sixteen times, when she was only fifteen months old and never get dizzy, then turn and go back the opposite direction without missing the rhythm.

Her hands are always open and flat on the floor when she runs. I think the pictures show the position of her head better than I can describe it.

I hope this additional information may be of some benefit to the research work you are making. I shall be interested in receiving information as you make progress in your work and will send any further information you may desire or anything which I would consider of importance.

> Very truly yours,
> Mrs. J. W. Armstrong,
> Carlsbad, Calif.

August 4, 1928

Dear Sir:
I have been told that you are collecting data concerning children who walk on their hands and feet instead of creeping on hands and

knees. Our little son progressed in this fashion, very rapidly, from his tenth to his fourteenth month, approximately, when he abandoned this method for walking. After he began to walk he seemed very sure of himself, never having any hard falls, and now at the age of 22 months he runs more than he walks, and climbs anywhere, surely and without mishap. A four-foot wire fence was put around his play yard when he was 18 months old to keep him in bounds, but he straightway climbed over it. A cherry tree in the yard is a favorite climbing object now and a step-ladder is one of his most desired pieces of play equipment.

He is the fourth child and absolutely sturdy—thirty-five and three-fourths inches tall and weighing thirty-two pounds.

> Respectfully,
> MRS. H. LOUIS AUTEN,
> Oak Park, Ill.

October 10, 1927

DEAR DR. HRDLIČKA:

I am taking the liberty of calling your attention to the case of one of my daughters.

At the age of about $10\frac{1}{2}$ months she began to adopt the practice of running on all fours and within a couple of weeks attained great proficiency and high speed. Before she was a year old she went up stairs and down stairs backward on all fours. At the same age she would stand erect but did not adopt the practice of walking on two feet until when over 14 months old. She adopted her peculiar method of locomotion without instruction and so far as we know without any suggestion. She was in other respects a normal child and is now at the age of nineteen a senior in Radcliffe College.

I enclose a photograph showing the child in action while running rapidly as the blurring of the moving hand and foot indicate.

> Very truly yours,
> G. P. B.,
> Tufts College, Mass.

April 2, 1928

DEAR SIR:

Our older daughter, now two years and ten months old, walked on hands and feet, placing both flat on the floor, for one month at one year of age, and more or less for perhaps two weeks before and six weeks after that time. She stood in her bed at nine months, walked around it at ten months, around a large pen at eleven months. She walked alone at fourteen months, and at exactly fifteen months walked very well and seemed to "make up for lost time" rapidly. She talked (three words upon recognizing the objects) at six months. At one year, she used forty words easily.

The second daughter, now thirteen and one-half months, is slow in talking and walking, said "Mama" at six months, "Daddy" at one year and recently tried a number (perhaps six) but none distinctly. She also shows the same tendency to walk on hands and feet, both started with both hands and one foot and one knee, then went to two feet. They both throw their hands out, opened, palms down, in falling.

Detailed information:

Race and nationality—Caucasian, American.

Sex—Both female.

What children in numerical order—First and second.

Health and robustness—First child average—second above average.

Has the phenomenon been observed in any other child of the same parents or among relatives?—Both of mine—do not know about relatives.

At what age has the child begun to run on all fours, and how long has it continued?—First child, 12 months; second child, 14 months. Continued two and one-half months in first child; two weeks in second.

Add description, etc.—Both started the all-fours motion by slapping the hands down on the floor, then curling one leg (right) under the other at about the knee, then progressing on outer right thigh and left foot, later raising themselves to both feet.

Position of the hands, etc.—Hands open, head oftener down, sometimes up.

Details, etc.—

"Mother" slept on knees, hands doubled under, up to age 4 or 5 months, not consistently, but for days or weeks at a time. Both children when coming out of the all-fours habit showed a tendency to stand on toes or heels instead of flat on feet. Second child when walking around pen, holding, crosses one foot over other instead of using a side step, *i.e.*, one foot away from the other sidewise. "Bess" is now trying to walk alone and walks in a sitting position instead of pulling up by a chair and then walking upright.

Mrs. W. W. Bacon,
Boulder, Colo.

June 27, 1928

Dr. Hrdlička:

My baby who will be a year old July 1 creeps on all fours. She started to creep at nine months; could stand by a chair before she tried to creep. Is perfectly normal in height, weight and health, and runs on all fours faster than any baby I ever saw on hands and knees. At almost a year she can walk if someone holds her by one of her hands and will walk by herself if she has something to hold onto.

Detailed information:

White—German-American.
Sex—Female.
Health—Good. Weighs about 24 pounds at sixteen months.
Child in order of birth—Second.
Any other cases of running on all fours in the family—No.
When began—At nine and one-half months. Started to walk at $12\frac{1}{2}$ months.

Hands and feet are flat on the floor. Head held so she can see straight. Now that she walks she does not bend her ankles when she takes a step.

Can make three or four circles and then start to walk without getting dizzy or falling down. When she started to walk she never crept any more and in a week she could walk as good as a child that had walked for a year. At fifteen months she began to climb and will climb as high as she can get though very careful not to fall. She is very observative and when she sees some one dance she will do the same steps (if simple) that they do.

Yours truly,
Mrs. A. R. Bahl,
Lake Park, Ia.

July 10, 1928

DEAR SIR:

I read with interest the account of your study of the "quadruped-like progression," in a recent issue of the *Literary Digest*.

Thinking you may like to have in your possession a picture of such action, I am enclosing a snapshot of our little girl (now four), taken at nine months. She went this way, however, for only three months, then walked—her legs very straight and sturdy. She has always been very strong, more like a boy, and exceptionally bright.

Detailed information:

Report by—Mrs. S. A. Bakalyars, mother.
Nationality—Czech, German, American.
Locality—Iowa.
Sex of subject—Female.
What child in family—First.
Age of subject when running on all fours—Nine to twelve months.
Health, robustness and mentality of child—Above normal.
Nature of peculiar behavior—For three months she "crawled" on all fours only.
Peculiarities in other children or members of the family—Father unusually athletic.
Additional peculiarities of behavior—Often both my girls (three and four) sleep hunched on all fours.

MRS. S. A. BAKALYARS,
Des Moines, Ia.

July 2, 1928

My little boy walks on his hands and feet and is learning to run that way. When he was five months and one week, he started sliding on his stomach and went all over the house that way. Now at nine months he started walking on his hands and feet. He is ten months old and walks on all fours by chairs, tables, windows, and doors, also climbs that way upstairs by himself.

As far as those three cases you reported, I believe my little boy, Stuart, is walking on his hands and feet earlier than they.

Yours truly,
MRS. K. E. BALLOU,
Clarion, Ia.

March 26, 1928

My Dear Dr. Hrdlička:

I read with interest the article entitled "Children Who Run on All Fours," in the March tenth issue of *The Literary Digest,* and am enclosing some snap shots and information of my own little daughter, Catherine McKinney Barker, who comes under this group. (See Plate II, p. 23.)

Catherine was born on July 23, 1927, in Johnson City, Tenn., and was eight months old the day that these pictures were taken, March 23, 1928. She is a breast-fed baby and has never been sick, save for a slight cold at present. She is a decided blond, with very fair complexion, bright blue eyes and golden hair. She is 27½ inches tall and weighs 19½ pounds. Her arms are 10 inches long, (hands included); her legs, 10½ inches long; and her body (shoulders to hip) 9 inches long. Her hip measure is 16 inches; her bust measurement, 17½ inches. Her bones are small but she is quite plump, as you will note from the pictures. She has no teeth yet.

She began "crawling" at five and one-half months of age and has always progressed in this manner—on all fours—at no time letting any part of her body touch the floor. She generally runs on the bottom of her feet, with her hands open and forward, and her head up and forward, in the direction in which she is moving. When she goes very rapidly, however, she runs on the ball of her feet and toes, rather than planting the entire foot on the floor. She is unusually strong, goes all over the house very quickly in this manner and never seems to tire. At the same time that she began to run thus on all fours (about a week later) she began to sit entirely alone, getting up by herself. About two weeks later, she began to grasp things and pull herself up on her two feet, standing as long as she wished. Now, at eight months, she pulls herself up on her feet by merely placing her hands against something, such as the wall, it not being necessary to grasp with the hands. Holding to the chair or other object, she now steps around it.

My baby (white) is of Scotch-Irish-English descent on both the maternal and paternal sides of the family. The past four generations of the families have been born in America. Her father is a lawyer, mother a college graduate.

Race and nationality—American, white, Scotch-Irish-English descent.

Sex—Female.

What child in numerical order—Second.

Health and robustness—Unusually strong and healthy, and has a perfect disposition.

Has the phenomenon been observed in any other child of the same parents or among relatives?—I do not know with regard to relatives but it did not appear with my little boy.

At what age has the child begun to run on all fours, and how long has it continued?—Began at a little past the fifth month. At ten months she still runs in this manner.

Position of the hands, etc.—Hands fully open and forward, head up and forward, foot on floor, knees slightly bent, except when moving very rapidly.

Details as to any other peculiarity of behavior of the child, or any other children in the family—She always indicates sleepiness by scratching behind the ear; and she always sleeps on her stomach with knees drawn up under her, and hands and arms stretched out above her head.

Yours truly,
MRS. HENRY N. BARKER,
Bristol, Penn.

July 1, 1928

DEAR DOCTOR:

Thought you might be interested in these pictures of my little son Earl, now aged one year. From the age of 8½ months he walked on all fours. He has never crawled like other infants have. He weighed 8 lbs. at birth and present weight at one year is 30 lbs. He is the second child in the family. His brother also "crawled" on hands and feet at about the same age but walked at nine months. The mother was quite worried about the way little Earl runs around until I read her your articles in the *Medical Journal* and *Literary Digest* recently regarding the same. He is just taking his first steps now but much prefers to run around like a little bear, his feet flat on the ground and his hands usually half closed. In this manner he gets around with remarkable speed, holding his head up most all of the time. He always sleeps on his elbows and knees, his back up in the air and his head turned to the side. He is remarkably well developed, and quite holds his own with his two-year-old brother, who is also quite a little husky.

Nationality of parents: Mother—English-Canadian; father—French-Russian.

R. DE ROHAN BARONDES, M.D.,
Salinas, Calif.

FIG. 7.—"Sunnylad" Barondes, at ten months and at one year.

September 20, 1928

DEAR SIR:

At the instigation of Dr. John McLeod of the Massachusetts Eye and Ear Infirmary who, while visiting me, remarked on the fact that my daughter walked on all fours, I am writing such information as I can, in the hope that it may be of use.

Her mother is of German-Irish extraction, two generations back, and her father is American on both sides since colonial times. The child is abnormally healthy (if such a term may be used), for she has never had a sick hour in her thirteen months and a half. Never a cold, constipation, stomach disorder, etc., which are common to children. She is very strong physically but is somewhat small. She is the first child.

When running on all fours her fingers are spread and her elbow and knee joints stiff. She began moving on all fours at about eleven months but with one knee on the floor and one foot. After about two weeks she rose onto both feet and propelled herself thus until, at a year and two weeks, she stood upright and now at the age of a year and one and one-half months she runs easily about the house carrying books, etc., from place to place. Occasionally she drops to all fours if she cares to go particularly fast. Her leg and arm movement is that of a trotter rather than a pacer, and her head is held erect.

Being a teacher of biology as well as the parent of the child I am interested in any unusual development which the child shows.

Very truly yours,
W. L. BARTLETT,
Gloucester, Mass.

First letter:

September, 20, 1928

DEAR SIR:

I want to report to you on my little boy. He is,
White—American (Ancestry British).
Male.
The first child.
Apparently in good health now, but a pound or so underweight for his height. Had a bad year and a half following his only illness —measles (at 18 mos.).
No other cases of running on all fours known in family or among relations.
Ran that way from eight months to thirteen and one-half months (never did it after he ran easily on two).
Hands open and flat on floor, feet flat on floor, knees stiff, face front, progression very rapid. When he first began to walk upright, he would take 4 to 5 steps then simply lean forward until his palms touched the ground and continue to walk. As I remember it, he paced, *i.e.*, same hand and foot almost together, the hand a little preceding the foot. His legs, even as a baby, were so much longer than his arms that his hip seemed to stick straight up in the air.
Not peculiar in any other way unless punctiliousness of speech from the very beginning and an early interest (2½ yr.) in letters

and numbers as well as to what promises to be real mechanical genius, are peculiar.

Mrs. C. F. Baud,
Cleveland, O.

Second letter:

January 2, 1929

Dear Sir:

As a follow-up to the information I gave you several months ago about my son, Angus Fordham, who "crept" on all fours, I wish to state that my baby daughter (now 13½ mo.) has been changing her style of creeping from the usual hands and knees to, first, the left knee and right foot, a lame duck effect, and now to both feet, knees extremely bent, on her toes. (In contrast to her brother's flat-footed straight-kneed, hips-in-the-air progress.)

Very truly yours,
Mrs. C. F. Baud.

March 12, 1928

Dear Dr. Hrdlička:

After reading a copy of your article in the *Literary Digest* I wondered if you would be interested in the case of a child one year old that runs on all fours.

English mother and Scotch-Irish father.

Male, Leonard Reed Baxter.

Second child.

Exceptionally robust and healthy.

There are no other children among the relatives that I know of who crawled on all fours but an older child, a girl, Barbara Jeanne, also ran on all fours. She was small but seemed to be quite healthy.

Leonard began to run on all fours when seven months old and continued to do so until 11 months 2 weeks. When running this way he kept his hands partly closed, the fingers being barely curled. And he looked down and not looking where he was going, frequently bumped his head against things. He very seldom puts anything strange into his mouth and it is also very difficult to persuade him to eat any food he is not familiar with.

He is afraid of tortoise shell rimmed glasses and of anyone wearing them but does not seem to mind any other kind.

My daughter, Barbara Jeanne, also ran on all fours from eight months until the day she was 13 months. She held her head up and looked ahead. When a year old she started to eat soap every time she could find any and seemed to enjoy it though she would be sick afterwards. At fourteen months until eighteen months she would run away to go out into the orchard to eat dirt. And she seemed to be very particular which piece she ate, carefully selecting it and then eating with evident relish. Also she ate anything given to her but candy or cake.

Perhaps it would interest you to know the second and third toes on both of Barbara Jeanne's feet are grown together almost to the end. Leonard's feet are normal.

Sincerely,
MRS. GLADYS BAXTER,
Oakland, Calif.

July 11, 1928

DEAR DR. HRDLIČKA:

We were very much interested in your article in a recent issue of the *Literary Digest*, regarding babies who walk on "all fours."

Our baby, a boy now 13 months old, developed this mode of travel when about a year old, and is able to make considerable speed. He has gone through three different stages. At first he crawled on his stomach, then on his hands and knees, and lastly on his hands and feet. He walks on two around a card table or while holding on to his pen, but has made no effort to walk unaided. He has always been very strong and healthy.

Details:[1]

Report by parents, Mr. and Mrs. Loraine A. Becker.

Father and mother, native Nebraskans; maternal grandparents, American-born, grandmother, Scotch-Irish; paternal grandfather, native of Canada; grandmother native of Germany.

Male. First child.

Present age—fourteen months.

[1] Some of the data under "Details," in this and other cases, are derived from later correspondence.

Good health; free from colds; sturdy and strong, bright, quick; has unusually large chest and shoulders.

Started walking on all fours at age of one year. First locomotion pulled himself along on stomach, later on hands and knees, then on hands and feet; sometimes changes from third to second means now. Goes backwards (on all fours) quite a bit just now. Often pulls himself on his feet by holding to another person. Pulls himself up quickly by means of objects. Since year old, sleeps on hands and knees or with knees drawn up under him, at one end of bed. Before year old always slept on back. Began climbing up stairs before he was a year old. Climbs from chairs up to tables. (See Plate X, p. 189.)

Father's brother walked on all fours.

MRS. L A. BECKER,
Lincoln, Neb.

June 26, 1928

MY DEAR SIR:

I saw the news article in the current number of the *Literary Digest*, in reference to children that walk on their hands and feet, and note the fact that you desire reports of such children in order that a study may be made of the condition. I have to report that my son, Milton Omar Beebe, Jr., now in his fifteenth year, progressed in that manner as a baby. He began to move on his hands and feet—not his hands and knees—when he was about fourteen months old and continued it until he began to walk.

I gave the matter little thought at the time but presumed that it hurt his knees to crawl on them and he substituted his feet to save himself the discomfort. However, judging from your statements, I presume that there is something of larger importance than this to his actions.

I am interested in psychology and can understand your interest in this subject. It will be a joy to have you examine my son, if you care to do so, at any convenient time.

Details:

White, native-born American. Born at Concord, New Hampshire, August 20, 1913.

Male.

He is the first and only child.

His health has been excellent through the years. He has had the usual childhood diseases though nothing serious.

No other cases of such nature are known of in family or among relatives.

He began to run about on all fours at about the age of ten months and four days, and continued this until he was approximately fourteen months of age. He left it only when he began to walk.

The progression was by using his hands and feet. He would usually get on his hands and knees, then raise himself to his feet, using the balls of his feet only He could move very rapidly—much more rapidly than a child crawling on the hands and knees. I used to characterize the whole procedure by calling him a "mule" or by saying that he walked like a mule. A picture of him is not available.

I do not remember the position of the hands distinctly, though I am of the opinion that they were open. I believe I would have noticed it if they had been closed. His arms being shorter than his legs, he had to raise his head to see where he was going. I do not recall any other peculiarities.

He is the only child in the family. In every way he has seemed to be a perfectly normal child. His intelligence is at least average. Certainly he is not retarded in any way. He seems to eat, sleep, play and study, and work just as any other child.

> MILTON O. BEEBE,
> Chaplain, U. S. Army,
> Washington, D. C.

DEAR SIR:

At eight months my baby started running on all fours, and could always make great speed this way. At ten months he walked on two by himself. He had no fear and perfect control, could balance himself with no effort and went steadily. Now at eleven months he carries things in each hand, can run and turn and seldom falls. He is now starting to climb on chairs, tables, etc. Has four teeth and weighs twenty pounds.

Later information:

Child—American male; doctor has pronounced him in perfect health, very strong and has never been sick.

Is the only baby.

No other cases of running on all fours in family or among relatives, as far as known.

Began to run on all fours at the age of eight months. Did this for two months, then suddenly got up and walked at the age of ten months. Has never walked on all fours since he has walked on two.

Have no photo. Held hands flat and feet flat, and could go along in this way for fifteen or twenty feet before stopping.

The child is very smart, talks now, walks anywhere alone, and has done this since ten months old. He is now fourteen and one-half months, twenty-nine inches high, weighs twenty-five pounds, full chest and broad shoulders. Several doctors wanted us to enter him in baby contest, but for the child's sake we did not. They claim he could have walked away with first prize. He is afraid of nothing at all, goes up to anything. He never did creep or crawl.

> Yours very truly,
> Mrs. M. Berney,
> Des Moines, Ia.

First letter:

July 14, 1928

Dear Sir:

I was very much amused and interested to discover that there is something unusual in a child's walking on his hands and feet. Judging by the article in the *Literary Digest* in which you were quoted on the subject, I thought you might be interested in hearing of another case.

Instead of being displeased with my child for walking on his hands and feet I was pleased because hands and feet are more easily laundered than clothes. Incidentally I may say that my little boy rarely had shoes and stockings on until he was over a year old.

He was an extraordinarily active baby, showing a strong desire to climb with his arms while his feet were still helpless—so much so that we could not leave him in a baby carriage without watching him constantly. When he was put in a baby pen he would not play with his toys but tried to pull himself over the fence by his arms. For fear he would succeed in getting over and tumble on his head we abandoned the pen.

Before he could stand upright on his feet he could go up and down stairs on his hands and feet. We had to avoid gates or stairways, such as are used to keep babies from falling downstairs, because for him they were only hurdles to be climbed over.

He walked on all fours at nine months, stood alone at eleven and walked upright at one year.

Now he is nearly seven. He is very sure-footed; he delights in using his toes as fingers. He has never been ill save for an occasional grippe-cold. He attends an open-air school. At six and a half he has finished the second grade. He has no interest in reading, although he excels in spelling and has an unusual vocabulary and real feeling for language. His vision is perfect. This lack of interest in reading is peculiar because his father and I, both college trained, read a great deal. Perhaps this is only a passing phase in him.

Additional information:

Report by Alma Murray Bevis, mother.

Child—white, American, born Cincinnati, Ohio, U. S. A.; parents old American.

Male, near seven years, first child, health excellent.

No other children. Father can use toes to pick up articles.

Comment I recall: His father used to say that he showed clearly that it has not been long since his ancestors came down out of trees.

Evinced strong dislike of being held in one's lap. Began to squirm away even before he had finished nursing. Generally slept with arms raised above head. Still does. Rarely has covers pulled up to his shoulders. As a little baby keeping him covered was a problem because he did not kick off covers but climbed up out of them and then crouched down on arms and legs on top of the covers. The other day he said, "I wish I could curl up like Brownie (dog) or kitty when I go to sleep." Moves a great deal in his sleep, but does not awaken or have disagreeable dreams. Occasionally tells of a simple, pleasant dream—generally a repetition of an ordinary event such as seeing a friend.

Mrs. Howard L. Bevis,
Cincinnati, O.

Second letter:

July 25, 1928

The only additional thing I can say about my son's use of toes as fingers is that he seems to derive real pleasure out of picking up things with his toes. Perhaps he enjoys a feeling of superiority over me because my toes are utterly useless for such purposes. I notice his dexterity with his toes is less marked now than originally.

My son's feet are not large, nor are they small. The ankle bones are not as far from the sole of the foot as is usual.

I regret that the only picture I have which shows Murray walking on all fours is pasted in his baby book and the original film has been destroyed.

Had we realized there was anything peculiar about Murray's method of locomotion, we would probably have noted other facts that might be of interest to you. Since reading the excerpt from your article we have inquired among our friends and have not been able to find anyone who has known of another child who walked on all fours.

Yours sincerely,
MRS. H. L. BEVIS.

June 27, 1928

DR. HRDLIČKA:

My baby was one year old on June 20. At the age of nine and one-half months he moved across the floor slowly while in a sitting position but with one foot under him. By the time he was ten and one-half months old he was using both hands, the right foot and the left knee, which method he is still using with high speed. He is of a very cautious nature and although he can balance himself well and walk easily around his play pen he will not step alone.

My other boy, who is three years older, although he learned to creep in the usual manner, was very daring and at eleven months, before he could stand alone, he would go and walk quickly across the room to some other object or until he would fall. It was several months until he learned to stand alone or get up from the middle of the floor to start walking.

Both children were very healthy active babies and weighed twenty-five pounds at one year.

Yours truly,
MRS. L. C. BIERMAN,
Harrisburg, Pa.

February 22, 1928

Dear Dr. Hrdlička:

I have been much interested in your articles about children on all fours, especially because I have a case in my family.

This is a boy, my son Robert Otis, born March 28, 1926. He began to walk without assistance on his first birthday, March 28, 1927. By September he could walk a quarter of a mile. It was during late August and early September, 1927, that I saw him going on all fours. It was always in play and in the house. He would go in this way for some distance, eight to ten feet perhaps. I was not able to get any photograph. While walking on all fours, the legs were flexed at the hip and extended nearly straight at the knee, with the soles on the floor.

Details:

Anglo-Saxon, old American families on both sides, with some Celtic admixture.

Male; very healthy and robust; only child.

As far as I know running on all fours has never been observed in any other member of my or my wife's families.

Age about 18 months, observed only three or four times, during a period of probably a month.

The action lasted only a few minutes at a time, and occurred during play in the house. The boy would be running, and then suddenly throw himself forward and run for a short distance, the length of the room, on all fours. I think that the hands were open and the head up. It was a frisky action and rapid.

The child began to walk normally when one year old, and at two years walks up and down stairs without assistance.

> Very sincerely yours,
> R. P. Bigelow,
> Massachusetts Institute of
> Technology,
> Cambridge, Mass.

March 11, 1928

To the Smithsonian Institute:

I heard you were looking for information about children who walk on all fours instead of creeping.

I have two little girls, one six years old and the baby one year old, and they both started by walking on their hands and feet.

Sincerely,
Mrs. David Billings,
Everett, Mass.

I learn that you are interested in hearing of babies who walk on all fours.

I know of a baby, eleven months old, who walks on her hands and feet with great rapidity. She seldom uses any other method of locomotion, but can walk on her feet if held up.

She began to walk on all fours when she was about nine months old. She is the second born—her older sister showed nothing unusual. No other case of this nature (running on all fours) is known of in the family. The child is healthy and strong, and so far has shown no other striking peculiarities.

Sincerely yours,
F. J. B.,
Washington, D. C.

June 29, 1928

Dear Doctor:

I have a very fine son who will be thirteen years old July 25. As a baby he was perfect physically. At the age of nine months he was put alone on the floor and soon traveled on all fours outside as well as inside the house. At twelve and one-half months he decided to stand and take steps and in a couple of weeks used his hands no more in that way and would laugh rather disgustedly if it were suggested.

Details:

White race. Nationality—One-fourth German, one-fourth English, the rest New England Yankee.

Male, health and robustness fine, third child.

No other cases of running on all fours in family or relations, as far as known.

Began to run on all fours at near 10 months of age, and continued for three months.

Stood up at 9½ months but did not have confidence to walk off. All at once he found he could navigate by using his hands too and straightway proceeded on fours to go where he wanted to, very soon acquiring considerable speed. He raised his body up and walked very much like a bear when he uses all fours. It was quick and graceful. He often would sit to survey the situation or examine something. I have one snapshot but do not have the film.

The hands were open, the head thrust forward and not up very much. The feet turned out some. When he stood up he was very erect and sturdy. He is positive in all his ways of behavior.

He is the only normal child in this family. I, his mother, think I am normal but have had a hard married life. Last March the father of our two children hung himself. He was always extremely nervous and hard to live with. The youngest child is afflicted with hydrocephalus and is blind. But is very bright and a really good piano player at the age of ten, the radio being his only teacher.

Mrs. S. B.
Lamont, Ia.

First letter:

June 27, 1928

I am writing about my baby who creeps on her hands and feet. She started to creep when nine months old, at first pushing herself along every way, but now at ten months of age she goes along on her hands and feet freely. We thought it unusual, but had not given it much attention until we read your article. She is a perfectly normal healthy baby, developing in every way a baby should. Her legs are very sturdy and chubby.

Mrs. B. F. Bliss,
West Bend, Ia.

Second letter:

October 4, 1928

Here is the more detailed report you desired on Evelyn A. Bliss, 13 mo. and 1 wk. old, who creeps on all fours.

Caucasian Race—American nationality.

Sex—Female.

Health excellent, average robustness.

First child.

The phenomenon has not been observed among relatives.

She began to run on all fours at nine months 3 weeks of age, and still goes that way at thirteen months.

I am enclosing a photo of her in the act.

Her hands are fully opened while creeping and her head is in its natural position, not up. She can run quite fast in this way. She walks some now but more often "creeps" this way.

She has no other peculiarities that we notice. She is a very bright child.

Yours truly,
Mrs. B. F. Bliss.

March 26, 1928

Dear Sir:

Dr. Free's article in a March number of the *Literary Digest* interested me because my eight months old daughter has just started to "crawl" in this peculiar way. She gets up on her feet, legs almost straight, with hands wide open, and moves very quickly for one who has just been at it about ten days. Everyone says it is unusual.

I would be glad to tell you all about her if this interests you.

April 5, 1928

I have been waiting for a chance to take a picture of my baby before writing to answer your questions but will have to send that to you later.

Answering your questions by number:

White race; American.

Female.

First and only child.

Extremely healthy and robust. Weighs 22 pounds and is only nine months old.

This phenomenon has never been observed before in families of parents.

She began at eight months.

She gets up on her feet like in walking, with hands with outstretched fingers flat on the floor; head held up like a turtle and

. 129 .

moves very rapidly all over the house. She is very strong and large for her age. She has always had loads of fresh air and sunshine and slept outdoors almost every morning all through the winter. She gets her bath in the big tub half full of water and loves it; does not mind when she slips and fills her ears, eyes, and nose full of water. Part fish, I think.

I am certainly very interested in this and would be awfully obliged if you would tell me something about it or refer me to some article on the subject.

Yours very truly,
Mrs. Louis M. Bourne,
Quantico, Va.

March 7, 1928

Dear Sir:

Having read of your desire to have reports of children who run on all fours instead of creeping, I write to tell you about my first born.

Family History: Parents—White, of American stock for several generations on both sides. At birth of child, which is the first, mother was 36, and father 37. Both parents have A. B. and M. D. degrees.

Personal History: Normal birth and infancy. Child crept at 9 months—but already could walk around inside her crib by holding on to the rail. About a week later she began running on all fours, and could soon go so rapidly that it was difficult to catch her. She did not establish walking upright until almost fourteen months of age. She just seemed not to find walking necessary—it was not a matter of strength, certainly, for she had already walked around walls and chairs for several months. Stopped running on all fours in fifteenth month.

She held her hands open while running. The head was somewhat retracted so as to bring the face forward. Ran just as a bear does.

Two subsequent children of ours have not exhibited this phenomenon; and so far as known there has been no such case among our relatives.

The child in question has been precocious both physically and mentally. At seven years she was 52 inches tall and weighed 70 pounds. She is now at 7½ years in the fourth grade in school, and seems the equal in every way of her classmates who are 9 and 10 years old.

I am especially interested to report this. I enclose a snap-shot which, though not good, seems to show necessary details.

Very truly yours,
MRS. ALBERT BOWEN,
Fort Myer, Va.

First letter:

March 12, 1928

DEAR SIR:

In the last issue of the *Literary Digest* I have noted your interest in the child who runs on all fours. I am submitting the following observations of my second son aged one year and two weeks.

At the age of eight months, having learned to creep in the ordinary manner he suddenly began to literally run on all fours. He got around at an amazing speed considering his age. His knees were stiff, the palm of the hand flat, using, however, the ball of the foot, keeping the head on the same angle as the trunk. He continued this mode of "walking" until two weeks ago, when he began to really walk. And we have noted that since discovering the erect position he prefers it, in spite of numerous falls incident to a child's first steps. But at times even now, when wishing to get some place in a hurry, he reverts to all fours.

I am his mother. My father was born in this country of Irish parents, who in turn, trace to the Danish and French. My mother, on her mother's side, was English and Welsh; my maternal grandfather was Scotch. Mr. B.'s father is an American since 1640, that family having come from England and Wales.

As far as we have been able to trace ancestors on both sides, they have been farmers, teachers, preachers, engineers. At the present time my own family boasts of our most eminent statesmen and jurists, and a scientist equally high in the service of our country.

Yours truly,
MRS. A. N. B.,
Jackson Heights, N. Y.

Second letter:

DEAR SIR:

It has taken me until the present time, to make inquiries concerning peculiarities in others of our family.

I will take your additional questions and answer them as they come.

At the time of birth, and until Howard, the subject of these letters and our second son, was about three months, he had a growth of hair, or more properly fuzz, beginning at the base of the spine, and spreading possibly one-fifth of the way up the back. It has completely disappeared.

Arthur, my first son, had none of Howard's peculiarities. He (Arthur) is quiet in manner, thoughtful, and not very active.

Howard is a regular cyclone. Not still one waking moment. In fact, when the house is asleep, he frequently wakes, in a darkened room, and bounces up and down in his crib, sometimes as long as two hours. He is above average in strength and development. This last from three doctors. Also he seems way above in intelligence. I say this advisedly, because of the well-known platitude concerning mothers and their children.

No other child in either family, on the available data, has ever run on fours or had any outstanding peculiarity.

I have tried to get the picture of Howard in his own peculiar motion. They (the pictures) have not been successful so far, because of the difficulty in making him be still long enough. I have not given it up however.

Let me thank you for your information on this subject. It will be a source of satisfaction to me, that I may have contributed a tiny bit to the great work you are trying to accomplish. It wouldn't be a bad idea to delve into the past of some of our U. S. Senators for prehuman characteristics, since you are right on the spot in Washington.

Sincerely,
MRS. A. N. B.

First letter:

March 11, 1928

DEAR SIR:

In the March 9th issue of *Science* you ask for information about children who have before walking run on all fours. I have three girls, and the oldest was the only one who did that, the younger two crept and then walked in the normal manner. Esther (the oldest), from the time she could sit up in arms would hold her arms and hands as a dog does in "begging," hands drooping. She did this until she was about eleven or twelve months old. Aside this, she sat on the floor, and instead of creeping would "hitch," using her heels as one would oars in a boat, and she would go so fast! This lasted, as I recall, from about seven to ten months of age. Then she began to run on all fours, which lasted until she learned to walk properly at about fourteen months. She became very expert on the fours, and could go almost as fast as I ordinarily walk.

Both my husband and I are American born, white. She was our first child. No one else on either side ever did these things as far as I know. She has always been in normal health. Never missed any time of any account in her school career, which ended in a university. She has now been teaching some time. I have no photograph. As I recall, her hands were open, the weight seemed to be mostly on the fingers, which are "double jointed," as are her toes, like her father's and his mother's. Her head was even with her body, raised, if anything, that she might see better. She has always been easily controlled, sensitive to suffering, and full of energy, very apt to use up too much of her nerve force. Very successful in her personal contact with boys and girls.

MRS. A. P. BOWER,
Reading, Pa.

Additional information:

March 22, 1928

DEAR SIR:

You ask in your letter of March 17 what I mean by "double jointed fingers." I mean the power to bend the fingers back at the three joints almost as much as most people bend them towards the palm of the hand. Sort of throwing them out of joint. A very awkward movement. The toes also to some extent, not as much as the fingers.

Our second child also had this peculiarity, but not so marked, otherwise she was and is a normal girl, above the average in intelligence (Phi Beta Kappa, Phi Kappa Phi, member A. A. A. S., and some other societies).

No one on my side of the family have anything out of the ordinary, and on Mr. Bower's side I know of none excepting what I said in my first letter.

Sincerely,
MRS. A. P. BOWER.

January 16, 1929

If you are still gathering data on "children running on all fours" I would like to submit the following case:

White, American, male, in good health but not robust, being pale and undernourished, first child, no other known cases in family tree; first began to run on all fours when twelve months old, and still continues, at the age of fifteen months. The hands are wide open, the head elevated, and the legs extended when running; started to creep in ordinary fashion before he attempted to draw himself up.

LOUIS J. BRAGMAN, M. D.,
Syracuse, N. Y.

August 29, 1928

DEAR SIRS:

I notice an article in this week's Sunday *Times* about "Babies on All Fours" and think you may be interested to hear of another case. My daughter, who is now nearly seventeen, crawled in this way. She never went on hands and knees like other babies but always on hands and feet and consequently got about much faster than other children.

This always amused us and our friends very much, but although we thought it peculiar and have never seen any other baby do it, we did not realize that it was anything extraordinary.

We thought it might have been a desire to "feel her feet," because, as she was a particularly big baby (eleven and one-half pounds at birth), we never put her on her feet until she pulled herself there and showed a wish to walk.

Details:

English mother, American father of all-English ancestry.
Female.
Health—Good.
Only child.
No other such cases known in the family or among relatives.
Exact time of beginning and ending uncertain.
Ran with knees straight, feet flat on floor, action of horse or dog, weight being equally distributed between hands and feet. The hands were fully open, head raised.
Is very left-handed.
She has noticeably hollow back. She weighed eleven and one-half pounds at birth; now, at seventeen, weighs 148 pounds and is 5 feet 1½ inches tall. Can still walk on all fours. There is a very pronounced tendency in her father's family to rupture in the groin. Unfortunately we have no photograph.

Mrs. A. W. B.,
London, England.

March 16, 1928

Dear Dr. Hrdlička:

On page 23 of the *Literary Digest*, issue March 10, 1928, I note your request to send certain observations of children to you.

In the summer of 1895 my occupation as a newspaper writer gave me an opportunity to visit various sections of a western state, principally to visit farmers in remote parts. On one occasion, about noon of a blistering hot day, I approached a farm residence after having hiked more than ten miles from the home of the nearest neighbor. As I came to a rude gate I noted a small boy lying in a shallow water hole, rather mud hole, beside a dog and a pig. As the boy heard the noise I was making trying to open the gate, he aroused himself, raised himself on knees and hands, and to my consternation barked at me in perfect imitation of the racket the dog was putting up. I said "to my consternation." You may imagine what I felt when the boy, about four years old, began then to grunt like a pig. I stood there. Off in a field I saw a woman at work. I went over to where she was, explained who I was and what brought me into the isolated section of the state. Tears came to her eyes, as she asked me how her little boy had behaved. The woman told me her husband was at work in some scrub timber some distance away and that soon he would be home. When he came, then the parents explained to me that their little boy—the only child—had acted in the manner told in the preceding since he was two years old, and that he then lacked two months of being four years old. Not being a physician, I could give the parents no competent advice. The following morning I hiked to a town thirty miles where resided a studious country doctor, and that evening I told him my experience. He agreed that the boy must have children as companions, and this was within a month brought about by the parents adopting an orphan child, a little girl of three years. [Just how the case went on is uncertain.] Years later I again was at the home of the parents—by this time a prosperous home. The boy was a youth, and the girl was blooming like a rose. Both were as normal as they could be.

Again I saw that boy, still later. He was leaving for a training camp, having volunteered for service in the army the day after the United States entered the World War. He went to France, became a commissioned officer, and is still serving as such in the army. He is married happily, and so is the little orphan girl. Not longer than two years ago I saw and spoke to both.

I refrain from giving names of parties. The occurrence took place in an intermountain state, and all concerned are as fine people as are to be found on this planet. I have read of you often, and I know that you are seeking information for the good of the world. As to myself I am a bachelor, but I love children.

Yours,
JOHN BRISTOL.

September 23, 1928

Our son Elwyn, now five years old, first got around by walking on all fours. He started to walk on hands and feet at about six months of age; never tried to creep. Could stand upright at nine months but would not walk that way. Am sending snapshot taken when he was about eight or nine months old, hiking on all fours.

Father, English and Scotch. Mother, part Spanish.
Male.

Complexion light, hair light, eyes blue, of delicate build and rather tall for age. Always quite healthy except has fever at times by stomach being upset.

Sixth child. Oldest child a girl, second a boy, third a boy, fourth a girl, fifth a boy, and this one the youngest.

No one else in family known to have run on all fours.

Began to walk on all fours at about eight or nine months and continued to do so for three or four months or until he began to walk upright, but for some time if he was in a hurry to get somewhere he would drop to all fours and make better time that way.

He placed his hands flat on the ground or floor also soles of the feet flat on ground and when moving had his head up looking ahead. At the time snapshot was taken he had stopped to look at something on the ground. He never showed any other peculiarities. He is very bright, quick to learn and of a good disposition.

Sent snapshot.

> Yours respectfully,
> A. J. Brooks,
> Lemmon, S. Dak.

July 5, 1928

Science Service,
21st & B Streets, N. W.,
Washington, D. C.
Dear Sirs:

In response to your radio request this evening I am writing to tell you of my son, fourteen and a half months old, who frequently runs about on all fours like a bear.

This youngster, Brickman Brown, born April 18, 1927, started to creep in the usual manner on his knees when he was not quite eight months old. He was very strong and active at that time and could always move very fast. He kept up the usual form of creeping until he was about a year old and then he started running on all fours occasionally, although he didn't give up his old method of creeping. He started to walk at 13 months and now walks fairly well, but he frequently runs on all fours when he is in a hurry. Now he does it only once or twice a day, perhaps.

Just after Brickman started to creep, his father taught him to slide off backward from a low davenport we have. He has had very few falls because he applies that method of climbing off of chairs, bed, or anything he manages to get up on. In the parks he often crawls backward in getting down off the curb to the sidewalk. Sometimes, after he has discovered where the curb is, he crawls backward on his hands and knees for as far as twenty feet to be sure to approach the curb the right way to climb down. When he is being cautious like that he never uses the all fours method.

Cordially,
MRS. ART BROWN,
Washington, D. C.

DEAR SIR:

Recently I have noticed several articles reporting that children in some cases walk on hands and feet rather than creeping. I have three youngsters in my family. Two of these three used this method of locomotion for several months. I doubt if any of the details which I shall add will contribute anything new but I will add a little more of detail regarding these two children.

They are twin boys. Their health when young was not good. When they were three months old they weighed only five and one-half and six and one-half pounds respectively. They suffered from no particular illness and after six months of age grew normally though they never have been quite up to average in weight. They are now thirteen years old and, except for being slightly under weight and height, are ordinarily active, vigorous boys. When they were from ten months to fourteen or fifteen months old they moved about most commonly by walking on hands and feet, rather than by creeping. They had some aluminum cups with which they played and within a short time after they began walking in this way, they began taking an aluminum cup in each hand to lengthen their arms to nearly the length of their legs and it was common for three months after that for them to find two aluminum cups and walk around on all fours.

I am quite sure I have seen several other children walking in this way more or less.

Additional information:

White—At least ¾ English and Welsh; French, German.
Male—Twins.

Mother died when they were four days old. Weakly babies for six months. Health excellent now. A little below average in weight at 13 years.

Twins, first children.

No other cases of walking on all fours in the family or relatives—not that I know of.

Began to walk on fours at about eight months, continued for six months.

No photo available of children "in action."

Hands fully open or very often holding an aluminum cup in each hand to lengthen arms. Sometimes face downward, sometimes face upward.

Nothing else which seems peculiar to me.

PROF. F. E. BROWN,
Department of Chemistry,
Iowa State College,
Ames, Ia.

MY DEAR SIR:

I read an article in the *Literary Digest* stating that you are interested in observing "Children who run on all fours."

I was most interested to learn that the habit was being studied, as I have a son who has always got around that way. At the age of seven months he began to get up on his hands and feet—knees never touching the floor. He soon started to move that way and after a month gained great rapidity. He actually ran along. He kept his hands open, fingers well apart, and carried his head erect. He is now just twelve months and is walking on two feet most of the time, although if he is in a hurry he gets down and runs along. Each day, however, now he seems to be walking more and running less. I have often wondered why he did locomote in such a way.

At first I thought nothing of it, but when friends and neighbors expressed surprise at the way he got around I began to wonder if he was abnormal. He is apparently a bright, happy child, perfectly healthy and normal in every way. I am an American, his father is an American. In tracing our genealogy, have found only Scotch, English, American in family.

Details:

White—American, male.

Perfectly healthy and robust.

First child.

No other case of running on all fours known in family.

Began at seven months, nearly stopped at twelve months.

He trots along like a dog and sort of sways his legs from side to side. He keeps his hands open and carries his head up. He can go along with considerable speed. He is now a year old and walks most of the time. I have not noticed anything additional peculiar about the child. Neither have I noticed any peculiarity in the other children in the family, unless lack of a full set of teeth could be called such—my boy has a boy cousin seven years old who has never had two teeth upper and two lower that he should have. This may be nothing but it has been a wonderment to all the family why he should not have. They are front teeth too. My youngster has different eyes than most children. Instead of being pointed in the corners they seem to have a cord that comes down straight (epicanthus). It is awfully hard to explain it and it is not particularly noticeable, but I had a brother who died and his eyes were the same.

I should be much interested to hear your deductions on this whole thing.

Yours truly,

Mrs. Donald W. Bruce,

Waltham, Mass.

July 10, 1928

Dear Sir:

After creeping in the approved orthodox fashion for babies for about six weeks, all of a sudden last Saturday my year old son Billie got upon his little feet and placing his hands flat on the floor walked in the most approved bear fashion!

The whole household exclaimed over this for none of us had ever seen a child do so or had we heard of one. We thought it was so cunning and his father believed that the small boy had of himself found a way to keep his knees off the floor because we had within two days put him into short socks.

Imagine my surprise upon picking up the *Literary Digest* of June 23, to find quotations from an article relative to researches which you had made in this very matter. Apparently it wasn't the half hose after all!

We note particularly that you have found the children always strong and well. My son has never been ill in his year of life, is sturdy and strong in every way apparently. He had twelve teeth on his reaching one year of age. He walks along beside of things after pulling himself up but has not tried for himself at all. Since Saturday he has crept but very, very little, using his "bear walk" almost entirely.

If this is all of any interest to you in your researches or if there is anything further I can tell you I shall be most happy.

Additional information:

Report by Amie M. Buchanan.

Mother—American from before the Revolution, of English and Welsh origin prior to that. Father—Nova Scotian of Highland Scotch descent.

Subject—Male, born June 20, 1927. Bear walk first noticed July 7, 1928.

First child.

Always perfectly well since birth. Weighed seven pounds, eleven ounces, at birth; height 18½ inches. At one year weighed 26½ pounds and was 28 inches tall.

Walks with his feet flat on the floor and his hands also flat on floor, the peculiar sidling gait of a bear. I hadn't thought of it before but as one of our friends said "He's a pacer." Have not noticed any other peculiar habits.

I don't know what to say about mentality. I guess it is hard to tell at one year. The first and only child after twelve years of married life, he seems to his admiring adult relatives the brightest and most wonderful child there ever was.

I will send a picture when and if I am successful in getting one in action.

> MRS. WILLIAM R. BUCHANAN,
> Athol, Mass.

June 9, 1928

DEAR SIR:

I read an article in a Boston paper some time ago concerning your interest in youngsters who travel about on all fours instead of creeping.

I have a daughter who never crept but always got around on all fours. Her legs were almost straight and her hands were pointed straight ahead with the fingers parted. As for her head, I cannot say definitely, but I believe she held it more down than upward.

Your inquiry about children moving about in this unusual manner is of great interest to me as I have always been very much surprised and amused in watching my child go about in such a strange way. Nurses, doctors, and friends who have been at the

FIG. 8.—"Peek-a-boo," between the legs, while on all fours, Miss Budke.

house and have seen her have always remarked about it, but I did not realize that it was anything out of the ordinary.

My daughter is now twenty months old and has been walking about four months. Every now and then, nevertheless, she reverts to going around on all fours. She has another strange and unusual habit when she becomes cross and then she stands with her head on the ground, her legs straight and in a position to take a somersault.

Detailed information:

September 14, 1928

White race; American (of Scotch, German and English descent). Female; health, excellent; first child.

The phenomenon has never been observed in either of the parent's families to our knowledge.

My daughter began to go about on all fours at about the age of fourteen months and continued up to two years of age.

The enclosed photographs explain the position of head, hands, feet, etc.

The picture in which you can see the head between the legs is the position which the child takes when she displays anger or temper. She sometimes takes this position and kicks with her feet as a dog might do when scratching and sometimes she breaks out in crying. This is the only peculiarity the child has.

I sincerely hope the above remarks are clear and that they may be helpful to you.

MRS. JOHN F. BUDKE,
Franklin, Pa.

January 28, 1928

DEAR DR. HRDLIČKA:

In the *Journal of the American Medical Association* of Jan. 21 I read your note regarding Children Who Run On all Fours. A nephew of my wife did this until he was about five or six years old, although he had begun to walk perfectly well at about one year of age. It was a source of considerable amusement to his family and it became a sort of game with him. I have seen him travel as much as a quarter or half a mile on all fours when he was about five years old. The sequence of hands and feet was sometimes a trot and sometimes it was much like a fox trot. I cannot give many details.

I give such facts regarding the performance as are at my command: (1) race, white; (2) nationality, American for at least seven or eight generations on all sides; he is a great-grandson of Edward Hitchcock, the geologist, also a great-great-nephew of John Randolph; (3) male; (4) always healthy and robust; now 24 years old, over six feet tall, 210 pounds, powerful and active; (5) second child; (6) the gait was sometimes a square trot, sometimes a running walk or fox trot. When he was four or five years old he would cover ground at a rate somewhat faster than a man would ordinarily walk; he never seemed to tire; (7) the hands were fully open, but I do not remember whether the whole hand touched the ground or only the fingers. I am not sure of the position of the head, but believe it was kept raised.

Yours truly,

DR. J. B. B.

First letter:

March 31, 1928

DEAR SIR:

Our daughter, who is now over five years old, is another example of "physical behavior atavism," for she began walking on all fours at the age of ten months, after crawling in the usual manner for a few weeks. She attained such speed on all fours that she did not seem interested in learning to walk, and she was over fourteen months old before she took her first steps unsupported. However, she became at once very steady on her feet, and her carriage has always been very erect. She is now a rapid runner and a fearless jumper, and shows excellent muscular control in the use of her hands and arms as well as her legs.

We are white Americans, of English and Dutch ancestry.

Second letter:

April 4, 1928

MY DEAR DR. HRDLIČKA:

In answer to the questions in your letter of April 3, I am glad to give you such additional information as I can. Our little girl is the first and only child. I have not heard of any other children in either branch of our family displaying this peculiarity. I am sorry that we have no photograph of the child "in action." We did not realize that there was anything remarkable in the performance.

She used to place her hands fully open on the floor when running on all fours. I do not recall how she held her head.

I believe there is nothing further to add, except that she seems somewhat advanced in both physical and mental development (not only in our prejudiced eyes, but by comparison with standard tables prepared by recognized authorities).

Yours very truly,

MRS. T. K. BURCHARD,

Cherrydale, Va.

June 26, 1928

Our baby has always been more or less of a miracle to us. But, of course, we have never thought his running on all fours anything really unusual, thinking that a good many babies do the same. But from Dr. Hrdlička's report there are evidently not many babies who run thus as early as ours did, so I would certainly like to tell you about him.

This little paragraph is taken from his memory book. So I have all these records.

"You are five months old and you are doing the 'Australian Crawl,' (that is what we called it jokingly; we even said he had gone back to the Stone Age evolution) using hands and feet as fast as you can."

He walked right up on his hands and feet with his feet flat on the floor. He never creeped at all. At nine months old he walked upright all over, and at ten he was walking outdoors over rough ground any place he wanted to go. Mother said I walked when I was nine months old so we did not think much about it.

Every day we are marveling at the way he develops. He is now eighteen months old, and can say anything you ask him. Even hard words like Norway, Sweden, Greece. Counts up to ten with us. Puts three words together. Like "write, Hoyt, come." That is a man's name Mr. Byerley writes to and who has been to see us several times. "Ding, dong, bell." "Cow, daddy's barn." And any number of such phrases and everyone understands them. No baby talk about it.

He weighs thirty pounds and is thirty-four inches tall. Wears No. 6 shoe and two-year-old suits. Feeds himself. Asks for his chair, helps to dress himself and puts his toys away. He has done a good many of these things since he was eleven and twelve months old.

At birth he weighed 8 lbs. 10 oz., 23 inches tall.

May 5 when he started on his hands and feet he weighed 17 lbs. 8 oz., and was 28 in. tall.

Oct. 5—31 in. tall—24 lbs. 3 oz.

June 5—34 in. tall—30 lbs.

From Memory Book:

Baby smiles on Jan. 5, 1927. Baby smiles for Daddy on Jan. 9, 1927. Five weeks old, smiling for everyone. Jan. 9, turned completely over in bed whenever he desired. Outgrew six pairs of shoes before he was six months old.

First tooth at six months. Six months old he pulled himself up to his kiddy-koop and to chairs.

He was a breast-fed baby up to eight months, and bottle to one year. Drinks one quart cow's milk every day. Has never been sick a day in his life, only three days after a serum, and that was because the Doctor that gave him the second shot gave him "antitoxin," instead of "toxin antitoxin" and he had the rash that comes from "antitoxin reaction."

I am enclosing a snap picture of baby.

Mrs. L. G. Byerley,
Leachville, Ark.

July 28, 1928

Dear Sir:

In the *Science News-Letter* for June 30, 1928, p. 408, is an article reporting some investigations you have made regarding babies who walk on all fours, rather than creep. The enclosed kodak pictures were made of a little niece of mine when she was about 14 months old. At the time these pictures were made she was learning to walk, but before she walked she had amused the family very much with what we supposed was a very peculiar method of locomotion. The family called it "walking like a bear."

She would scuttle across the floor in this fashion quite rapidly. I was also amused with her odd squatting position which I caught in picture No. 3, as she was examining my camera case.

Report by Mary R. Calvert.

Child—American born, Tennessee, female.

Ran on all fours between 14 and 15 months.

First child, fairly healthy and robust, good mentality.

I only saw the child just after she had learned to walk. She would even then at times drop on all fours and "walk like a bear" across the room.

Mary R. Calvert,
Williams Bay, Wis.

My Dear Dr. Hrdlička:

I read with great interest an article in the *Literary Digest* of June 23, on the subject of babies who walk like bears. My daughter who is eighteen this summer walked exactly that way from the time she was a year old until she was eighteen months or nearly two years, as well as I can recall the time.

She is one of the strongest persons that I have ever known. Our family doctor has told me that she is just like a sturdy little animal. She has missed only a few days from school in her whole life. She is rather small in stature but is perfectly healthy in every respect. Her physical examination this spring was so nearly perfect that a doctor from away from here commented on it.

I really believe that she is above normal mentally too. She graduated at the head of her class at High School this year with the highest mark for the four years. There were 178 in the class so I do not feel that being my child would cause me to make a biased statement about her. I understood that you wanted to know something of the kind of people that these children came from. Our families from both sides are English and Scotch-Irish. They came to this country in the seventeen hundreds and fought in the Revolution on the side of the colonies. They pioneered into Virginia, Tennessee, and South Carolina.

My daughter's great-grandfathers were both very able men. One rose very high in the ranks of the church and the other in the state. I tell this simply as information of the sort that I believe you want.

So many of our friends commented on the strange way that our child walked. Some called her a coon and some a bear. She would run away sometimes and could go faster than we could walk after her, over to our next-door neighbors. She never crawled or tried to go any other way except this until she walked naturally.

I am sure that this is a most interesting line of study that you are carrying on.

Yours sincerely,
MRS. GABRIEL CANNON,
Spartanburg, S. C.

March 21, 1928

DEAR SIR:

I notice in the *Literary Digest* of March 10th that you would like accounts of children who walk on all fours.

As I shall be eighty-four next May, it may interest you to see from my case that the habit meant nothing unusual in after life.

I have often heard my mother speak of my walking on all fours at the creeping age, before I began to walk upright, and judging from her description of my very funny appearance, I must have walked with my knees nearly stiff. This threw my body forward, and I must have looked somewhat like a kangaroo when on all fours.

My legs were evidently especially strong, and all my life they have been particularly stout and firm.

In New York we can measure distance by the blocks, and I generally walk about a mile, more or less, every day.

Details:

Race and nationality—Pure New England blood, of English ancestry.

Sex—Female; health and robustness—ten-pound baby at birth. What child in numerical order—Fourth.

Has the phenomenon been observed in any other child of the same parents or among relatives? I never heard of any case.

At just what age have you begun to run on all fours, and how long has it continued? I don't know.

Details as to any other peculiarity of behavior of the subject, or any other children in the family—None.

The baby being myself, I can only repeat my mother's description. I walked with my body tipped very much forward. Evidently therefore, I kept my knees stiff.

Mrs. Alice P. Carter,
New York, N. Y.

First letter:

March 11, 1928

Dear Sir:

In a recent magazine article I read of your request to the American Medical Association for help in finding instances of "children who run on all fours." I was very much interested in your request since my little daughter ran on all fours. I have never known of a case like hers and will be very glad to give any information you desire, if it will be of any value to you. I shall not attempt to give a history of her babyhood here but if you consider my observations helpful to students of human evolution you have but to ask any question you wish.

Mrs. A. L. Casseday,
Astoria, L. I., N. Y.

Second letter:

March 25, 1928

Dear Dr. Hrdlička:

This is in answer to your letter of March 17 concerning my little daughter, Jeannette, who ran about on all fours.

She was born July 8, 1922. Her father's family and mine are descendants of Scotch and Irish pioneers who came to America before the Revolution. She is an only child. As far as we can find out no other child in the family has gone about on all fours.

At six months she was able to sit alone. Never at any time did I encourage her to sit up or stand on her feet. When she learned to sit up I then put her on the floor for certain periods each day. Very soon I discovered she moved herself about without moving! She merely jiggled herself up and down and after a while seldom failed to arrive at the piano with her little feet wedged underneath. The all-fours habit just seemed to evolve out of this so gradually, it is impossible to state exactly when, but I think it was at about eight and a half or nine months. She then ran about like a little race horse with hands open and head up. In many respects she was like a chicken—very carefully going over every inch of the floor searching for the tiniest particles to put into her mouth. Everything she could find went into her mouth. Everything she could lay hands on was destroyed—toys, books, papers, music. She delighted to drag torn papers, cushions, shawls, etc., into a little cage formed by a gate-leg table when closed. She amused herself for long periods in this way. Most of the time she was scampering rapidly about hunting for trouble. As early as three months she seemed to like colors, like blue and lilac, but screamed in terror when a relative clad in mourning came to see her. She showed a most intense dislike for people with grey hair as early as five months. At first she seemed afraid but soon it seemed she simply loathed the sight of a grey-haired person.

From the time she was able to grasp anything she grasped it properly. For example, a ball with a string attached. She seized the string to make the ball rattle. She had one toy she loved and was unable to destroy and she always grasped it properly and upon being undressed, very carefully changed it from one hand to the other as her sleeves were removed. During the time she was running on all fours she found a magazine cover of very slick paper. She discovered she could make a great deal of speed by resting her hands on the paper and using her legs only. I assure you it was a good show. At eleven months she began standing by pulling herself up with the aid of furniture. She was soon walking by holding on to something. Before her first birthday she was quite ill and she did not walk alone until she was a little past fourteen months. However, she did not revert to the all-fours gait after she found she could stand and walk by holding to something. She always has been keenly aware of everything about her, and intensely active, too active. She is very well formed, except her ears—they do not match.

As she was going from one phase to another she seemed quite normal, except in learning to talk. She developed a language of her own of which I understood only a few words; however, when I asked her to repeat she always repeated the same sounds. I was very much alone with her until she was over two years old and as we were strangers in a strange city I think perhaps that accounts, at least in a measure, for her slowness in learning to talk. At two and a half years she could put but few words into sentences and it was not until we went South to visit our relatives that she really learned to talk. Now she has a vocabulary much beyond her years.

I am so sorry I have no pictures that would be of any value in this case. I am not sure that the condition of her health has any bearing on this matter. She seems to have certain disorders that her father and grandfathers were subject to, a delicate stomach and asthma. Certain traits in disposition, etc., are almost identical with those of her father, her father's sister, and my mother, but one would say without hesitation that she is almost exclusively of the Casseday family in character and disposition.

I do hope that you will find something of interest in this.

With very best wishes, I am

Very truly yours,
Mrs. A. L. Casseday.

P. S. I forgot one thing that perhaps is of interest. Since she was one month old she scratches gently on her pillow as she is going to sleep. She has a tiny pillow which to this day she takes to bed and cuddles in her arms and scratches on. If she wakes up in the night I hear this gentle scratching until she goes to sleep again.

Mrs. A. L. C.

March 16, 1928

DEAR SIR:

In a very recent issue of the *Literary Digest* there is a statement that you are interested in reports of children who ran on all fours. My son, Francis M. Chaney, was such an infant.

He was born in Mexico City, of American parentage of English, Irish and German ancestry, August 2, 1911. Largely because of agility in the pre-walking stage, he did not walk upright until the age of 15 months. Earliest creeping was in a sitting posture, or nearly that; then, leaning forward led to locomotion, to grasp articles just out of reach, and creeping on hands and knees had begun; and then, for a brief period in the fifteenth month, he traveled with considerable speed on hands and feet. In one instance I ran, in a park, to catch him, and am sure he did on his all fours a gait of $4\frac{1}{2}$ miles per hour. He proceeded up the steps of a band stand, and was photographed with a hand upraised for the next step. His movements were with open hands and head raised for vision ahead.

This Kodak picture has been preserved, and can be sent to you for copying, if it is of interest. The posture, as photographed, does not appear abnormal, due to the incline of the steps. Any child, just having learned to walk, might have been caught in a similar posture; but he had not yet learned to walk.

Details:

Race and nationality—American, English-Irish-German descent.
Sex—Male; health—excellent.
Numerical order—First child.
Has the phenomenon been observed in any other child of the same parents or among relatives? No.
At what age has the child begun to run on all fours, and how long has it continued? Began at twelve months, hands-knees; thirteen, hands-soles (all fours); 15, walked.
Add description, as detailed as possible—See photo. This was taken as the child completed a long, fast race on hands and feet but before he stopped.
Position of the hands, etc.—Hands fully open; head raised for vision ahead; movements very quick and complex—for instance, side vision without halt as shown in the photograph herewith, taken just before end of "quadruped" period.

Details as to any other peculiarity of behavior of the child, or any other children in the family—

Now 16½ years of age, has extraordinary muscular control of scalp, ears, of Adams apple. No other child in family.

E. V. CHANEY,
Texarkana, Ark.

First letter:

January 30, 1930

DEAR SIR:

I have become interested in your article with regard to children which run on all fours. My young son who happens to be in Honolulu at the present time, and is fifteen months old, has taken to running on all fours. He travels long distances and can run so rapidly that it is necessary for one to run in order to catch him. I am requesting that motion pictures be taken of him. If you are interested I will be glad to furnish some information. (See Plate III, p. 29.)

Very truly yours,
ROYAL N. CHAPMAN,
St. Paul, Minn.

Second letter:

March 13, 1930

MY DEAR DR. HRDLIČKA:

I have just received 100 feet of standard 35 mm. motion picture film, showing him in various poses running on all fours. I have found this particularly interesting to study frame by frame as it shows the manipulation of the arms which makes a very interesting study. I am not sure that I fully understand at the present time just how this manipulation is carried out.

Very truly yours,
R. N. C.

Details:

Race and nationality—White, American of English, Scotch, and Holland extraction, 300 years back.

Sex—Male, fourth in family.

. 152 .

Health and robustness—Good and strong at present, but encountered bronchitis, measles, and whooping cough after the third month of life.

Has the phenomenon been observed in any other child of the same parents or among relatives? No, never at all; others were girls.

At what age has the child begun to run on all fours, and how long has it continued? When about fourteen months old and it lasted six or seven weeks, I guess, until he could walk erect.

Details as to any other peculiarity of behavior of the child, or any other children in the family—None that are unusual.

DEAR DR. HRDLIČKA:

I read this morning of your interest in babies who get about on all fours. My little girl who was born March 28, 1927, has done this from the time she was nine or ten months old. She first began to creep in an ordinary way but she soon began to go on one foot and one knee, and then on both feet. She still uses this method of locomotion as she does not walk alone yet. Occasionally she creeps on hands and knees but for the most part she prefers to go on all fours. She is very quick and can run away in this manner very rapidly.

She is my first baby, and was a normal child at birth, weighing seven and one-fourth pounds. Everybody has remarked on her peculiar method of getting about and it is a comical sight to see her running around like a little puppy. She walks just as you have described in your article, and there is no restraint in her movements, just a naturally easy manner. I also have a younger baby boy who was born April 1, of this year, and I am anxiously waiting to see if he will follow in his sister's footsteps. I sincerely hope my letter will be of interest to you.

Yours truly,
MRS. ANDREW B. CHASE,
New Bedford, Mass.

July 4, 1928

DEAR SIR:

In the *Literary Digest* of June 23 my attention was directed to an article entitled "The Baby That Walks like a Bear Need Not Alarm Its Mother." It piqued my interest as I read it, and then

I started a search for an old photographic plate. After a search of an hour or so I found it. It was taken on July 4, 1905, at the address given below, when my daughter Ruth was thirteen months old.

It shows her walking on all fours towards her mother "like a little bear or tiger."

I am a Vermonter who can trace his direct line back to Benjamin Child who came to Boston with Winthrop in 1630; my wife was born in Beacon Hill in Boston. Her father was born in Glasgow, and her mother in northern Nova Scotia, of Scotch parentage.

Our daughter walked first like a bear and stood upright and walked at about fourteen months. She is now twenty-four years old. She has always been perfectly normal, owns her own car, has her own job, spent three months in Europe last summer at her own expense and, being her father, I will have to admit that I am very much sold to her.

Our son, who was born three years earlier, crept in the conventional fashion.

Additional information:

July 10, 1928

White, American, of English-Scotch extraction, female, health excellent, second child.

No other cases of bear walking in the family, as far as known.

Started to run on all fours at about nine months and continued till she was about sixteen months. Was able to walk upright at thirteen months.

Sorry I cannot recall any minute details regarding the performance. We always said that she ran "like a little bear," and I should say that her hands were open and the head held fairly well up so she could see where she was going.

I always considered her to be a normal child in every way, and her peculiar manner of running did not give us any concern whatever.

My son, who is three years older, crept in the conventional style, and both children have grown up to maturity in a perfectly regular and normal manner.

> Very truly yours,
> E. T. CHILD,
> West Orange, N. J.

September 12, 1928

DR. HRDLIČKA:

Herewith a report on another little subject that runs on all fours.

Frederick Carl Flindt; 60 per cent New England stock, rest mixture of Irish, Scotch, Dutch, English, French, and German.

Male, born Sept. 26, 1927; strong and robust; weight at eleven months 20 lbs., ht. 31 inches.

First and only child.

No other case of that kind in family or among relatives, according to our knowledge. Crept at nine months and walked on hands and toes 10th month. Now stands almost alone.

When on all fours, holds palms of hands flat down with fingers turned slightly in.

Fingers spread. Head up.

Will take hold of a person's leg and stand and with very little help will crawl up leg to sit on arm, holding thighs flexed and knees bent. Sleeps a great deal in the knee-chest position. Will try and get photo later.

Yours truly,
DR. CARL D. CLAPP,
Utica, N. Y.

DEAR DOCTOR:

My granddaughter began walking on all fours at the age of seven months. She was very happy with a new dolly till it cried; then she dropped it and darted away two or three yards, sat up and looked at it longingly and astonished. She then returned to it slowly on all fours and picked it up, only to get the same cry, drop it, and get away at such amazing speed.

At eight months she was left on the bed asleep. When she awakened she slipped off, got to the corner table and stood there clinging to the table legs when I found her. At nine months she went on all fours upstairs, also attempted to walk, but was not allowed to do so by her parents lest it harm her legs, until the twelfth month.

She is now almost five years old, very strong and well, physically and mentally.

Her mother crept at seven months on the left knee and walked on the right foot. Everyone thought it quite unusual and her speed was very great. Was so efficient that way so that she did not walk till fourteen months.

And I, the grandmother, was placed on the floor in short dresses at four months, to kick my way through, walked all around by chairs at nine months. On my first day of the tenth month walked straight out across the room.

Details:

Child—white, American, female.
Health, splendid.
First child.
Walked on all fours, eight months to fourteen.
Ran about on all fours with great speed, going upstairs at nine months as easily as straight ahead. Could pull herself up and walk holding things, or pushing a carriage from nine months on, but was not inclined to walk by herself as the four-legged way was so much quicker. The knees in action were never bent but held firm and seemed to aid speed. Hands full out on floor, head with face facing floor.

Child is now five and seems to have talent for dancing, is very quick and is considered by a local physician (who has observed her a great deal) a precocious child. Her health and mind are in the best condition, and all habits have developed regular, although she is inclined to be a little nervous.

Mrs. Jessie W. Clark,
Utica, N. Y.

First letter:

January 20, 1928

Dear Dr. Hrdlička:

My two children never crept on their knees but ran on hands and feet. Their "on-fours" period was however very short, as Margaret, aged five now, walked at ten months of age and Albert, now two years old, at eleven months—in both cases, curiously, on the date of their birth. After they walked and when Albert was little they liked to play "doggy" the same way, that is on all fours, but never oftener than two or three nights in succession for every month. I have not seen Albert amuse himself that way lately but Margaret has great fun by herself walking on all fours occasionally. While running that way both children, so far as we remember, applied their hands and feet flat to the floor.

As to details, they are the only two children we have. Both were from birth and are now healthy and strong. They show no other marked peculiarity or anomaly. As to relatives, I asked my mother-in-law in Indiana whether anyone else in the family crawled on all fours, and she remembered that a cousin of my husband did it, a man now about thirty-five years old. My own family lives in Germany and an answer from there cannot be expected for a few weeks.

Very truly yours,
Mrs. Betty S. Clarke.

Second letter:

I should like to give you little additional notes on the behavior of my children.

We did not take snapshots of them in the "on-all-fours" position. I think that they did not use their hands more or less closed as that would probably be remembered by me as I washed them usually personally. I do remember that their knees did not need the same attention they need now when both play on the floor. Another fact of interest might be that one dozen pairs of stockings that both children wore when babies (there are two sizes of six each) do not show wear or mending except on the heels and there are no holes in the knees. Both children moved on all fours between seven and ten months, Albert until eleven months.

We did not pay great attention to their way of running, but friends who came to the house usually watched Margaret, as they thought it cute.

Margaret was ambidextrous but prefers her left hand more as she grows older.

B. S. C.

April 11, 1928

Dear Doctor:

I have read several articles relative to the infants who go on "All Fours," and I should like to make the following report.

I have two children, one a girl over ten years of age, and a boy sixteen months of age. Both of these children went about on "all fours," and at no time did they crawl upon their knees. It is also true that while asleep they occasionally would assume the attitude in which they were, face down and with their knees drawn up underneath. These children are very active and the boy, in particular, is very sharp and quick. He walked upright at the age of ten months.

I have been informed by my father that I too went about on all fours when an infant.

Respectfully yours,
H. L. CLAUSEN,
Chicago, Ill.

March 18, 1928

DEAR SIR:

In Saturday's *Chicago American* I noticed your article on "Children Who Run on All Fours," and was interested because we have a baby girl who moves about in that manner.

Joyce was one year old on February 26 and belongs to the white race. At first she moved about by rolling. At about nine months she started to move on all fours. She pulls herself upright and has, since she was eight months old, and walks around objects in the room but does not try to walk upright alone.

She holds her hands open while moving, holds her head slightly raised and looks ahead. We have enjoyed watching her move about because the two older children went on hands and knees as most babies do.

We haven't a picture of her moving in this manner but if you wish it, we will have one taken.

Details:

Race and nationality—White, American.
Sex—Female.
Health and robustness—Very healthy.
What child in numerical order—Third.
Has the phenomenon been observed in any other child of the same parents or among relatives? Not that I know of.
At what age has the child begun to run on all fours, and how long has it continued? At nine or ten months; for five months and still continues.

The enclosed picture is as good as we could get with a small kodak in the house. Hope it will show all you care to know; if not, will try to get a better one when it is warm enough to take one outside. Runs with hands fully open, head slightly raised.

Details as to any other peculiarity of behavior of the child, or any other children in the family—None known of.

Yours respectfully,
Mrs. Glenn R. Closson,
Benton Harbor, Mich.

July 8, 1928

My baby girl is now eighteen months old but when she was eight and one-half months old she began walking on her hands and feet. She did not walk upright until she was twelve and one-half months of age, but when she started to walk she never faltered or wobbled as most babies do.

She is very strong and healthy, in fact she has never been sick one day since she was born.

Sincerely,
Mrs. Ruth L. Coeyman,
Newark, N. J.

June 28, 1928

Dr. Hrdlička:

In the *Literary Digest* for June 23, I read the article about the baby that walks like a bear. I became very interested and hope you will write to me regarding the fact.

My little girl is fourteen months old, and has been walking for two weeks. For three or four weeks before she walked upright, she ran on all fours—never crept. We all laughed at her, and most of the relatives thought it a big joke. She seldom walks that way now.

Shirley is a big plump healthy child—always rosy, because she is healthy and always outdoors.

I should appreciate it very much if you will write to me about the meaning of this.

Yours very truly,
Mrs. E. C. Conn,
Boonton, N. J.

March 22, 1928

DEAR SIR:

I notice an article in the *Literary Digest* regarding children that run on all fours. I have a case in point with my grandson, Charles Cooke Peyton, Charlottesville. This little fellow ran on all fours and never did crawl; he was bow-legged and pigeon-toed so much that my daughter took him to a specialist and wanted to put his legs in braces but the Doctor told her they would grow straight of their own accord, which has been the case. This child is now over a year old; was very active, could climb up on anything, was sure-footed and never fell. He would climb the steps like a dog, not touching his knees and when sitting on the floor with his legs folded under him he would get up without touching his hands to anything. He is very bright and smart; a perfect specimen of a child.

Yours truly,
CHAS. B. COOKE,
Beaver Dam, Va.

September 24, 1928

DEAR DOCTOR:

We have two daughters, one six and the other four. The oldest, when a baby, walked on her hands and feet. We thought it nothing unusual until I read your column some time ago. She used this method altogether from the time she was about ten months until a year old. All at once she stood up alone and walked from then on. She merely laid where she was until ten months old. She has always acted old for her age. She has been to school one year but reads, writes and spells as well as children several grades ahead of her. She grows so fast and is larger than most children of six. Has always been healthy. When two years old she spoke every word as plainly as we did. We think she is much more advanced than other children of the same age.

Very sincerely,
MRS. D. W. CORNELL,
Goldfield, Ia.

April 27, 1928

Dear Dr. Hrdlička:

I am sending a snapshot of our little girl, Margaret, taken when she was eleven months old, showing how she runs on all fours. She started to "crawl" thus when about eight months of age and from the first went on all fours with both hands and feet flat. She soon developed considerable speed and even now (twelve months old April 15) that she is walking upright, she frequently gets down on all fours if she wishes to make speed. When walking in this position she holds her head down in a horizontal position until she reaches a certain objective, and then sits back on her haunches so that she can look around and select a new objective. (Plate IX.)

Her parents are both Americans of Anglo-Saxon descent.

I shall be interested to know what facts of interest have been developed in this connection.

Details:

May 21, 1928

Race and nationality—American of Anglo-Saxon descent. Sex—Female.

Health and robustness—Health good. Robustness fair (6¼ lbs. at birth; 19 lbs. at 1 year).

What child in numerical order—First.

Has the phenomenon been observed in any other child of the same parents or among relatives?—No.

At what age has the child begun to run on all fours, and how long has it continued?—She began to run on all fours at about eight months and continued until she was fairly proficient in walking upright, which was accomplished at about twelve months. At thirteen months she still occasionally reverts to all fours if speed is desired.

Description of the performance, etc.—It is difficult to describe the performance except to say that she seems to have perfect ease in walking on her hands and feet and has possibly a little side motion which is probably done to obviate interference between her hands and feet, which nearly come together during the operation. She has always walked in this way, never having dropped to her knees in the process of walking.

Position of the hands and of the head while running on all fours— During the performance her hands are fully open except when she is carrying something, which is frequently done. Her head is held in line with her body, with her eyes down. She generally starts after having determined upon a definite objective and as soon as this has been reached, she settles back on her haunches so that she may look up and determine upon a new objective.

Details as to any other peculiarity—I do not know of any other peculiarity on the part of her behavior which is not common to other children.

> WILL C. CRAWFORD,
> Superintendent,
> Department of Public
> Instruction,
> Territory of Hawaii,
> Honolulu, U. S. A.

June 23, 1928

DEAR SIR:

The *Literary Digest* for June 23, 1928, speaks of your interest in children who as babies walked on all fours. My brother's son used that mode of locomotion for about three months, then learned to walk upright and never reverted to the all-fours method.

He will be fourteen next month, is 68 inches tall and well developed, has perfect teeth, and makes above the average grades in school. He is very healthy, has had a perfect attendance record for the last four school years. He is fond of and good at outdoor sports.

Additional information:

July 3, 1928

Both parents are American born with ancestors dating to Colonial days, all of whom lived in the South.

Child, male; first and only child.

Has always been healthy, is large and well developed, at 14 is often mistaken for a large boy of 16. Has never had a serious illness.

No other case like it in family or among relatives, so far as known of.

Started on all fours at about ten months and ran thus for about three months, then began to walk.

PLATE IX.—*a*. Albers, boy. *b*. R. E. Cunio, Jr., ten and one-half months. *c*. Margaret K. Crawford, eleven months.

He started crawling in the usual way but that seemed too slow, so he would rise up on hands and feet and run rapidly.

The hands were fully opened and in placing on the floor the fingers were put down first then the whole palm; the ball of the foot seemed to carry the weight of the rear part of the body. The head was carried well up so that he could look ahead and from side to side. He usually went straight to the object desired, but sometimes he approached it with a funny little sidling motion, such as sometimes employed by puppies. There was nothing particularly unusual in his behavior other ways.

The daughter of my other brother, now seven years old, did not crawl in the usual way, but hitched herself rapidly across the floor by the use of one hand and one foot. I might add that my mother has told me that I never crawled but lay down and rolled over and over in any direction to reach the place I wished to go to. All three of us are surefooted, agile climbers.

Yours very truly,
MISS LUCY CROOKS,
Pine Bluff, Ark.

December 26, 1927

DEAR DOCTOR:

My attention has been drawn to an article in *The Star* of Dec. 26 in which it appears that you are interested in certain cases of locomotion of children in which they go upon hands and feet rather than on hands and knees. We have a child born Jan. 28, 1927, whose first mode of locomotion was of this nature. I do not think that this method is very rare, for if my memory is correct I have a younger brother who learned to run in this way. However, we have two other children and neither of them learned to progress in this manner.

The present child (a boy) learned to go on all fours at approximately eight months of age, and for four or five weeks this was his only method of locomotion. He was often allowed upon the floor dressed in the ordinary way with shoes and other clothing extending well below his knees. These hampered him considerably and so he learned that better progress than on all fours could be made by going upon his hands and knees. Much of the time now he goes thus upon hands and knees though he still frequently goes

. 165 .

upon all fours. He is now eleven months old and has not as yet learned to walk alone though he stands alone and seems a normal average baby in every way.

As the wife and I are both interested in science we shall have no objection to your observing the child if you care to do so.

The position of the head varies somewhat depending upon the circumstances. When he is running for some object his head is held so that his eyes obtain the fullest view of the desired object. His head will be considerably more elevated when running for an object on a chair than when for one on the floor.

His hands are placed flat upon the floor (unless carrying some object in his hand when running) with the fingers extending forward (the hands turned slightly inward at an angle to the axis of the body) nearly parallel to each other. The thumb is held at an angle of 45 to 60 degrees to the fingers. The weight of the body is placed very largely upon the palm of the hand the fingers supporting practically no weight.

The way he places his feet upon the floor also varies somewhat with the rate of movement. If he is moving leisurely along he will bring one foot forward and place it practically flat upon the floor. As his body moves forward his heel is raised from the floor and when he is again ready to carry the foot forward only the toes and ball of the foot will rest upon the floor. If his movements are rapid his heel will frequently not touch the floor when the foot is brought forward.

His right hand and left foot go forward at practically the same time. This results in some time that the right foot is stretched farthest backward. I think this is of particular interest as it is the usual method of locomotion of most animals from the reptiles on up. (I have noticed that most men in walking swing the right hand forward at the same time as the left foot is carried forward.)

The enclosed pictures were taken upon the lawn with an inexpensive kodak. They show fairly well the position of body, head, hands, and feet. He is traveling rapidly in all the pictures but slowest in No. 4 which shows the natural position better than any of the others. He was eleven months of age when these were taken.

It might be of interest to state that both father and mother are scientifically trained. We each have Master of Science degree and have pursued further graduate work at the University of Chicago.

I judge that we are of average mentality for scientists. The child seems to be of normal average mentality.

Sincerely yours,
C. W. C.

June 29, 1928

I had not realized that it was anything unusual for a child to run on all fours.

My eldest daughter who is now 24 years old moved that way and could run like a little deer. She began creeping thus when about eight months old and walked upright when 13½ months old. She could walk nearly as good when she began as she can now.

Yours very truly,
Mrs. Roy Cumberworth,
Ashley, Mich.

June 14, 1928

Dear Sir:

A relative of mine sent me a copy of the article in the *St. Paul Pioneer* of June 10, which told of your research work in the quadruped progression of children.

Our boy baby never learned to creep but at the age of eight months started to walk on hands and feet. He is nearly ten months old now and makes excellent progress in the house or out on the lawn.

Our boy was very ill the first three months of life due to a pyloric stenosis. This condition was, however, soon overcome by the aid of medical and nursing care. He was also a "blue baby." His present condition of health and exceptional muscular strength I attribute to the sun baths and mode of dressing since birth. He lives out of doors with no clothes except a diaper, and his skin is a coat of tan. He weighs twenty pounds now and was a seven-pound baby at birth.

Detailed information:

Child—White; American of mixed (English-French-Italian, etc.) parentage.

Born with pyloric stenosis; ill three months; since then, very robust. First child.

. 167 .

No other cases of running on all fours known in the family.

Began to move on all fours at seven months; still using that method at eleven months.

Posture—Hands flat on floor, fingers spread, head up. Right leg and left hand move at same time.

When younger would pick up doll in mouth and carry same in mouth. Will try to "lap up" water from ground. Shoulder and arm muscles exceptionally well developed for age. Climbs up his father's trousers to lap without help. Alert mentally. (See Plate IX, p. 163.)

Respectfully yours,
Mrs. R. E. Cunio,
Miami, Fla.

August 17, 1928

Dr. Hrdlička:

Our girl started to creep on hands and feet at eight months. We called her a little puppy dog, and she sure could go. Then at ten months we could no longer keep her off her feet and she got up and walked.

At four years old she is forty-two inches tall and—hold your breath—weighs forty-seven pounds. Needless to say she is a hearty eater but likes everything. I have to watch the sweets. Is advanced mentally above the average, too, we think. I was over forty-one and her father fifty when she was born.

Details:

White—American; female.
Health, very good.
First child.
No other "bears" in family.
Began to run on all fours at eight months, continued for two months.
Trotted around like a puppy.
Hands spread flat on floor.
Developed rapidly both physically and mentally.

Yours truly,
Mrs. Bertha Curry,
Lesage, W. Va.

November 20, 1927

DEAR DR. HRDLIČKA:

I have been very much interested in your paper in the last number of the *Journal of Physical Anthropology* on plantigrade progression in infants. You may be interested in the case of my boy. Of my three children, the oldest, when about eight or nine months old, progressed by irregular rolling and sliding motions. He next learned to stand, supporting himself by furniture. Then he crept in the normal manner for perhaps a month, after which for a period of a month to six weeks, he walked on all fours in the manner described for some of your cases. Neither of the other children ever showed any inclination in this direction.

Sincerely yours,
C. H. DANFORTH,
Stanford University, Calif.

July 10, 1928

DEAR SIR:

I noticed in a late issue of the *Literary Digest* that you were interested in receiving information about children who had walked on all fours.

Our boy started going in that manner. I do not remember at just what age he started doing this but stopped when he got so he could walk well at about sixteen months of age.

He made excellent time with his mode of travel and kept his legs very straight. We did not think of it as being anything especially peculiar.

He was quite a climber and could climb before he walked. When he started to walk he could rise up in the middle of the room and start going but had to be helped to get down again.

Before he was three years old he had been on the roof of the house twice when some workmen left a ladder by the house and had been to the top of a tall ladder in a cherry tree.

He also seemed to delight in picking up heavy things and carrying them. I will not take up your time by telling you what a fine child he is.

He has a sister just as physically fit as he who propelled herself by scooting on the floor. She did not walk quite as young as he did. She was in better health at the creeping age.

Details:

Male, American, first child.

Ten years old now, above normal.

No other peculiarities noted.

Sincerely yours,

Mrs. Chas. E. Darling,

Van Nuys, Calif.

June 28, 1928

Dr. Hrdlička:

My baby walked on all fours, and personally I have never known another that did. At the time I was terribly worried about it and now when I tell anyone they seem doubtful, but he is now eight years old and as bright and sturdy as any little fellow you ever saw. He is perfectly normal in every way. He began walking on all fours at nine and one-half months, and two days after a year old he raised right up in the middle of the room and walked upright from then on. Up to that time I had never seen him take more than half a dozen steps alone.

Details:

White,—American, male, first child.

Health, first class.

No other cases like it in family except my sister's boy who is creeping at the present time.

Began running on all fours at eight months and continued until one year and three days. Suddenly he began to walk and never again went on all fours.

I have no photograph and he is now eight years old but he just reminded one of a monkey the way he got around and then sat upright.

Held hands fully open. He would look up to see what he wanted or where he was going; then sort of duck his head and away he would go.

I have no other children but Mother had ten and not a one ran on all fours; but at present as mentioned above, my fourth sister has an only child running on all fours.

Sincerely yours,

Mrs. J. H. Daugherty,

Bedford, Ind.

First letter:

April 21, 1928

DEAR SIR:

My attention was called recently to a newspaper article describing your study of some types of prehuman behavior in young children. I wish to describe an observation of one of the types which, according to the article, is rather infrequently seen, and which I observed some years ago.

At that time I was teaching country school in Indiana. One of my pupils was a little girl of six years. (As I remember it, her age was given me as six, but I suspect she was a little under six.) One day at intermission I looked out and saw her climbing a small tree perhaps four or five inches in diameter. She was going up in the manner of the Australian natives, with hands grasping the trunk (or rather hooked back of it, as the trunk was too large to grasp) and with the soles of her bare feet pressed straight against the trunk as if she were walking up it. When I saw her she was up nearly ten feet. As she was a rather "chubby" little girl with comparatively short legs, she greatly resembled a little bear as she climbed. She seemed to go up without great difficulty and would probably have gone higher if I had not brought her down to avoid a possible fall. She climbed with her body well out from the tree trunk, with legs not much flexed.

This little girl came from a family of six children, as I remember it (there may have been more). Father a farmer. Family of average intellectual ability. The four children who came to school to me showed about the average run of intelligence, evidencing no exceptional aptitude for learning. The boys of the family were inclined to slenderness, while the girls were more stout but healthy and rather attractive. I have had no opportunity to observe the little girl who did the climbing, since that time (1909), so my judgment as to her mental and physical characteristics may not be very accurate. Exceptional abilities might easily escape notice in a young child under the conditions prevailing in a country school at that time. My impression, however, is that she was average in intelligence and physically sturdy and healthy.

I am Asst. Prof. of Physics at Iowa State College, now on leave of absence while doing research in the Physics Section of the Mayo Clinic.

Very truly yours,
GEORGE E. DAVIS,
Rochester, Minn.

Second letter:

July 20, 1928

DEAR DR. HRDLIČKA:

I hope you will pardon my unavoidable delay in replying to your letter of April 26 in which you ask for further information in regard to the little girl who climbed trees like a bear, reported in my letter of April 21. I have obtained the following information from one who knew the family well.

Derivation of subject—Grandfather, Pennsylvania Dutch. All immediate ancestors white. Grandfather a stout, strong man with a heavy growth of black hair. Father very much like grandfather. Brothers of the mother were strong, muscular men with much hair.

Female; well built, rather fat little girl, apparently in excellent health; fourth child.

No other unusual behavior in family, so far as I know, excepting peculiar monkey-like climbing habits of an older brother.

Do not know at what age the bear-like climbing tendency was shown first nor how long it continued. Child was six years old when I observed it.

When this observation was made, the child was climbing a tree about five inches in diameter. The hands were hooked around the trunk, as the trunk was too large for her hands to grasp properly. Arms straight or nearly so. Feet almost flat against the trunk, as if walking up the tree. Legs not much flexed. Body held well away from the tree trunk. The child climbed without great effort, apparently. Reminded one strongly of a little bear. Climbed up to first branches, about eight to ten feet high, at which point I took her down to avoid a fall.

An older brother (second child) exhibited peculiar climbing tendencies when about ten years old. Would climb up on to high objects (trees, etc.) and squat there for an hour or so at a time. Rather monkey like tendencies. Ears broad at the top, with rims rounded at the top and down about one-third of the way.

Very truly yours,
GEO. E. DAVIS.

June 29, 1928

DR. HRDLIČKA:

I have a baby boy who adopted the peculiar method of running on all fours at the age of seven and one-half months. He is now nine months old, weighs twenty-three pounds and has never had a sick day.

Details:[1]

Child, white and American; male; first child.

Health perfect.

No other such cases in family, so far as known. Began the practice when 6½ months old, kept it up 4½ months.

Hands fully open, head up, when thus running.

Yours very truly,
Mrs. L. F. Davis,
Indianapolis, Ind.

September 26, 1928

Dr. Hrdlička:

You wanted to know of babies who run on hands and feet. My baby boy, aged 11 months, does. He started to crawl on hands and knees when 9 months old. Before long he began using his feet part time. When crawling on the rug, he uses his knees, but on the polished floor he goes on his feet. He is a normal baby; weighed 10 pounds at birth. My sister's son has the same record as to birth, weight, and running on hands and feet. He is an only child.

Details:

Child, white; American; male; particularly strong and healthy.

First born.

Sister's Boy:

My sister's third child, boy, developed same habit; no others known.

Progressed on all fours from nine months till twelve months.

When moving on all fours held hands fully open, head high, went at a fast speed. He walks now. For five days he both walked and ran on fours, then walked exclusively. People remarked on how well he walked from the first. His legs are well developed. He weighs thirty pounds at thirteen months, is 31½ in. tall, and looks like a child of eighteen months or even older.

Am interested in this investigation. Let me know your conclusions.

Sincerely,
Mrs. Ernest Day,
Grimes, Ia.

[1] See footnote p. 120.

Jan. 25, 1928

Dr. Hrdlička:

I have a seven-year-old son who started to move upon all fours at about the age of seven months. This method of locomotion he preferred until he was two years of age, as he had acquired considerable speed and got fewer tumbles than when in the upright position. Never at any time did he crawl on his knees. He began to walk at thirteen months, but when playing with his brother after that he would often drop down on all fours to keep pace.

He is the second child of a family of three boys; ages, nine, seven, and six. His brothers showed nothing unusual in way of locomotion. He was a full term baby, eight and a half pounds, spontaneous delivery, breast fed until eleven months old. Very rugged, alert and acrobatic all his life.

Since reading your article in the *Journal,* I have had him repeat his performance, and I note that he goes with his hands flat to the floor, fingers extended, lower extremities straight, with no flexion at the knees, and the hips a bit to the right. He can still travel at a sharp clip by this method, and I notice in playing, in the evening, that he frequently resorts to it. He has rather short legs and can put the entire palm of his hand to the floor without bending his knees. The head is thrown back a bit, enough to allow vision ahead. Another point, which may be of interest to you, is the fact he has always had a marked desire and ability to climb. In spite of three fractures acquired in this sport, he is still unafraid and only two weeks ago I learned from his brother that he has been walking an eight-inch cement guard rail, one hundred feet long and about sixty feet from street below.

He is very aggressive and alert mentally, does well in his school work, which is the second grade. The boy is of American-Scotch-Canadian ancestry. So far as now known this phenomenon has not been noticed in other relatives.

Very sincerely yours,
Dr. O. J. D.,
Kansas City, Mo.

First letter:

June 28, 1928

Dear Doctor:

We have a baby boy fifteen months old. At the age of five months he was able to balance himself on all fours and at six months was running all over the house in that same manner. Never crept any other way. He sure had speed too. At seven months he pulled himself up to chairs and could stand alone. He was walking alone at ten months and was not one bit unsteady.

His little body and legs are as straight as can be and I think for a baby of his age he is extra strong. We, of course, think him exceptionally bright. My girl, now seven, did not walk until sixteen months and rarely crept though she was healthy in every respect and talked plainly at a year old.

Very truly yours,
MRS. WM. DODSON,
Jersey City, N. J.

Second letter:

September 24, 1928

The following are the answers to your list of questions:

Child, white; American; male; second born.

Very healthy and robust, large for his age, is 17½ months old, weighs 26¼ pounds, stands 32 inches high.

No other cases like that in family or relatives, as far as known.

At five months he began to raise himself on all fours. He would get up and then wobble and face sideways. By the time he was six months old he was running across the floor on all fours. At seven months he was standing by chairs and able to go very fast on fours. He walked at the age of ten months, just simply walked off one evening. He never crept on his knees and even now when the occasion arises he runs on fours, as when his Daddy gets down on the floor and plays with him making believe to chase him.

Have no photo but if I can ever get one will send it.

His hands when running on all fours were flat and spread wide, his feet would be flat, his head was held up. Before he was able to stand up and push a door open he would push it with his head. I had a screen door leading to the back porch at which he would do the pushing.

No other peculiarity. He is very straight.

I have another boy now three months old. Should he do the same I will write you and give you details.

Very truly yours,
MRS. WM. DODSON.

DEAR SIR:

Noting an article in the N. Y. *Herald Tribune* of Sunday last in which you are quoted as wanting instances of children walking on all fours, instead of creeping, I can mention that of my great-nephew, who never crept, but for many weeks covered the ground with great rapidity in animal fashion until he learned to walk.

He is now six years old, and an unusually precocious child, perhaps the result of his early mode of locomotion.

He is not now in Washington, but I can refer you to Dr. Edgar Snowden, 1712, 21st St., N. W., as to the perfectly normal condition of the little boy, whom he examined a few weeks ago.

It may not be a very rare occurrence for babies to walk in this manner, for several of my friends who saw the child "doing it" spoke of their own children having employed a similar method.

> Very truly yours,
> (MISS) SOPHIE W. DOWNER,
> Washington, D. C.

DEAR DOCTOR:

I am sending this account of my son's creeping. When he first began to move around on the floor, he hitched along on his bottom going from side to side in a rocking motion. He soon found that too slow and began to tuck one foot underneath and using the corresponding hand he paddled sideways. That also was too slow and after repeated experiments he decided on all fours as the best method. In this way he could go nearly as fast as his sister (two years older) could run.

I always thought the reason he crawled that way was because his legs were so short. From the top of his thigh to his knee is very short and his body is long in comparison.

When he first started to walk at fifteen months, he was very bow-legged indeed. His weight was normal and he was very good about eating anything I fed him. The only reason I could see for his bow-legs was the way he had crawled. At two years his legs were as straight as arrows and he could walk and run like any other child. He is eight years old now.

The upper section of his legs has always remained short in comparison to the rest of his body. I have to buy him twelve-year-old knickers in order to have them long enough through the crotch, then I cut off four inches at the bottom to have them the right length at the knee.

Sincerely,
Mrs. A. L. Downes,
Attleboro, Mass.

December 28, 1927

Dr. Hrdlička:

Several days ago there appeared in the *Evening Star* an article which referred to your interest in children which run naturally on all fours. Enclosed I am sending you a photograph of our daughter which shows her running in such a manner. This was her regular method of locomotion for several weeks until she was ten months of age when she began to walk like a human being. She was exceedingly rapid in her movements. With this one exception she was a perfectly normal child and is now a Junior in George Washington University. Our three other children crawled around on their knees as most children do.

The child in question is the first born. She was always healthy and very active. She liked to climb trees. There is no knowledge of any other child in the family or relatives having run on all fours. There are no mental or physical anomalies about our girl.

Hoping that this note and photograph may be of help to you in your investigations, I am

Yours respectfully,
H. D. D.,
Washington, D. C.

May 12, 1928

Dear Sir:

I was very interested to see in the *Free Press* paper an article re—"On All Fours."

My little boy ran on all fours for about three months or more—until fourteen and one-half months old never crept at all. He is perfectly normal, in fact rather above the average in mentality. He is now six and one-half and is in most subjects in Grade 2 at school.

Details:

Father—English for generations.

Mother—Irish parents, but born in England.

Male.

Rather subject to colds, but while epidemics have been in school, such as measles, mumps, etc., has been immune; has not had any serious illness. Had tonsils and adenoids removed last year; is rather delicate looking because of exceptionally dead white skin of a very fine texture.

Second child of mother having had a daughter by previous marriage.

Not any record or knowledge of phenomenon in family or among relations.

Started running on all fours at about 12 months of age and continued up to 15 months, when he walked normally. Legs were particularly straight and carriage of body erect when walking. Was heavy for age and therefore not encouraged in walking.

Photograph enclosed. Could travel at a great speed on all fours, quicker than his mother could walk.

When running thus had fully open hands, head erect, feet flat on ground.

Nervous child, highly imaginative and very ingenious. Uses expressions in conversation such as adults would use (quite big words). Remarkable memory, even to minutest details. Spoke at 10 months, and at 20 months memorized quite a number of nursery rhymes. Clever with pencil. Has very high arched foot with prehensile toes, can grasp anything and walk with objects grasped with the toes. The child has small appetite but drinks lots of milk, does not like vegetables nor care much for fruit, but is very fond of meat and chicken.

I am enclosing photograph, present day, to show skull formation, etc., also snaps. Will you please take care of them and return same to me as they are the only copies I have.

I wonder if the following is of any additional interest:

My boy will not, when sitting in a chair reading, put his legs down on ground, but will curl them around front of seat supports, for instance in a Morris chair his body and legs are all on the seat part, the legs curled around the arm supports. Do I make it clear enough for you to understand? I trust I do.

MRS. CHRIS DUNHAM,
Heatherdown P. O.,
Alta., Canada.

March 8, 1928

MY DEAR DR. HRDLIČKA:

An article in *Literary Digest* of March 10 calls attention to your interest in babies walking on all fours.

My third child, now seventeen years old, never learned to creep but made rapid progress on all fours. He is now five feet nine inches tall and weighs one hundred sixty pounds. In four years of high school he has not lost a single day or class because of illness. Of my four children he has had the least illness. In fact he has never been ill excepting with the usual contagious diseases of childhood. The other children showed nothing peculiar.

At birth his trunk was noticeably long and thick, after the monkey type, as Professor Tyler of Amherst mentions in his book "Growth and Education." His legs and arms have since developed to make him unusually well proportioned.

Very truly,
MRS. FRANK C. DUNN,
Gardner, Mass.

July 10, 1928

DR. HRDLIČKA:

Our baby, now just 12 months, always walks on all fours. We thought it was a common variation of creeping as our other children often used this method and one (now almost three) always got around this way until he walked. The older children would say, "He's walking like a cow."

A friend of ours called our attention to the peculiar way our baby had of creeping and later showed us an article relating to this in the *Literary Digest*.

Details:

Father—American for generations, of British descent. Mother —English.

Male.

Health, physical and mental—Both exceptional. Weighed ten pounds to start and has steadily gained. Has not been sick. Sturdy and well proportioned. Physically and mentally splendid.

Fifth born. All healthy and bright.

The previous boy, now three years old, used to get around this way until he walked at thirteen months.

Began on all fours at eight or nine months and continued until about fourteen months. He would take six or eight steps alone at a year old, but preferred going about like an animal on all fours, and for a couple of months would walk a little way and then go back to the old way. It was surprising how fast he could go. He would run at a great rate when on all fours, and occasionally he does it yet.

I regret very much not having taken a picture which would have been easy, but I did not think of it. The position was hands and feet on floor, only. And the seat of his pants was the highest portion. The hands were fully open. Head not thrown back much.

No peculiarities in any of the children. Unless perhaps in these last two boys who both had a love of climbing and getting into one thing after another which was quite different to the three previous children (two girls and one boy).

Yours very truly,
MRS. GLADYS EDWARDS,
Waukegan, Ill.

September 5, 1928

DEAR DOCTOR:

Having noticed mention of your interest in children who move about on all fours before walking, I am writing to tell you that out second boy did that thing.

He was kept in a play pen as soon as he became too active for a crib, and he soon learned to walk by holding on to the railing at seven months. But as he grew older he fretted at the confinement of the pen so we gave him the run of the library and at first he hitched himself about with one foot on the floor and the other knee bent under him. Thus by gradual stages he took up four-footed progression.

When he adopted upright walking (to his delight and pride) he still dropped to all fours when he wanted to make speed. He never did creep on hands and knees.

His paternal heredity includes blood lines running back to a Thayer who came to Massachusetts with Governor Winthrop in 1630 and on the other hand is Scotch. His maternal heredity is also old Yankee stock, Scotch-English.

Details:

Boy; second child; health good, strong for age; quiet.

To our knowledge no other such case in family.

Began to go on all fours at about eight months. Walked at twelve months. Walking began suddenly and quadruped progression ceased altogether.

In running on fours, held hands with thumbs turned in, flat on floor, toad like; feet with toes turned out giving a kind of push with inside of foot. Head held up, looking straight ahead.

Otherwise normal. His brother about normal as far as we can judge.

Sincerely,
RALPH A. EDWARDS,
Atnarko, B. C.

First letter:

July 3, 1928

DEAR DR. HRDLIČKA:

My boy's creeping record runs like this:

9 months—Got everywhere by gliding on his stomach; 9 months, two weeks—One knee and one straight leg; One year—Both feet and hands in a rapid bear-like gait; 13 months—Walked.

Details:

Race and nationality—Father, American; Hebrew-German parents; Mother, English and Huguenot, Puritan stock.

Sex—Male.

What child in numerical order—First.

Health and robustness—Good.

At what age has the child begun to run on all fours, and how long has it continued?—12 months, continued for one month and two weeks.

Add description, etc.—Started creeping at 9½ months, used one knee and one straight leg until 12 months old; can't remember exact details of act itself; walked at 13 months and 2 weeks.

Position of hands, etc.—Hands open.

Details as to any other peculiarity of child—This child was ambidextrous until well along in elementary school.

MRS. PAUL ELIEL,
Berkeley, Calif.

Second letter:

May, 1929

I now have a baby who is also "creeping" on all fours.

Eleanor Eliel, born June 13.

Note on February 3, says: 7 months, 3 weeks old; advances by moving arms forward a little way and then throwing whole body forward on stomach; gets up on all fours, hands and feet, and teeters back and forth.

February 10: Crawling on all fours for short distances.

March 1: "Crawling" everywhere, alternating between all fours and hands and knees. Starts on all fours, goes two or three steps, then is knees for one, then all fours again.

Later: Tears around on hands and feet, hands open, feet spread out, using instep side, flat on floor. Uses left arm, right leg; right arm, left leg. As she slows up goes to knees and sits down.

Details:

Race and nationality—Father and mother Americans (father a Hebrew).

Sex—Female.

Health and robustness—Excellent.

What child in numerical order?—Third; second living.

Has the phenomenon been observed in any other child of the same parents or among relatives?—First child of same parents. (A boy, see *ante*.)

At what age has the child begun to run on all fours, and how long has it continued?—Eight months old. Still doing it—is now one year old.

Position of hands, etc.—Hands open, fully. Head is carried in line with body with slight tip-back to see ahead.

Details as to any other peculiarity of child—Very active; pulled herself on to feet at eight months also.

MRS. PAUL ELIEL.

September 21, 1928

DR. HRDLIČKA:

I am writing you in regard to my little girl. She has been a child that has gone on all fours. She walks entirely on the palm of her hands and the flat of her feet. We have never noticed her on her knees more than one or two steps. She is eleven months now and walks alone. She has always been a very strong baby and so much older for her age than average babies. She weighs twenty-three pounds. It has been very interesting to watch her develop into walking.

Details:

White, American.

Female, first child.

Very healthy and full of vigor, very well- and firmly built.

Such walk (on all fours) never before in either family.

Began to run thus at seven months and kept on until she walked upright at ten and one-half months.

When proceeding on all fours she held her hands palms down, fingers spread flat on the floor, feet flat on the floor, body held in a straight line parallel to the floor. Head held in the same line with the body. She would practically run instead of walk this way.

At one year of age she could say words. She feeds herself entirely from the plate with her spoon.

We now have a little boy eight weeks old and are anxious to see if he does the same as she.

> Yours truly,
> MRS. CLIFFORD ELLIS,
> Mapleton, Ia.

April 2, 1928

DEAR DR. HRDLIČKA:

I am glad to reply to your personal request regarding the behavior of my daughter who walked on all fours previous to walking upright. It is hardly necessary to give details about nationality and race. I had better answer the questions as appearing on the outline you gave me:

White, of old American stock.

Female, first child.

Good health but small-boned, weighed six pounds at five days of age. Eighteen years old now, in college, and doing excellent work. Weighs 100 pounds.

My brother's twins, one boy and one girl, the eldest of four children, also walked on all fours. Younger children, two, did not use this means of locomotion.

. 183 .

Started on all fours at about ten months and kept it up until walking at fourteen months. Walked like a dog, left hand and right foot being moved in unison. Did not put entire foot on floor, but hands were well spread. Could go as fast as one could walk, possibly faster, as I had to positively run to catch the child. Child sat alone at five months. Started to walk suddenly and never, that I can recall, went on all fours afterward.

I am sorry I can send no pictures of her doing this "dog walk" stunt.

With warm personal regards to you from both my husband and myself, I remain

Very truly yours,
ANNIS T. EMLEY
(MRS. WARREN E.),
Washington, D. C.

First letter:

August 2, 1928

DEAR SIR:

An article on babies who walk on hands and feet, interested me very much, and I thought you might be interested in a friend's baby who never crawled but moved on all fours.[1] He is now five years old and a good deal above the average in mentality, and is very strong and healthy. His chest measurement is $1\frac{3}{4}$ inches over the average of his size and weight. He tells stories to his mother who copies them down in shorthand as he tells them. She does not correct or change any of the wording. Here are a few:

"Whenever I go by the Mother Cat
I stop to look in her eyes.
Her eyes are as green as a forest,
And her fur is as black as a black bear's fur."

"The Moon is in his house tonight,
His house is all lit up,
All night long he sits in a chair,
Holding a lighted lantern in his hand."

"In the morning Mr. Snake goes out to hunt for bugs while Mrs. Snake cleans up the house and tends to the babies. Mr. Snake brings the bugs home to the babies. The babies eat them. They say,

[1] See also F. W. Mason.

'Daddy, please give us some more bugs.' So they have more bugs for dessert. Then they all go out for a little walk."

Alan has several more "stories" which have been published on the children's page of the *Portland News*. Alan's mother is a college girl, and his father a business man. Is this a case of atavism?

My own little baby, six months old, catches hold of his bottle, or anything else handed to him, with both his feet and hands, the feet usually get it first. Nearly all babies do this.

> Yours very truly,
> MRS. H. H. ENGELMANN,
> Portland, Ore.

Second letter:

> September 23, 1928

I am sending you a picture of my son grasping his bottle with hands and feet, a picture you requested some time ago. We took exposures several weeks before without clothes but the pictures did not come out well. This baby was seven months old when this picture was taken, weighed nineteen pounds, and is a "bright" baby. He is in excellent health, even though bottle-fed from birth. Hoping you will be able to use this picture, I am

> Sincerely yours,
> MRS. H. H. ENGELMANN.

Third letter:

> June 18, 1929

Last summer I sent you some pictures of Alan Mason walking bear fashion. I do not know if you are still collecting cases of children who walk in this way, but am sending these snapshots of my son on the chance that you may be still interested. I sent you in August a picture of my seven-months-old son grabbing his nursing bottle with his feet, but the picture was not very successful as I could not get it without his clothes. He began walking on his hands and feet at the age of nine months and I took these pictures at the age of eleven months. He stopped walking this way at thirteen months so I was never able to get any pictures without his clothes on.

My youngest sister walked in this fashion, also one member in my father's family. This baby weighs now, at sixteen months, twenty-nine pounds and is very strong. He has a peculiar habit of sitting on the floor with his legs doubled back close to the body. He also can, by bending at the waist and keeping the knees stiff, lick the contents of a dish on the floor in front of his feet. I think he is imitating the puppy as it is the dog's dish!

Sincerely yours,

MRS. H. H. ENGELMANN.

June 18, 1928

DEAR SIR:

To assist your research as to "quadruped progressors" I am writing to inform you that my little boy walked that way between the ages of eleven and fifteen months. He is our first and only child, a good-tempered little fellow, extremely healthy, somewhat larger than the average for his age, and, we are told, a little more active. At eight months he would roll from one end of a room to the other; at nine he was beginning to creep, but always went backward. Then one day he suddenly, without practice, began creeping forward. After about three weeks of this, at the age of ten and one-half months he began to creep with one leg and walk with the other, that is, he put his weight on his right knee and his left foot.

It was a funny, awkward gait, which soon, when he learned to use both feet instead of only one, developed into exactly the walk you describe, resembling it in every detail. He could get about quite rapidly, and continued this until he began to walk upright at fifteen months. Since then I have rarely seen him walking on all fours just for fun. In the park at nineteen months of age he watched with keen interest a dog that passed by. When it had disappeared he dropped to all fours and began running up and down on the grass exactly as you describe and evidently in imitation of the dog. He could go quite fast.

Aside from this the baby has always seemed perfectly normal. He has never been ill. I sometimes think he is more fond of climbing and dancing in his bed than the average child. So far as I know none of his relatives ever walked in that fashion in babyhood.

I regret that the only snapshot we have of him in that position is a very poor one, but I will enclose a second taken at the age of one year which may be of interest in showing the type of child he is.

Very truly yours,

MRS. L. P. EVANS,

Buffalo, N. Y.

October 1, 1928

DEAR SIR:

We are in receipt of your letter of the 28th of September, stating that Dr. Clapp has informed you that we have a child who walks on hands and toes, and asking us to give you certain details. Here they are:

The child has descended from American-English parents on the father's side and Irish parents on the mother's side.

The sex is female.

She is the first child.

Her health was excellent for three months but thereafter there was quite a good deal of trouble weaning her and she lost weight for the next three or four months and for a time it was doubtful as to whether or not she would live. She finally accepted a milk diet and was very healthy and gained weight rapidly until she was a year old. She then acquired an attack of diphtheria and had a temperature of 105 on two successive days. She recovered within the next two days and has been in the best of health ever since. She is now 19 months old and weighs about 23 or 24 pounds and is an exceedingly active child and seems to be healthy and normal in every way.

We have not heard of the phenomenon in any other children of the relatives.

The child commenced to run on all fours at the age of nine months and she continued until the age of 16 months.

She soon learned to move over the ground. Her hands were fully opened. She walked mostly on her toes but occasionally her feet would be flat on the ground. The head looked straight ahead except when it was turned sidewise and looked up. The knees were stiff and so was the back. During the time she was walking on all fours she would grasp any object and stand erect or walk around it while holding on to it. We have no snap-shot of the child while walking, but have moving pictures which were taken with a home camera. In these pictures the child was fully clothed or wore what is known as a sun-suit.

She has no other peculiar details of behavior.

Very truly yours,
GEORGE F. FERRIS,
Utica, N. Y.

April 19, 1928

DEAR SIR:

In the current issue of the *Pathfinder* occurs a paragraph evidencing your interest in children running on all four rather than creeping or on two legs as children ordinarily do.

The writer's son, who is now six years old, used this method of travel when a baby; in fact, he used this method much longer than children do that creep.

Ordinarily children's creeping activities are confined to the house. This boy, however, used this method of locomotion to transport him all over the neighborhood.

He is entirely normal in every respect and I attach two kodak snapshots taken of him, one showing him traveling on all four and the other taken a little later, I would say at about the age of two years, which shows his well-developed physical condition.

Details:

White race and of English descent mostly, although a strain of Scotch, Irish, and Dutch or German blood can be found.

Male; second child.

Health and robustness of the very best. Weighed twelve pounds at birth and has always been robust and healthy.

No other cases of walking on all fours known of among relatives.

Began to run thus about the age of nine months and continued till about seventeen months of age.

On all fours this boy traveled all over the neighborhood, attaining much more speed than he could by creeping. The hands were spread wide open and palms down, head erect, looking forward—not down. No other peculiarities were noted.

> Yours very truly,
> H. DUDLEY FITZ,
> Fairmont, Minn.

November 12, 1928

DEAR DR. HRDLIČKA:

You asked for details concerning my baby's peculiar method of running, and of throwing himself out of chairs. In the last month he has learned to crawl down, feet first, so perhaps his former method will not interest you now but I will explain what my father meant by his statement.

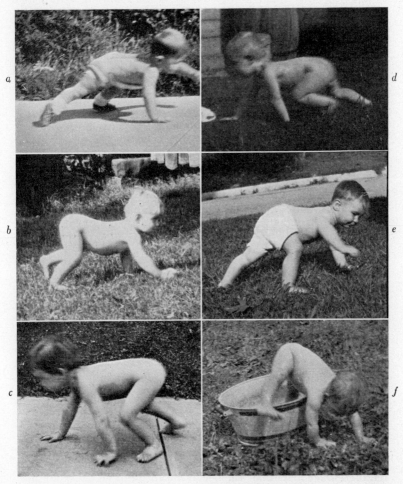

PLATE X.—*a.* L. W. Becker, boy thirteen and one-half months. *b.* Carl Flindt, eleven months and three weeks. *c.* Molly Harper "bear walking on the lawn." *d.* Ivey, boy. *e.* L. S. Gift, boy, twenty-two months. *f.* Kough, girl.

Carl can walk a little now, but still prefers running on his hands and feet as he can go so much more rapidly.

When he was about a year old he began climbing into chairs and would then turn around and throw himself off with hands outstretched. After he got a few bumps (in spite of the cushions I put under all chairs) he became more cautious and slid along on his stomach, head first, until he was able to touch the floor with his hands. After a little practice he was able to do this very rapidly and looked as though he was diving off. It is a little hard to explain, but I hope I have made myself clear. The way he handled his arms and legs reminded me of a cat jumping off something.

I hardly feel flattered at my son's peculiarities as one of my friends calls him "The Missing Link."

Sincerely yours,
RUTH C. FLINDT,
Schenectady, N. Y.

July 2, 1928

DEAR DR. HRDLIKČA:

Seeing an account of an interview with you, in regard to children who walked on their hands and feet, I wished to tell you that we had one of the little "freaks," who never crept a step in her life, but ran about like a spider, or as my husband said, "like a stink bug, all up-ended."

I am an American, for eight generations back, a D. A. R. and of a healthy, long-lived race of out-door men and women. Mr. Florance is a Canadian of Scotch-English ancestry and in neither family is there any tradition of a child of such habits.

Edna came when I was 25 and her father 32. I was exceptionally well prior to her arrival, but the child was rather delicate and required much attention. She began to run about on her hands and feet when she was about old enough for creeping and traveled in no other way till she began to walk, just before she was ten months old.

When she was seven and a half months, she would raise up in the center of the floor and balance herself there for some minutes, then lower herself and travel as before. As soon as she could walk, she "spidered" no longer. At 5 she learned to read, just *had* to learn, it seemed, and from that time on, she has been continually busy, feeding her mind. She entered school in the fifth grade at 9, for the school authorities insisted upon it. She did exceptionally good work in English and in Latin in both the High School and the University of North Dakota. Took also Greek, French, and German, specializing in Art, which was her choice of studies and in which she was Student Assistant.

This year she has been doing Post Graduate at Radcliffe, fitting herself for Museum work in which she hopes for a position some day. I have always tried to hold her back, striving to develop body and heart as well as intellect.

Her brother, four years younger, was a sturdy boy who did everything normally, creeping, walking at one year, entering school at seven and doing average work all through, hating English and liking mathematics as all boys do.

Edna's queer method of propulsion was much commented upon at the time but I had nearly forgotten it, until I saw your article in the *Literary Digest*.

Yours very truly,
MRS. JAMES FLORANCE,
Humboldt, Minn.

December 29, 1927

DR. H.:

We have just received a clipping from the Washington, D. C., *Evening Star*, edition of December 26, in which mention is made of your observations of children who walk on their feet and hands in their natural efforts at locomotion.

We have a son who is almost twenty months old, who just abandoned the means of locomotion referred to. The young man is physically normal, to the best of my knowledge. He is healthy and vigorous. His mental development is such as may be expected of one of his age. His first efforts at getting around were very much those of a little quadruped. This was when he was near eleven months old. He never crawled on his knees for he discovered, apparently, that he could get around much better on his hands and feet. He became very skillful at this and could make incredible speed. Neither his mother nor I have made any efforts to encourage him in his choice of locomotion nor did he learn this method by imitation of other humans. His method of getting about was entirely natural with him. He did not learn to take steps until he was about fifteen months old. After he learned to walk he reverted to the "all-fours" method when he happened to be in a hurry. At the present time he occasionally goes around on "all fours," though he can walk and run perfectly well.

We thought that his method of locomotion was unusual and invited the attention of several physicians to his habit and they were struck by the facility with which he could get about. We took some pictures of him in action with a Filmo motion picture camera and have the films now. The child is the third in order, having two older sisters, neither of which showed the peculiarity. There is no knowledge of any similar case in the two families. The boy behaves normally otherwise, but is retarded in speech. As an interesting incident may be mentioned that once in running on all fours he picked up an apple with his teeth.

Sincerely,
CHESTER L. and MRS. FORDNEY,
Saginaw, Mich.

July 13, 1928

DEAR SIR:

We saw your article in the St. Louis *Globe Democrat* asking for data on babies who move on all fours.

Our son, William Martin Foy, Jr., who is eleven months old today, July 13, moves on all fours when he wants to get around.

Bill Jr. is our first baby, and to our knowledge is the first child in the family to move on all fours. He started to crawl on the bed at six months and after a week of this we put him on the floor and he started moving on all fours as if he was used to it. He still continues to go that way although he is walking holding on to things now. He also has taken a few steps alone and stands alone quite easily, and we believe he will be walking freely in another month's time. However, if he wants to get any place or get something he always goes on all fours.

He places his hands and feet all flat on the floor and his head fairly down and eyes straight ahead as you can see by the enclosed pictures.

Bill Jr. is a bottle-fed baby and weighs twenty pounds, and we believe in every way is a perfect baby. He has so far never been sick. He also is not afraid of strangers and will go to anyone.

He has a great tendency to want to climb up everything. He also will not go to sleep without his pillow at any time. He never sleeps on a pillow, but must have one to toss with his feet and hands while going to sleep.

We think, however, Bill Jr. has been slow in cutting his teeth. He has six teeth now consisting of four upper and two lower ones.

FIG. 9.—The Foy boy.

He did not cut any teeth until he was nine months old and then cut them all in one month.

We hope Doctor this information will help you in your work and also would like to hear from you as to what you think of our son.

Very truly yours,
MRS. WILLIAM M. FOY,
St. Louis, Mo.

June 29, 1928

At the age of ten months my baby girl began going about on all fours. She never went any other way. She is now 12½ months old, but does not walk any yet. She climbs up to everything and does not seem afraid of falling. She can go almost as fast on all fours as my other girl can walk. As it is unusual for babies to crawl this way, I thought I would report it to you.

> Yours truly,
> MRS. EFFIE FRANCIS,
> Glover Gap, W. Va.

March 24, 1928

DEAR SIR:

My daughter never put her knees to the floor. We never encouraged her to walk. All at once she started on finger tips and toes; I do not remember about her head positively; held up slightly I think. This mode of moving continued for nearly two months, then as her Dad came in, she stood almost erect, and walked to meet him. She was about six months old when she first started on all fours. The iceman who saw her thus said, "That is the sign of a brainy child." She is now twenty years old. She is a very efficient stenographer and pianist, has a fine sense of rhythm, has four certificates, piano and theory, from McGill University, and a gold medal from Bridgeport High School, Connecticut. She is not rugged. Purely Scottish descent, no mixture. I am interested. Do not forget me. Some time send me the result of your observations.

Details:

Purely Scottish.

Female, first child.

Not very rugged.

No knowledge of other such cases in family.

Began on all fours about seventh month; continued about one month.

After 20 years I look back and think it was a pacer trot. Supported herself on finger tips and toes. Hands spread. Head slightly raised.

Sucked her big toe of left foot, when not watched.

Enthusiastic over a crowd, would sing or shout. Our minister said she was the most observing child for her age that he had ever noticed. While too young to be seated up, she looked him over very carefully. Before she could speak a word, or move her body, I found her making shadows on the wall with her fingers, and looking back a little at the shadows. Her breasts were full of milk and the nurse squeezed it out every day for three weeks. She would hold her hands up and study them for hours turning them round and moving her fingers, wondering what they were for, no doubt. When her Dad put a new pair of pretty beaded moccasins on her feet and held them up for her to see she yelled and would not be pacified until her pink ones were put back on her feet. If I made the slightest change in my clothing she would stare until she was tired. When born she had a head of heavy brown hair and weighed 10½ pounds. She came in a heavy thunder storm. A hard instrumental birth. Her first call to me was a natural bleat like a lamb "mam"; I can hear it yet.

MRS. JAMES D. FRASER,
New Glasgow, Nova Scotia

February 20, 1928

DEAR DOCTOR:

F. F., aged 12 months, is the fraternal twin of W. F. Both boys are in good health, weighing respectively 24 and 22 pounds. F. F. weighed 7 lbs. 3, and W. F. 7 lbs. 10 at birth; F. F. cut his teeth

FIG. 10.—The Freeman boy.

first, having now eight; F. F. sat up first, held his bottle first, pulled to his feet first, and is more aggressive. F. F. is a better eater, more active in his movements, laughs and cries with less provocation than his brother. He also sleeps much more. He pulled himself to his feet at 11 months whereas W. F. was doing so at 8 months. Until recently, while W. F. was creeping normally F. F. has sat on the floor, moving about with the right leg curled under him and the left leg as a prop; has not crept in normal fashion. Recently he has been "climbing over" his curled-up right leg and then setting the foot to the ground and progressing on all fours.

The child's ancestry is English and Irish. Male sex. Health excellent. Robust, very. Child is number 3. No other similar phenomena noted previously in other children or relatives. The child began to run on all fours at 12 months (February 1). The hands are open, fingers point somewhat inward, the head is practically straight and not pulled backward, the legs are flexed at the knee so that the back is nearly horizontal. The left leg is pushed out more to the side, and is straighter than the right.

DR. WALTER FREEMAN,
Washington, D. C.

May 26, 1928

DEAR SIR:

I have noticed recently several articles referring to your interest in children who run on all fours.

My oldest boy, who is now fifteen, did that when he was a baby and although it amused us we never thought there was anything particularly unusual about it.

I have hunted through our photographs to see if we had any picture of him and I have found the enclosed snap.

As you will note from the print, he held his head as high as he conveniently could and his hands are open. It was a habit he picked up before he was able to walk and was apparently acquired through his desire to get about quicker than he could by crawling. He would crawl when he was not in a hurry and run on all fours when anxious to make speed. This may possibly have delayed his walking to some extent although on that point I do not remember. I recall walking clear around the block with him while he ran along at my side on all fours.

My folks on both my father's and mother's side are Hollanders for several hundred years; but, as the name indicates, the family was originally French and came from Lorraine during the sixteenth century. My wife's family are Americans for three generations.

The boy was always well and strong. He was the first child.

The phenomenon has not been noted among any of the other of our children, nor have I heard of it among any of our relatives.

We never noticed any other peculiarity of the child.

Yours very truly,
JAMES DE FREMERY,
San Francisco, Calif.

April 10, 1928

DEAR SIR:

A few weeks ago I read of your communication to the American Medical Association asking members thereof for descriptions of children going on "all fours" instead of creeping. I see it again today in the *Pathfinder*. The article states you have learned of eleven cases, from that it must be rare.

Your call aroused my interest for the reason, I had a granddaughter who did not creep but went on all fours, and she is the only one I ever saw go that way. She probably went that way six or eight weeks and then began to walk, and only went back to that way when in a hurry, because she could make better time than by walking.

Her hands were placed flat on the floor and she slapped them down with force enough to be heard over most of the house. Her face sometimes faced the floor, at others she looked at the object she was headed for. She is a normal child in every way, but I think more observant than the majority of children.

She has now abandoned the all-four habit of walking. When she was going that way for her own amusement she reminded me of a turtle walking.

One of the doctors has his office across the hall from my office; I called his attention to your article, and he said he had seen a number of cases, but was only able to cite one.

Details:

Race and nationality—White, U. S.

Sex—Female.

What child in numerical order—First for mother, second for father.

Health and robustness—Health good and normal in every way.

Has the phenomenon been observed in any other child of the same parents or among relatives? No.

At what age has the child begun to run on all fours, and how long has it continued? At about one year and continued for about 6 weeks, when she began to walk.

Add description, as detailed as possible, of the performance itself, supplemented when this can be done, by a photograph of the child in the act—Cannot give any better description, and no photograph was taken.

Describe position of the hands (whether fully open or partly closed) and of the head, while running on all fours, as well as any other peculiarities of the child's behavior—Hands fully open and struck the floor with force enough to be heard over most of the house. Either looking at floor or the object headed for.

Details as to any other peculiarity of behavior of the child, or any other children in the family—Normal in every way, but she appeared to me to be more observing than the great majority of children. She reminded me of a turtle when on all fours, especially so if in a hurry, as she always was when I came into the house; she is my granddaughter.

J. C. FRICK,
Rockwell City, Ia.

March 18, 1928

DEAR SIR:

The heading "Children who run on all fours" in the *Literary Digest* of March 10, 1928, attracted my attention immediately upon my reaching page 23 of that issue. My son, who was one year old on March second of this year, has never moved from place to place in any other way than on all fours, bear-fashion, until he pulled himself upright to a standing position in the middle of the floor without holding on to anything at the age of about eleven months. While he walks quite steadily at present he often drops down to dash after something which he can reach more quickly on hands and feet than by walking on just feet. But he never gets down on his knees when in motion, and he can go much faster than his three-year-old sister can who sometimes imitates his gait because she thinks it so amusing.

I am enclosing a snapshot taken last summer. At that time Crawford was just starting to try to go from place to place on his hands and feet, and I was fortunate enough to get a picture of him as he started after a boy. It seems strange that my little girl never walked in this bear-fashion but always hitched on knees and elbows until she learned to walk.

Mr. Fritts and I are both college graduates, he of Colgate and the Albany Law School, and I of Mount Holyoke College. We are both intensely interested in evolution, and shall appreciate your comment on our son's case if you can find it convenient to write us.

Details:

Race and nationality—White, American.

Sex—Male.

What child in numerical order—Second.

Health and robustness—Splendid health, vigor, and activity.

Has the phenomenon been observed in any other child of the same parents or among relatives? No.

At what age has the child begun to run on all fours, and how long has it continued? Began about age of six months. Now walks, but occasionally turns to all fours. Age 13 mos.

Added description, etc.—Hands fully open, legs fairly wide apart.

MRS. HAROLD E. FRITTS,
Hudson, N. Y.

First letter:

March 18, 1928

DEAR DR. HRDLIČKA:

After having read in the *Literary Digest* of March 10, an extract from Dr. E. E. Free's article in *Week's Science*, I thought that perhaps you might be interested in having some information about one more instance of a child who ran on all fours in preference to creeping.

My son, now ten years and three months old, stood erect on both feet at the age of five months.

He walked on two legs, by taking hold of his pen, at seven and a half months.

He traveled on all fours mostly, from place to place, until the age of eleven months, and walked alone on two legs thereafter, also traveling on all fours in diminishing amount until the age of three.

His hands were open, and his head usually held up. I do not exactly remember at what age the all fours habit started, but I do remember that he got up on his hands and knees at the age of nine days, as we have a photograph taken at that time. As an infant it was never safe to leave him sleeping on a bed unprotected by some kind of a fence, as he would awake quietly and roll off, for the sake of the excitement. This was true as early as the first day. On the first day too, he turned his head to look at a big yellow chrysanthemum which stood on the dresser. He was being carried by his nurse at the time, and there was no doubt about his interest in the thing. His was not a delayed birth.

> Sincerely yours,
> SUMNER F. GADDAS,
> Northwestern University
> Medical School,
> Chicago, Ill.

Second letter:

April 16, 1928

DEAR DR. HRDLIČKA:

Your letter of March 21 has for a long time been unanswered, but with the help of Mrs. Gaddas, who has spent this winter in New Hampshire, I am now able to send you answers to the series of questions you so kindly enclosed in that letter. Some of the questions I was not able to answer with certainty, but these answers furnished by her are quite accurate and dependable. I am also enclosing some photographs which she has furnished, on the backs of which you will find data as to the boy's age at the time and some explanatory notes.

Child—American, with Scotch and English ancestry.

Male, first and only child.

Health excellent. Slender girlish build and features.

No other case of such kind known of in the family.

Began to run on all fours at the age of 10 or 11 months, but walked upright holding on to steady objects at 7½ months. Walked alone at 12 months, but still ran on all fours for greater speed. Continued on all fours in decreasing amount up to 15 months or more, and still does it very easily at the age of 10 years.

Child's head was up, hands open, heels raised, back horizontal. Ran fast and never ran into things.

Other peculiar characteristics:

Ability to lift head at age of 11 hours;

Ability to turn over and get up on arms and knees at 9 days.

Mrs. Gaddas and I will be glad to assist in any other way that may be in our power.

> SUMNER F. GADDAS.

August 24, 1928

Dr. Hrdlička:

In connection with your collection of cases of quadrupedal locomotion—instead of creeping—in children, I wonder if my own experience has any interest or significance.

I have had several times dreams, generally nightmares, in which when pursued I was forced to run on my hands and feet in order to escape. In all of these dreams I realized that this was undignified and felt humiliated at being compelled to resort to it, and yet I knew that I could run on all fours faster than on two feet.

My psychologist friends maintain that this is my pet complex, dating back to some scare that I had in infancy, but they do not attempt to explain why I never creep in these dreams—unless I am one of your cases.

Almost invariably I can identify every single item of my dreams and tell exactly where I got it—except this one item.

Very truly yours,
E. V. Gage,
Tallahassee, Fla.

First Letter:

June 30, 1928

Dear Doctor:

My baby started to creep at nine months on both hands, one knee, and the other foot. In about two weeks he changed to all fours, and he sure could travel. At thirteen months he stood up in the middle of the room and walked. He seemed to be very sure of himself and hesitated but very little.

He was born May 17, 1927, weighed a generous nine pounds and was twenty inches tall. He was breast fed until he was nine months old and then put on the bottle; at eleven months he voluntarily gave up his bottle to drink from a glass.

At one year he was twenty-eight inches tall and weight twenty-two and a half pounds and at thirteen months, twenty-five pounds.

Mrs. Walter A. Gahm,
Rolfe, Ia.

Second letter:

October 1, 1928

The child is white; American; male; first born.

He is exceptionally healthy, having been really sick but once with what is called "summer complaint." He is well built, rather stocky, full chest, flat back and rather broad. At sixteen months he is thirty-one inches tall and weighs about twenty-eight pounds.

So far as we can find out, no one else related to either parent crept this way.

He started to creep at nine months. At first he crept on his hands, his left foot, and his right knee. He kept this up for about a week and then traveled on all fours until he walked at thirteen months.

He put both hands flat on the floor with the fingers spread out. He also put his feet flat on the floor. In moving he used his hands the same as a baby that creeps on its hands and knees. Instead of bending his knees he allowed his foot to slide back and to one side and then forward. When he did this, he bore most of his weight on the big toe. The big toes seemed to be extra strong as he could stand clear on their tips and bear his entire weight. Part of the time he held his head up, looking forward, and part of the time he looked down. He never bumped into anything while creeping and he traveled unusually fast. When he stands he is very bow-legged; his knees being about six and a half inches apart and his feet about five inches apart. We have no picture of him "in action."

Sometimes I think he has been rather slow to learn the little tricks that babies do, but this may be because he is alone and has no one to play with. It took us nearly four months to teach him to "patty-cake" and now he won't do it. He cut his teeth all out of order. First the two lower ones, at five months, then two outside upper ones, then the outside lower, and then the middle uppers; now at sixteen months he has both eye teeth, but no double teeth. He dearly loves to be out of doors and play in the water; does not care much for fresh fruit except apples.

Very truly yours,
Mrs. Walter A. Gahm.

July 16, 1928

Dear Sir:

. . . I was attracted to your article on children who run on all fours owing to the fact that my son about a year ago when he was first beginning to walk took this method instead of creeping. We did not give it much thought at the time, but did notice that it seemed peculiar. Our next boy who is just starting to do the same thing attracted our attention more strongly, and having read this article, I am writing you. The child was born on August 22, 1927, and is just about eleven months of age. The past week has been his first attempt at crawling and he uses all his effort to get up on his feet, not using his knees at all. His hands are kept open and his head in line with his body unless attracted by something to draw his attention away.

I might state that my ancestors as far back as I know were born in Ireland and my wife's folks on her mother's side were German. Her father's folks as far as they know were born in America.

I would be very glad to hear from you or do anything that will enable you in any way in your research work of this kind. We will try to get some pictures later when he is a little stronger on his legs.

Yours very truly,
JOHN F. GALLAGHER,
Dash Point, Wash.

March 6, 1928

DEAR DR. HRDLIČKA:

I noted a short article in the *Literary Digest* for March 10, that you desired information or reports on cases of children using "all fours" as a means of locomotion. We have been more or less amused and interested in the case of our own boy and I thought possibly the case might interest you.

Our boy, Billy, is or was, very adept in getting about on all fours, being able to travel as speedily, or more so, in that fashion than when erect. He began the practice when just a little past three years of age. For nearly a year and one half he has used that means of locomotion almost entirely when at play about the house, some, but not as much, when at play out of doors, and even to some extent when he was coming in answer to summons or going upon simple errands. For several months, about a year ago, he used it almost exclusively. Now, at four years, eight months, he has almost entirely abandoned the practice.

He developed a great love for a toy "Teddy Bear" and an interest in the "Goldy Locks and Three Bears" story, and he himself has been impersonating a bear. He is "Billy Bear," not only during just a part of his play time, but practically all the time, and has been "Billy Bear" for well over a year, perhaps during all of this period when he has been using all fours as a means of locomotion. He still is "Billy Bear" a great deal of the time but now he frequently forgets his assumed title.

We were interested and amused by his "antics."

The boy is perfectly normal mentally and physically, in fact, we think, quite a little above normal in both respects.

Details:

Child in numerical order—First.

Has any other child in the family or among relatives shown the same phenomenon?—No.

At what age and how has the child begun to run on all fours?— Three years, six months.

When and how has he stopped?—He is gradually stopping it now at four years, eight months. Just seems to be outgrowing the habit.

How in running thus, did he place the hands and feet?—Very much as the animal he is impersonating (bear) gallops about. Hand open and flat.

How did he hold the head?—Head up.

Note any additional peculiarities of behavior, or anomalies, if any, shown by the child during that period—None at all.

R. W. GANFIELD,
Attorney at Law,
Minneapolis, Minn.

First letter:

March 25, 1928

MY DEAR DR. HRDLIČKA:

In response to your request in *Science* of two weeks ago for cases of children who could run on all fours before walking, I have a good case to send you, although, unfortunately, as I did not then know the rarity and interest of the procedure, my records are scanty, and I took no photographs.

The case is that of my own young son, William Francis Ganong, Jr., born July 6, 1924. We have nothing to show when he began thus to run, but his mother and I both remember that he did this perfectly spontaneously, and before he crept in the ordinary way.

We recall that when a little over a year old, in late July or early August, 1925, this method of locomotion attracted great attention at a large family picnic where, he happening to be wearing a brown wool suit, those present watched him thus running about, and designated him "the bear," for his mode of locomotion.

The first actual record I have is one dated Sept. 6, 1925, when he was fourteen months old, which reads: "Francis is 14 months old today. A very healthy, active, growing, developing, handsome boy. Does not yet walk, except with support, though he can raise himself upright and stand a second or two alone. Runs very fast on palms and soles (not knees), and pries into everything." Again on October 6, 1925, when 15 months old, a note says "Healthy, strong, big, handsome, lively, overbright for age, and physically in finest condition. Has all of his front teeth, fine and strong, and just cut one upper premolar (left) with others imminent. Does not yet walk, except by holding on to things, but runs very fast on his hands and soles. Goes up and down stairs alone . . . says many words . . . very good tempered . . . Gets what he wants by pointing and saying an imperative 'dah.'"

He did not walk until 18 months old, and a month or so (his mother thinks about 2 months) before that he took to creeping on his hands and knees, in normal posture, abandoning the "palms and soles" method. The speed with which he could get about on all fours, as well as on hands and knees, enabling him to get to his objective so much more quickly than by attempting to walk, was a reason, we thought, why he delayed walking so long.

Once in a while, I have noticed, even now he will when romping on the floor take a few steps in the old "palms and soles way."

The only feature that we can correlate with this was a remarkable facility he had in using his feet to draw towards him things that he wanted. He would reach out with a foot and draw a toy towards him in this way instead of using his hands, though there has never been any lack of handiness in using his hands but rather an unusual facility in this respect. He would work objects closer by use of a foot and then would often grasp them between his feet; once I saw him place a cup between his feet and then, lying on his back, swing it back and forth through the air.

He has a sister fourteen months younger than he and much like him in many respects, but she never showed either the palm and sole locomotion (learning to creep on her knees in the ordinary way), or any tendency to use her feet to reach after or grasp objects. She walked earlier, at sixteen months.

The boy is now perfectly normal and healthy, very active, somewhat large (especially tall) for his age, and has shown no other peculiarities that I can think of.

He was our first child (my first and his mother's also), born when I was sixty and his mother nearing thirty. His mother is of unmixed Norwegian descent, I am almost wholly of English origin with a strain of French. Neither of us know of any like case anywhere among our relatives.

In running thus, we are perfectly sure he kept his hands wide open (the expression in my notes runs on "palms and soles"), and our recollection is that he kept his head horizontal, in line with his body, and his eyes on the floor beneath and somewhat ahead of him. We have many photos of him at all stages, but none that show him in the act.

Very truly yours,
WM. F. GANONG,
Professor of Botany,
Smith College,
Northampton, Mass.

April 3, 1928

Additional data concerning William Francis Ganong, Jr.:

I have found an additional note which reads:

June 17 or 18, 1925, when nearly a year old. "For first time he really crept (instead of just rolling and hitching) going from one room to another." Unfortunately the note does not say how he crept, but his parents are both sure that he went from the first on his palms and soles, *i.e.*, on all fours.

In going this way we recall clearly that his legs and feet were spread well out at an angle with his body, bringing his feet well outside the line of his hands, which were directly beneath him, his arms being vertical.

A peculiarity which might be correlated with this mode of progression is the fact that he is somewhat knock-kneed, though not very markedly so. But his younger sister has this peculiarity at least as marked as he—if anything more so—and she never showed the least tendency to travel in that way.

Prof. W. F. GANONG.

April 1, 1928

DEAR SIR:

After reading your article in *The Evening Star* of March 31, I decided I would send you a snapshot of my daughter demonstrating walking on "all four," and also sleeping on her stomach with arms and feet drawn underneath.

A few years ago our mothers—mine—would have been horrified—to leave baby on his stomach—"why he'd smother." The common practice now causes our "curious" little animal to raise its head to see the light and locate the sound and soon the hands and feet help raise the body. The spine, arm muscles, leg muscles, and bones, in general, strengthen. We called our little one "turtle" when her little head at the age of not more than three months was raised from her pillowless bed.

By ten months she was "speeding" on all fours and by fourteen months, walking erect, without so many usual hard "sittings down."

Details:

White, American; Scotch English ancestry.

Female, third child.

Health good; frail, but strong.

No other case of walking on all fours known in family.

Habit lasted approximately four months, tenth to fourteenth.

Gait rapid; position shown in photo. (Plate XI, p. 245.)

The child in question was from infancy unusually precocious, climbing over a high crib months before she could walk, talking correctly very early. At the age of five has adult vocabulary (due to constant association of elderly people). Father 48, Mother 45, at her birth. No child companions. Child of restless disposition, no accomplishments. Only quiet when being read to—books suitable for ten-year children; all of which I ascribe to being reared among gray-heads on a seventh floor.

My second child—normal, healthy, filled with music which he heard in most commonplace sounds, such as a pan hitting against a wall, would have been a wonderful study, but he was taken from us suddenly at 5 years 11 months. He did not walk on all fours.

Yours very truly,
MRS. A. N. GARDNER,
Washington, D. C.

June 28, 1928

DEAR DOCTOR HRDLIČKA:

Both my children ran on all fours at the age of ten months, walking at the age of thirteen months. Susie, aged eight years, and Harold, four, are both normal children. One of my neighbors, Mrs. Harold Wilbur, has two little boys who both moved that way. I don't know that I have ever heard of any others.

Details:

Children, white; American.

Health very good.

First and second born.

My sister's first child, a boy, ran on all fours. I do not know about others. Both began at approximately the age of ten months and continued until they walked at the age of about thirteen months.

As my daughter is now eight years old, I cannot remember very much about her creeping but will enclose a snapshot. A friend used to call her a "spider." The hands were fully open. The head was held high enough to enable her to see where she was going. With the boy much the same.

When the girl began to cut her teeth on the upper jaw the lateral incisors appeared before the central incisors. The same thing was observed when my father was a baby, also in my sister's third child, a boy. (See Plate IV*a*, p. 33.)

Yours very truly,
MRS. R. H. GIDDINGE,
Auburn, Me.

July, 1928

DEAR SIR:

Lawrence Spangler Gift is now twenty-one and a half months old. At the age of six months he started to run on all fours. At seventeen months he walked upright on two legs. After he learned to walk he reverted to the all-fours method when he happened to be in a hurry.

Whether indoors or outdoors he occasionally goes around on all fours of his own will and travels at a great rate of speed. Also, he has a marked desire to climb, being extremely cautious in all he endeavors.

The child has never been ill and his carriage is as straight as an arrow, due no doubt to the exercise in running on all fours.

Enclosed find several snapshots taken while "in action." (See Plate X, p. 189.)

Details:

Report by parents—Child, white; American; first born; male; now twenty-two months old.

Has never been ill. The child is slim and strong; also above the average mentally.

Walks on all fours like a bear. His speed is remarkable. Started to walk on all fours at six months. At seventeen months walked upright, but when in a hurry reverts to the all fours. Whether indoors or outdoor he walks in this manner of his own will. He is also a great climber, being very agile but cautious in everything he undertakes.

No other peculiarities; and no other such case known in relatives.

Yours very truly,
Mrs. Howard D. Gift,
Allentown, Pa.

September 26, 1929

Dr. Hrdlička:

My daughter walked on all fours. She is white and of Scotch, Irish, and German descent. She is in the best of health and is very robust, never ill except for the usual slight ailments of babyhood.

She is the first child and is the only one to walk that way in both branches of the family. When eleven months old she began to run about on all fours. She never crawled previous to that time.

The photographs will show you, the way she goes, better than I can explain. Her hands are fully open. (Plate XI, p. 245.)

In all other ways she is perfectly normal. All other children on both sides of the family are normal.

Respectfully yours,
Mrs. Marjorie Glenn,
Brooklyn, N. Y.

Report by Mrs. George A. Goss, mother:
Child, male; white; first-born; New England descent.
Seven at present. Walked on all fours from six to twelve months.

Strong, active child. Mentality good.

Never crept. Always walked and ran on all fours, until he walked erect.

No peculiarities of behavior in other children or members of the family.

Slept on stomach.

July 6, 1928

Dr. Hrdlička:

I have a daughter, Betty, who is now eleven months old. At about eight months of age she began to walk on her hands and feet, once in a while creeping in the regular way, but very seldom. She began to walk in this way as if she was in a hurry and could not wait to creep. She can go as fast as anyone can walk and sometimes even faster if she is trying to get away from you. She lacked one day eleven months when she took her first step alone, although she had tried standing up off and on for a couple or three weeks. She never falls, though she sits down rather hard after swaying on her feet a minute or so, and very seldom gets a hard bump. She is always pulling herself up against anything available and has done so right along. Of course we think she is very cute, and all the neighbors do also.

She has eight teeth, the last one coming through at ten and one-half months. I broke her from the bottle three weeks ago and she eats everything, drinks milk well and is gaining right along. Says a few words and jabbers all the time. Sleeps well nights as a rule and takes a couple or three naps a day. Goes to bed any time from eight to ten at night and is wonderfully good to take among kind strangers. She will go to nearly anyone.

She weighs twenty pounds or a trifle over. She took a quart of milk a day when she was on the bottle but now does not take quite that amount. Is very fond of potato, any kind of vegetable or any kind of fruit; eats crackers or bread and butter well.

She fusses quite a little sometimes when I put her in her crib for either the night or a nap as she is accustomed to going to sleep with her bottle. Sometimes she will take something to play with and not fuss at all.

She climbs up anything she can get a hold on and seems very strong with the exception of her ankles. They seem a little weak. I am wondering if that is because she was so strong in the arms that she pulled herself on her feet too soon. Her legs are a trifle bowed although I think not as much as when she was smaller.

I am sorry to say that I have never had a snapshot of Betty while she was walking on all fours.

Details:

On her father's side, Betty is of Scotch and Irish descent, on her mother's, Irish, German, and Swiss. Parents and grandparents born in United States or Canada.

Female; first child.

Is very well, was weaned from bottle at 10½ months, eats everything, no trouble with food disagreeing in the least. Weighed a trifle over 20 pounds at 11 months; 7 pounds 11 ounces at birth; average height; has not been weighed lately as she will not keep still long enough for scales to register.

No one else in either family has walked in this manner.

Betty began to pull herself up against anything before she was eight months old, soon after, perhaps about nine months of age, began to walk on all fours. At not quite eleven months she began to stand up and took one or two steps alone. Began to walk a few days after she was a year old and walks almost all the time now—was a year old August 4, 1928. Seldom now gets down on all fours.

Her hands were used palms flat on the floor, feet more as a person would walk on tiptoe than on the whole foot. At times she bent her knees very little, at others she would bend them down so they nearly touched the floor. Her arms were held rigid, without bending the elbows. Head usually down a trifle, unless looking at someone whom she was coming to. Moved very rapidly this way and was very sure of herself. When she began to walk she fell less often than most babies, if she lost her balance would go down on her hands rather than sideways or backwards, or catch herself in mid-air, hesitate a moment and straighten up and start again.

Has no other peculiarities that we have noticed.

Sincerely yours,
D. E. G.,
Oriskany, N. Y.

March 14, 1928

My Dear Dr. Hrdlička:

I read your article in *Literary Digest* about children who creep like animals.

My baby boy, now fifteen months, did most of his creeping that way, with palms open, head up. He began it around nine months and although he has been walking since a year, he now and then when on the floor will go clear across the room in that fashion, especially when he has something of the other child's he knows he should not have. Often he runs to a corner or under a table exactly like an animal. He can go more rapidly that way, he seems to think. When the weather gets warm I can send a picture, if you wish.

He is a normal child in every way, of very fine physical development and intellect a little above the average perhaps. He seems very imitative both of sounds and actions. When only a year old he would stand up and dance with the little girl and keep perfect time to the music, imitating her to a remarkable degree. He understands everything I say to him and will go all over the house to get things you tell him to bring.

Details:

Child—white; American; male; second born.

Very fine health, robust looking.

No other cases of walking on fours known of among relations.

Began at ten months, but only about half time, crept on knees and hands also, always went on all fours when he wanted to hurry, and now at fifteen months will gallop away if sitting on floor and run under table. Several times a day I catch him on all fours. He has a double crown and very heavy dark eyebrows. His conduct is about the same as that of all healthy babies. He has always been very active, is very happy and friendly. Has never been afraid of any one.

He held his head erect from the second week, also my other child; but she developed much more slowly and crept by sitting flat and using one leg as an oar.

My sister's child has an extra eye tooth and her hair stood up straight like a porcupine's at birth but fell down when it got long enough. She never crept at all.

Am enclosing some pictures of the baby and his sister, the only children we have. I can think of nothing else peculiar either in their habits or looks and I have never heard of anything among the children of the relatives that seems abnormal or peculiar.

When the baby runs on all fours he does it with hands out flat. If possible will get a picture of the baby on all fours and if you wish when we come to Washington this summer will bring him up for observation.

Yours truly,

Mrs. H. C. Graves, Jr.,

Verona, Pa.

July 10, 1928

Dear Sir:

I state the case of my son, Francis K. Green, born January 1, 1900, now a civil engineer.

He was the first-born child, a strong healthy baby, who could sit up and hold up his head at five months. At seven months he began to move about on his hands and feet just as you describe. At nine months he could stand erect by pulling himself up by the furniture, but did not walk alone till thirteen months, owing to a set-back from cold and vaccination.

He stopped going on all fours after he could walk. No other child in the family progressed in this way excepting a cousin of the same age who sometimes did it in imitation.

Details:

Child, white; American; of direct British descent.

Male; first born.

Health, excellent; more healthy than robust.

No other like case in family, except a first cousin who used to imitate my son. Our other child started progression by rolling about.

The boy began to progress on all fours at seven months. This continued until he was fourteen months and could walk. He was very strong.

"Hind limbs upright with moderate bend in knees, but nearly straightened as the limb extends when the child moved forward; fore limbs upright, body inclined slightly forward, and downward, head slightly raised. Soles of feet flat on ground turned slightly outward. Palms of hands applied to the ground extended. Fingers partly separated. Head slightly raised. Eyes looking forward." Progression quite fast. I quote your own description. It is the best possible.

Left-handed, now ambidextrous. Two of his cousins are left-handed. No other peculiarities in the family.

Mrs. F. B. Green,

New York City.

. 213 .

November 12, 1928

DR. HRDLIČKA:

I was very much interested in the article on baby locomotion, and am writing this letter in response to your request. Our baby used quadruped locomotion. She began moving on her hands and knees at nine and a half months. At the age of eleven months she began walking on her hands and feet. She found this method so satisfactory that she abandoned creeping entirely. She suited her speed to her needs, at times going slowly, or loping along when in a hurry. She walked in an upright position at thirteen months. She apparently had no difficulty for she walked off immediately when she discovered she could step.

She has always seemed to be strong from birth. When only a month old she would try to hold her head up when put on her stomach. She rolled over and over on the floor when five and a half months old and would get into a position preparatory to creeping.

She is now fourteen months and nine days. During that time she has had the best of health with the exception only of two days when she had fever caused from her double teeth. She has just completed cutting all her milk molar teeth.

Details:

Child, white; American; female; first born.

Splendid health, sturdy but not fat; weighs 24 pounds at 17 months and is 23½ inches tall.

No other children who walked on all fours known of among relatives.

Walked on all fours soon after she was 11 months old and did so for two months.

At first our baby got around by creeping but did so for only a short time. Then she began to raise her knees from the floor by straightening out her legs as though it annoyed her to have her knees touch the floor. She did this as though she were doing exercises, then she began walking along with her knees stiff and her hands on the floor. Walking in this manner she would have to throw her legs in an outward manner in order to get them in position for another step. She turned her toes in, especially the right one.

Her hands were fully opened, flat on the floor with the fingers spread apart. Her head was up so that she could see ahead of her. When wishing to take any of her toys with her she would put the article in her mouth and proceed on all fours. At times she would carry her "sack" doll in this manner letting it dangle as a cat would its kitten.

I can think of no other peculiarities of the child except that she refuses to take milk and has done so since she was ten months old.

> Respectfully yours,
> Mrs. G. H. Green,
> San Francisco, Calif.

June 29, 1928

Dr. Hrdlička:

My baby started walking on all fours when about eight and one-half months old. He never crawled over the floor. We thought it very amusing to see him walking on all fours but when he was ten months old he walked upright.

I never allowed him out on the floor until he started to walk on all fours. I kept him in the play-pen and swing and the getting up at the sides of the pen I think strengthened his limbs. He is very well developed and perfect in health. He is two years and six months old now.

Walking on all fours I know is unusual and he is the first baby I have ever seen walk that way, but I am sure it helped him to walk upright without any assistance at the early age of ten months.

> Respectfully yours,
> Mrs. John C. Grissinger,
> York, Pa.

March 22, 1928

Dear Sir:

It has come to my notice that Dr. E. E. Free, in his *Week's Science*, has indicated that you are interested in securing information concerning infants who "creep" on all fours.

The enclosed picture of Jimmie Halbe was taken a few days ago, a short time before his first birthday. This photograph was taken with Jimmie in motion and was not posed. Until he learned to walk erect, shortly before he was a year old, his only method of locomotion was on all fours, as shown in the photograph. He has never crawled on his hands and knees, but at the time when youngsters usually learn to crawl he began to move about with a great deal of agility on fours, as you see in the picture.

His movements have been the source of considerable amusement among friends and neighbors, but it was never deemed to be out of the ordinary until the article above referred to was seen.

Details:

Race and nationality—White; American.

Sex—Male.

What child in numerical order—First.

Health and robustness—Both excellent.

Has the phenomenon been observed in any other child of the same parents or among relatives?—No.

At what age has the child begun to run on all fours, and how long has it continued?—At about six months, until one year; but stood frequently after six months.

The position of the hands, etc.—Hands open, head down to see direction.

Details as to any other peculiarity of behavior of the child, or any other children in the family—Always unusually quick to grasp new things taught, such as imitating singing, blowing with lips, blowing nose, notices color in pictures. Frequently looking up.

Yours very truly,

L. W. HALBE,

Fort Pierce, Fla.

June 7, 1928

DEAR DR. HRDLIČKA:

Last April, at the meeting of the American Society of Mammalogists in Washington, I handed you a photograph of my daughter "Molly" in the act of walking on all fours, or "bear-walking" as we call it. Herewith are several additional photographs, and also some of the data you have asked for in *Science* of March 9, 1928.

Molly was born on May 13, 1926. Her ancestry on the paternal side is Scotch-Irish, English, and German; on the maternal side, Scotch-Irish and English. For two or more generations all her ancestors have been American. She seems to her parents, at least, exceptionally bright, lively, and intelligent. Her health and robustness have been excellent from the start. She is our first and only child. At present she has a vocabulary of more than a hundred words. The data on "bear-walking" can be supplied in considerable detail, thanks to a diary kept by her mother. The phenomenon has not been observed in any relative, so far as we are aware.

About June 20, 1927, she began walking on the sole of her right foot while still creeping with her other three limbs. At first she did this only when barefoot, and not with stockings on. Occasionally she stood on all fours, but did not progress in this position at that time. By July 3 she would climb up an embankment on all fours (see photograph).

On July 18, while "bear-walking," she lowered her head and looked back between her legs at a child behind her.

The photograph of July 21, handed to you in Washington, shows Molly's characteristic attitude in "bear-walking" at that period. So far as we have observed, she has always walked on the palms of her hands, with fingers more or less extended, and with the hands turned somewhat inward (pigeon-toed).

On July 24 she took her first upright steps alone. On the next day she took six steps alone, and "bear-walked" and walked upright alternately.

On July 28 she walked a good deal. She always "bear-walked" when turned loose naked in the yard.

By August 15 she was walking more and more. By August 22 she was running upright everywhere and seldom on fours. A photograph on August 29 shows her still "bear-walking." (Plate X, p. 189.)

The diary contains no record of "bear-walking" between August, 1927, and March, 1928, though we recollect that Molly indulged in it for a few seconds two or three times last fall.

On March 13, 1928, after reading your note in *Science,* I placed her in the position of "bear-walking," and with a slight urging she took up her old pastime. On March 14 she "bear-walked" with no suggestion from any one. Her palms were flat down.

On March 16 there was a little more spontaneous "bear-walking." On March 18 there was more, when not suggested, and still more when suggested. Up to April 8 she did it now and then, on request. Since that time, right up to the present, she has continued the practice, almost entirely without suggestion. When leaving her chair at the dining table to go to the nursery, she has an almost regular ceremony of "bear-walking" down the hall.

Last summer she went comparatively fast while "bear-walking." Now she goes very slowly and apparently with much greater effort. Also her head seems to be held lower now than last summer.

Up to a few months ago she would often go to sleep lying on her stomach with her knees bent forward beneath her, but this has not been noticed but once recently. She still runs on all fours occasionally in play.

Molly is more or less ambidextrous, using her right hand more for eating, and her left hand more for drawing. I might add that mimicking, in both words and actions, is one of her most pronounced characteristics.

Very truly yours,
FRANCIS HARPER,
Boston Soc. Nat. Hist.,
Boston, Mass.

April 26, 1928

DEAR SIR:

I noticed an article in *The Pathfinder* requesting physicians who observe children creeping on all fours to write you. I am not a physician but a mother and have three children. The oldest, a girl, crawled on her hands and feet, with her hands open, palms down, till the inside of her hands were calloused. She began to go thus at the age of nine months and three weeks, and at the age of twelve months and three weeks she began walking. She was an unusually fat and short baby, weighing nine and one-fourth pounds at birth, 20 pounds at four and one-half months, 33 pounds at 22 months. She never tried to creep at all until she could raise herself clear of the floor and go on all fours. She kept her head raised so much that she faced straight in front. The funniest thing to us was when running on fours she carried all her toys by holding them in her teeth. She is now seven years old and perfectly normal. She has never liked to climb and seems to have a fear of high places.

The next child, a girl, crawled on her hands and knees though she tried to go on hands and feet, but her ankles are weak.

The baby, a boy, progressed on his hands and feet just part of the time. I have known several children who ran on their hands and feet and it is a noticeable fact that they never do this until 9 or 10 months old and never very long. I wonder is it abnormal for a child to move that way. Mothers are always glad when they do because they are so much easier to keep clean.

Details:

Race and nationality—White; American; a perfect blonde.
Sex—Female.
Large. Always healthy except for tonsillitis and earache. Weighed nine and one-fourth pounds at birth, twenty pounds at four and one-half months, 33 pounds at 22 months. An unusually short baby, but now a little above average in height for her age. She is now seven.
First child. Born April 21, 1921.
Has the phenomenon been observed in any other child of the same parents or in relatives?—I have two more children, they crawled on hands and knees until just before they began walking when for a short time they went on their hands and feet.
At what age has the child begun to run on all fours and how long continued?—Began when ten months and one week old and began walking at twelve months and three weeks of age, so only went in this manner two months and two weeks.
Description of performance: Moved very rapidly on hands and feet. Feet being placed flat on floor as anyone would in walking. Hands were placed wide open on the floor. As my floors were bare her hands soon became calloused as a person's bare feet would. Her hips were elevated higher than her shoulders as she kept her legs straight when walking; her head was always held about as high as she could get it. Chin, up and slightly out.
She carried all her toys that she could get a hold on, in her teeth. Her doll or other toys would be clinched firmly in her teeth. Her sister was 22 months old before she walked. Her ankles are weak. She crawled on her hands and knees with her feet turned back and would raise up and sit on the soles of her feet. It seemed so queer for her to sit that way. She began crawling at ten months, at 14 months could stand alone and walk by holding on, but was 22 months old before she walked. The little girl who is the subject of this has always been a perfectly normal healthy child. Very fond of vegetables and fruits, doesn't care much for sweets. Did extra good work in school.

Mrs. Sam Harris,
Ingalls, Ark.

June 17, 1928

MY DEAR DR. HRDLIČKA:

In an article in regard to babies that walk like a bear, by Watson Davis, which appeared in the St. Paul, Minnesota, *Pioneer Press* for Sunday, June 10, 1928, it states that you are a Doctor and a Curator of Physical Anthropology and that you are anxious to hear from persons of all races who have babies that walk like bears. I herewith will comply with your request and let you know that I have a boy that walked like a bear before he could walk upright. He is now 2 years and 10 months old. The enclosed picture was taken when he was 11 months old. I am sending you his picture so you can judge him to some extent. He is very bright and aggressive. From the time he was born he was always in motion while awake. I think that babies have the instinct that they want to get on their feet and if they are strong enough they will rather walk like a bear than crawl.

I have only this child and have had no other children. If my child can be of any service to you in your work I will be glad to give you any assistance possible, and I also kindly invite your suggestions on the picture for my child.

At time of birth the baby weighed ten and one-half pounds. When six months old weighed nineteen pounds; at one year, twenty-five pounds.

Brief details:

Child, white, parents Norwegian.

Male, first born (we have no other children).

More than ordinary healthy.

We do not know of any other case of bear-walking in our families.

He started when he was about 10 months old, and occasionally he walks on fours yet.

Photograph enclosed. He likes to do stunts which require strength.

The boy is quite strong for his age and very bright, and likes to have lots of exercise and fun.

Yours very truly,
MRS. H. J. HAUGE,
Canby, Minn.

June 17, 1928

DEAR SIR:

An article in the *New York Times* today regarding babies moving on all fours states that you are interested in hearing of instances of this kind.

We have a little daughter, now nineteen months old, who never crept but moved around on all fours. At six months she said "Mama," "Dada," and "Hello." At seven months she moved on all fours. At eleven months she walked from object to object hanging on to one until she gripped the other. At twelve months she walked without assistance.

Now at nineteen months she has a vocabulary of at least one hundred words which we can furnish on request.

Last week she walked from our home ten city blocks to the River over the bridge which is one-half mile and for an hour through the Troy City streets. This child is the first of the family and no other child among relatives has shown the same phenomenon.

The method of getting about was identical with your description in today's article, so for this reason it is needless to repeat.

The child has always enjoyed excellent health, is strong and hardy and while a great many people remarked at the time that they had never seen a child get around like that we did not particularly think it other than odd until reading your article.

Enclosed find a photo at age of seven months. We never even dreamed of taking a photo on all fours. We shall be pleased to supply further information or confirmation of statements herein made on request.

MR. and MRS. HARRY E.
HAYNER,
Watervliet, N. Y.

August 3, 1928

DR. HRDLIČKA:

I wish to report the case of my son, Malcolm, who at the age of one year employed this method of locomotion (running on all fours) and became very expert. He could cover a great deal of ground in a short while. He was late walking (sixteen months). He plays with his toys even now in that manner pushing them around with one hand while the other hand and two feet propel him forward to the amusement of every one. He has a fine back and muscular arms and legs and I give this credit for it. He is three years old, bright for his age, very active all the time. He weighs forty-two pounds.

Yours truly,
MRS. HELEN A. HENLEY,
Richmond, N. Y.

June 26, 1928

DEAR SIR:

Our oldest boy, now nine, walked on all fours. He never creeped, but would walk on his hands and feet. He seemed to figure out that it was faster. He would start to creep a little but would soon rise up on his hands and toes and go like sixty. He could make twice the speed or better.

We have a very good snap-shot of his walking this way. One hand raised ready to thrust it forward, to take another step. I do not think we have the film any more, but if you would like a copy, we would try and accommodate you some way.

I do not recall how long this lasted but until he could walk. He was very quick and bright.

We have one other child, now 17 months. He creeped in the ordinary way and made no effort to do anything further.

Yours very truly,
DON J. HENRY,
Twin Falls, Idaho.

March 20, 1928

DEAR SIR:

Being much interested in an article in a Hearst paper printed in this city on the 17th inst., telling about the research work you are doing in regard to atavistic children, I am taking the liberty to write you a few facts concerning my granddaughter, Mildred Nadine Hill, born Dec. 7, 1926, at Clarkdale, Arizona, but who is at this time making her home with me here in Chicago.

If parentage has anything to do with children who develop this peculiar habit, will say that the child's mother is of English parents, is now about 19 years of age, and was brought to the U. S. when she was four years old. As to the child's father on his mother's side, the grandmother is of Bohemian parents and his grandfather was born of German parents. On my side of the family, there are several mixed American strains.

This child was brought here from Arizona when she was five months old. When she got to be about seven months and being very strong and robust, we would put her on the floor and we tried to teach her to crawl. But instead of going forward, she would back up. When she got along about eight to nine months of age was when she began to show signs of being an atavistic. She began to run on all fours. This was something entirely new to us, also all our friends and relatives. If anyone recognized the case, they did not tell us. But recently one day I came on an article in a paper that described the case fully and in that way we have learned the facts.

The child was fifteen months on the 7th inst., and has been walking since she was ten and one-half months of age. But even now there are times, when she is playing with a tennis ball that we got for her, that she will throw the ball and instead of walking toward it she will go flying along on all fours at a fast rate of speed.

Since reading the article regarding what you are doing and seeing the accompanying pictures, we regret very much that we didn't take a few kodak views of our little girl. But intend to try and get some at this late date.

Trusting that what I have been able to tell you here will be of some help to you, I am

> Yours very truly,
> M. L. HILL,
> Chicago, Ill.

June 27, 1928

DEAR DOCTOR:

My fourteen months old son is walking on all fours, in the fashion you describe. He began creeping, as in your Case 2, by wiggling along flat on his stomach. He now proceeds on his hands and feet almost entirely, sometimes using his knees.

Details:

White; one-fourth Welsh, one-fourth German, one-fourth Irish, one-fourth French and Pennsylvania Dutch.

Male; second child.

Very healthy and strong.

The phenomenon has not occurred to my knowledge at any time on either side of the family.

Tommy started running on all fours when about one year old. Before this, he wiggled, rather than crawled, flat upon his stomach. He started walking at sixteen months and has not gone on fours since.

We used to be surprised because the baby's progress was so very rapid. Flat on his feet; flat on his hands, fingers out-stretched; head well down between shoulders, but eyes ahead. His hands and feet moved in the same rhythm as a dog's or any animal, I suppose. I never was able to get a picture that was not badly blurred. In no other way has he been peculiar and neither has his older brother.

Yours truly,
MRS. ARNOLD J. HILLESHEIM,
Madelia, Minn.

September 18, 1928

DEAR DR. HRDLIČKA:

I am writing to say that I have baby twin girls, just a year old this month, who have been walking on all fours for several months. One of them goes on fours occasionally, but the other babe walks entirely on all fours. They are both very active children and since they were three months old have always had a lot of exercise before they were put to bed for the night . . .

Yours very truly,
MRS. A. W. HINDERER,
Richmond Hill, L. I., N. Y.

First letter:

July 31, 1928

DEAR SIR:

The enclosed clipping from a past issue of the *Literary Digest* was recently brought to my attention and I decided to send you a snapshot of my youngster taken at the stage of his walking on all fours. I hope it may be of some use to you.

This picture was taken on Dean's first birthday—he is five years old now—and he has been going on all fours from the time he was eight months old. He walked at fourteen months but for speed resorted to hands and feet even after two years of age. Even now, when he plays "wild animal," it's down on hands and feet—not hands and knees.

We never realized that this was a condition of special interest. In other respects he has always been quite a normal boy.

I am greatly interested in knowing what value you attach to this condition.

> Very truly yours,
> MRS. JOE A. HINTON,
> Phoenix, Ariz.

Second letter:

> May 19, 1929

Dean is our first and only child. He is now six years, exceedingly alert mentally. He is not robust. In play he squats on his feet instead of sitting down. In sleep we frequently find him curled up, lying on his side, his hands pressed tightly between his knees. He says it is the best way to get warm. He has always been cautious, so he has had very few accidents or tumbles.

> Very truly yours,
> MRS. JOE A. HINTON.

> April 22, 1929

DR. HRDLIČKA:

Knowing that you are interested in the peculiar methods of walking on all fours that some children develop before learning to walk upright, I am sending you a picture that I took about eighteen years ago of a son of mine who for a short time, perhaps a couple of weeks, walked as a plantigrade animal. The picture, I think, shows this very well and that was his ordinary method of locomotion during this time.

He is at present a Junior in Swarthmore College at the head of his class.

Details:

White, male, first child.

Health good.

No other case known in relatives.

Began to go on all fours one week before he was one year old, kept it up about two weeks.

> Sincerely yours,
> GEO. A. HOADLEY,
> Swarthmore, Pa.

March 5, 1928

DEAR SIR:

I have read your article about "Science Studying Children who run on all fours" and like to send you couple of pictures, the only two we ever took of my son in this way. He was born Dec. 23, 1926, in the Greenville Hospital, Jersey City. As he was eight months old (August 1927), he started in slowly to run on all fours. In September last year, he had already a great speed in that way to run. He never was creeping. He used to do a race on all fours all around the kitchen. His regular time for this race was from 8:30 o'clock until 9:00 o'clock every night for about one month (October, 1927). He is now 14½ months old, very strong and healthy, running upright since 14 days before Christmas, but, if it means safety first, he runs on his fours.

This week he is starting to speak, you can't understand him, but he shows with hands and one finger, what he means.

Details:

I am married the second time and this boy is my fourth child; he is the first child from my second wife. My wife is twenty-five, I am thirty-five years of age and we are both North-German.

Between seven and eight months he began to run on all fours in his crib. At about eight months he started to do the same on the floor. First slowly, after a while with a great speed.

Since middle of December '27, he is walking alone and only uses his hands and feet when he is in danger, it means safety to him to run then on all fours.

He places his hands and feet flat on the floor, as you would say, like a dog.

As you see in the picture, he holds his head most of the time high.

When he did his exercises at night, he stopped once in a while and looked and laughed at us, what we say *albern* in German and with a greater speed he did his exercises on the fours and would not stop until he was all exhausted.

Yours truly,
EMIL HOFF,
Bayonne, N. J.

March 9, 1928

DEAR SIR:

Referring to the article in the current *Literary Digest* for data on children who run on all fours, I am enclosing a photograph of a child which I made fifteen years ago. (See Plate IV*b*, p. 33.)

This child was about thirteen months old at the time and could run as rapidly on his hands and feet as his eighteen months older brother could do in the normal manner.

I only knew the people casually and so cannot give you definite information as to heredity; I only saw the mother and she appeared to be of the usual American stock.

Respectfully,
W. K. HOLMES,
Los Angeles, Calif.

July 24, 1928

Possibly it may be of interest to you to learn of children that never crawled, and yet did not go on all fours.

My aunt never crawled. She moved about sitting upright with her limbs doubled under her, and lifting herself with her hands, I have heard my grandmother tell. Heavy patches had to be sewed on her clothes underneath. She was very active and soon learned to walk, and when less than 18 months old walked an unbelievable distance when being taken to a neighbors.

She was of Scotch-Irish descent.

Very truly yours,
E. G. HOOVER,
Carlisle, Ind.

April 24, 1928

DEAR DOCTOR HRDLIČKA:

I enclose herewith two pictures of my granddaughter, Della Lou Dunbar, taken when she was one year old.

One shows her in her normal quadruped gait with hands and feet flat and chin up and one shows her about ten minutes later when she took her first steps alone. She began running on all fours at seven months.

. 227 .

She is the first child; her mother was 18 years old when she was born; her mother's ancestors were all colonial families, most recent immigrants from Europe 1800, English, Dutch, Irish in race; her father's ancestors are of about the same races, with a German grandfather.

Additional details:

Race and nationality—American, colonial; Dutch-English, German.

Sex—Female.

Health and robustness—Excellent, but not large.

What child in numerical order?—First.

Has the phenomenon been observed in any other child of the same parents or among relatives?—No.

Very truly yours,
THEODORE J. HOOVER,
Stanford University, Calif.

A white child, American. Oct. 28, 1926, evening, at the Union Station, Washington. Waiting for a train, I saw nearby a young woman, evidently a poorer country woman or mountaineer, with a child on her lap. Before long the child wanted to go down and was lowered to the floor, where it promptly and without difficulty got up on all four, and ran about thus, much like a little animal. It moved actively, though not actually running. Went thus again and again, on all fours, all limbs upright, only knees bent little forward, hands and feet applied very nearly flat to the floor. Now and then would turn and sit down, but soon be up again. Could barely yet stand alone. The whole performance was spontaneous and almost uncanny. The mother was evidently accustomed to the procedure, nevertheless did not seem to be wholly at ease when she noticed that I watched the child, enough so to prevent me from closer questioning. I found, however, that the child was a boy, fourteen months old. He looked healthy and normal. There was no chance of obtaining a picture.

REPORT BY DR. HRDLIČKA.

June 4, 1928

DEAR SIR:

With reference to the enclosed clipping from the *Literary Digest* of March 10, 1928, I am writing to say that a grandson of mine,

Jerry McCall, seems to get about in the manner therein indicated. This mode of locomotion on Jerry's part I had noticed before seeing the reference to it in the *Digest*.

The boy is now 11 months and four days old and is just beginning to walk.

To begin with—at about the age of six months he began crawling in the usual way, that is, on hands and knees, and at first crawled backward. About 6 weeks ago he began crawling on his hands and feet, not on his knees, and has been crawling in this way since. He goes at a rapid gait, much faster than when crawling on his hands and knees.

Now I became interested in his mode of locomotion for the reason that it seemed to offer a possible solution to a problem which had puzzled me to solve for a good many years.

When a child I used to try running on my hands and feet, but found it exceedingly tiresome for the reason that my legs being much longer than my arms my spine was directed downward and forward and this made it difficult to raise my eyes from the ground.

But Jerry has found a solution of this difficulty. As he crawls or runs in this way, his spine remains about horizontal and he is easily able to keep his head erect.

This he accomplishes in three ways. First, by placing his feet far apart; second, by keeping his knees raised but little above the floor; third, by keeping the knees bent. The hands are entirely open as he proceeds. The arms come nearly perpendicular at each stroke, but the legs are at all times directed backward. This mode of locomotion is not only rapid, but apparently very easy. The length of his arms and legs appear to be entirely normal. The toes when walking in this way are turned out so that the foot including the heel is nearly horizontal, with a tendency to walk on the ball of the foot. I have thought this may have been the mode of locomotion used by the ground apes at a time when the fore limbs were relatively short. Instead then, as I had hitherto supposed the ape in running had thus gone.—[Drawings.]

I find my daughter has noticed the same peculiarity. She says she has known one other case of the kind. The head in our boy is usually raised so that the eyes easily look forward and upward.

Jerry's ancestors were German, English, Irish, Scotch, and Welsh.

Yours very truly,

E. C. Huffaker,

Memphis, Tenn.

April 28, 1928

Dear Sir:

Having seen your remarks on atavistic children we wish to report that we have two unquestionably atavistic youngsters, both boys. The older is three years old and no longer uses the gait, although it was as pure a gait of that kind as would ever be found. The younger is now thirteen months and uses the gait considerably but also walks erect.

Neither of the children ever crept on their stomachs or knees, the acquisition of the all-four gait, especially in the case of the older boy, having been very abrupt and complete, *i.e.*, he suddenly chose this means of locomotion and appeared almost possessed of full operation of it from the beginning. He simply pitched his hind end up in the air and began to travel. And the speed that he could make this way was certainly remarkable. Even after he got started walking erect, if he really wanted to make time anywhere he would revert to this four-footed gait. His knees were never on the ground and the appearance was much the same as the manner of a cub bear even to the rolling back on the hind to sit up.

One thing I remembered about the older boy's use of the gait was the fact that no matter how short the distance was that he wanted to go, *i.e.*, even if only one or two steps, he would always go into the full form for only the few steps. The perfection with which he used this gait seemed at times to retard the acquisition of walking although he did not walk late.

Both of the children are extremely active.

Although I cannot place it at this time, we have a snapshot of the older boy in this gait. If we can find it, will be glad to send you a print. Would be glad to hear from you.

Details:

Parents—American born—I being German on my mother's side and Scotch on my father's side; my wife is Swedish on both her father's and mother's sides.

Both children are boys.

Both healthy and robust, and both have weighed much above the average for their age, without being fat. The youngest now 15 months weighs 30 pounds.

We have only these two children and both have used this gait; it has not been observed in relatives' children.

Both used this gait at from about 11 months to 16 months, beginning to use it at about the time they got to stand unsupported and continuing to use it, but more and more interspersed with attempts at walking, until by 16 months or so it appeared only in occasional bursts as full ability to walk had been acquired.

The photo is of the older boy (now 3¼) when he was 14 months and shows him in full tilt. The gait is conspicuously animal-like. A hand and the diagonally opposite foot being off the ground at about the same time—though I won't say exactly the same time because there is a slight difference in timing, so that only one member is actually being put down at a time. (In a horse I think it is what is called a "single-foot" gait.)

The hands seem to be fully open at all times. I would not say partly closed at all in the case of the younger boy, who sometimes seems to stretch the fingers out and spank the hands down hard. The head is held for the most part rather down without much regard for the view ahead. In fact I have frequently been apprehensive of their running hard into some sharp corner or object as after they have chosen their direction they seemed to take only an occasional glance ahead or would even stop, look, and start again. The glance never seemed strained ahead.

As to any other peculiarities I do not think there is anything except that they are bright and active and considered perhaps above the average by local M.D.'s.

I don't know much about the anthropological side of it, but there is one thing that it isn't, and that is imitation. I know imitation because I see it now in the older boy and most of the time he does it, it's imitation now but it wasn't when he was 11 months.

It simply means that they resort to it as being the most convenient to get around in.

> Yours truly,
> J. R. HUNNEMAN,
> Woburn, Mass.

First letter:

June 27, 1928

DR. HRDLIČKA:

My baby started at about seven months to crawl by drawing his left leg under him, then pushing himself along with his right leg. At nine months he adopted the hands and foot movement and now recently I have noticed he uses the "all fours" method exclusively. He is now 12½ months old, 29¾ inches tall, weighs 26 pounds and is just beginning to walk alone. He has been walking with the aid of chairs, etc., for the past four months.

Yours sincerely,
Mrs. J. L. Hurley,
San Francisco, Calif.

Second letter:

November 29, 1929

Referring to your letter of May 11 in connection with information on my boy, who ran on all fours, he was the first in the family.

He now has a sister who was born May 7, of this year.

If there is any information regarding the new baby that you desire, I will be very glad to answer any questions you care to ask.

Yours sincerely,
Mrs. J. L. Hurley.

Dear Doctor:

Herewith a brief report on a youngster running on all fours:
White, American.
Male.
Health, good.
Second child.
No other such cases in family.
Began at 8 months.
Hands fully open.
Left handed. (Plate X, p. 189.)

Yours very truly,
Dr. R. R. Ivey,
Asheville, N. C.

September 20, 1928

Dear Dr. Hrdlička:

My baby, Helen Colleen, has never attempted to crawl but started out at the first going on her hands and feet. She is now ten months and one week old. She seemed to be slow at everything first. She never sat alone until she was seven months old and at eight months she was going fine on her hands and feet and pulling herself up on her feet.

At nine months she cut one of her lower front teeth and two weeks later one upper front tooth and one next to it. Now the two other upper ones and the other lower front are coming through. She has got so she lets go of things and stands alone for a few seconds. Today she got up from the middle of the floor twice and stood for a few seconds before she fell. Everyone says she will be walking soon, but why was she so slow at first? She has always been real plump but small.

My boy was just opposite from her, as he was sitting alone at four months and had cut a tooth. He walked across the room three times at twelve months but fell, and he never tried to walk again until he was twenty-one months old.

> From a friend,
> MRS. WILLIAM JACOB,
> Reading, Kan.

May 5, 1928

DEAR SIR:

Reading in the *Pathfinder* of your interest in Children who run on All Fours, in place of creeping, called our attention to our own Baby Boy who formed that habit when he was ten months old in place of creeping. When he got going good it made his mother run to keep up with him, in fact he could beat a child who was running on its feet. He is now nineteen months old and has learned to walk and run on his feet alone; but he still sometimes gets on all fours. We are white, both my wife's and my own parents were born in Germany, while I was born in America and my wife in Germany. Am enclosing a snapshot of him on all fours when he was eleven months old.

> Yours very truly,
> J. H. JANSEN,
> National City, Calif.

DEAR SIR:

I have read your article in the *St. Paul Pioneer Press* and thought I would write. My baby walks like a bear on feet and hands.

He weighed 5½ lbs. when born, and is 14 months old and weighs 20½ lbs. now. Is a healthy strong baby. He is awful slow to cut teeth; has three now. Enclosed is a picture.

MRS. ROY JARMIN,
Stanley, N. D.

June 28, 1928

DR. HRDLIČKA:

I noticed your request for a report on any cases of children walking on all fours.

Our baby boy was very ill for the first six months of his life due to stomach disorder:—but when he outgrew his ailment he developed into a very healthy and sturdy youngster.

At ten months he would lie flat on his stomach and pull himself along by use of his elbows. He started walking on all fours at about a year. We did not allow him on his feet as early as he wanted to, due to bowed legs. He stood alone at fourteen months and did not walk alone until fifteen months. He is now sixteen months of age, walks considerable but still runs part of the time on his hands and knees and part time on all fours; however before he learned to walk he went on all fours almost entirely.

I did not realize the method of locomotion was very unusual but merely jokingly considered it the recapitulation of the race.

Yours very truly,
MRS. C. H. JEFFERSON,
Cedar Falls, Ia.

April 17, 1928

DEAR SIR:

In reading *The Pathfinder* of April 14, I noticed an article headed, The All-fours Habit, in which physicians and others were invited to send you their observations of such cases.

I am a Registered Nurse and am going to try to tell you of my second child, a girl. When she was old enough to begin creeping, she first learned to balance herself on her hands and feet then to take a few wobbling steps at a time and now can go on all fours much faster than the average child can running on their two feet. She is seventeen and one half months old and won't attempt to walk upright unless some one leads her.

She goes with her hands open and fingers spread quite widely apart; she holds her head up with her chin thrust well forward.

My husband and I had talked a great deal about her way of moving, but did not think much of it until we read your article, as other people said she was not the first child they had seen going that way.

We are white Americans.

Respectfully yours,
MRS. E. B. JONES,
Purvis, Miss.

July 18, 1928

DR. HRDLIČKA:

We have a little daughter, almost eleven months old, who uses the method you described. She was born August 24, 1927. She began creeping backward on March 17, 1928. This method was used until May 14, when she crept forward on her hands and knees. Two weeks later she started on all fours. She has attained a good rate of speed in this fashion.

When the stairs were discovered, the same method was used to ascend, but she is not able to get down again.

Yours truly,
MRS. H. K. JONES,
Mason City, Ia.

March 6, 1928

DEAR DOCTOR:

In *re* your letter in J. A. M. A., concerning children walking on all fours, I give you the following data concerning my daughter, Karen Beth, now aged two years.

Caucasian Race.

Father: American, Welsh—Pennsylvania Dutch.

Mother: American, Norwegian extraction.

Female child.

Excellent health; more chubby and better health than brother. Second child.

No relatives had any similar walking in family.

Started on all fours at about $6\frac{1}{2}$ months; continued until about 11, when drew self up on chairs, etc.

Posture when running on all fours:—Legs only slightly flexed, left more than right; face down, but looking up when approaching objects or persons. Very fast. At first was at times so fast with legs would fall forward on face. Hands, palms downwards.

I had no idea this condition was fairly rare and am sorry snapshots were not taken. Just considered it a very amusing type of creeping and it gave ourselves and friends quite a laugh.

Sincerely,
KENNETH P. JONES, M. D.,
Olive View, Calif.

First letter:

April 20, 1928

DEAR DOCTOR:

Our little girl ran on all fours.

Born November 11, 1926. Weight, 7 lbs. 14 oz.

Birth was easy and quick. Second child.

Mother twenty-six years old, father thirty-two. Both parents artists, of moderately well-to-do educated families, able to trace lineage for some centuries. Mother of Irish descent (second generation in United States); father of Polish birth.

At six weeks of age the baby was able to brace her feet against the lap of the person holding her, and to force herself erect. This athletic predisposition was not encouraged.

Dentition somewhat tardy and irregular. Lower central incisors at ten months. At eighteen months, upper central and lateral incisors and two molars, lower central incisors—eight in all.

Measurements at eighteen months: Length, 31 inches; weight, 30 lbs.; chest, normal, 20½ inches; forearm, 5 inches; upper arm, 6 inches; hip-joint to knee, 9 inches; knee to sole, 8 inches; circumference of head, 19 inches.

At three or four months the baby showed a disposition to lie prone, and when placed on her back or side would struggle to roll over on her abdomen. She was able to pull herself into a sitting position at six months and shortly afterward began to creep.

From the outset her "creeping" consisted of running on all fours, with the palm flat on the ground and her feet raised on the toes. She was able to travel with great rapidity—at ten months as fast as a man's brisk walk.

Coincidentally with her creeping the baby began to climb. This trait is perforce limited to furniture, all the trees on the place being straight-bolled elm and ash, and to steps and stairs.

She is more sure-footed in narrow footholds than either of her parents, and possesses an acrobatic sense of balance and no fear of height. She will with great rapidity climb to the arm of a chair and balance herself free-handed, run along a narrow stone coping on the brink of a deep brook traversing the place. Perhaps it is needless to add that these stunts are escapades, completed before she can be halted.

The baby has been walking since the age of fourteen months. She was reluctant to give up her four-footed mode of travel and had to be guided into walking long after she gave every indication

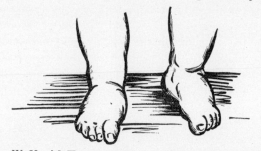

Fig. 11.—W. K. girl. Toes cramped, in walking on outer edge of foot.

of being able to navigate on two feet. Until recently she always reverted to the four-footed position when speed was desired.

In walking on all fours, she treads upon the outer rim of the foot and grips the ground with her toes. This gives her a decided pigeon-toed and bow-legged appearance, although in rest her legs are normally straight.

She still uses hands or feet, interchangeably, for picking up and holding objects. She will hold her bottle between her clenched toes in order to play with toys while drinking, or hold the bottle in her hands and pick up toys with her feet. She can pick up a safety pin with the toes of one foot, or a marble.

She claps the soles of her feet together to make a loud noise such as is produced by hand-clapping.

The child is of rugged, sturdy build. Her breadth of shoulder is one-third her height. Her fingers are quite long (2 inches, 2d finger) and she seems to possess unusual lifting power.

For example, she swings with ease a ten-pound African club with a terra-cotta head from her father's collection. She has a passion for hoarding large stones and rocks, carefully making a cache of them. She can hurl a piece of trap-rock as big as a man's fist for four or five feet with fair accuracy.

In appetite she prefers raw fruits and vegetables to the cooked sorts. She will spurn sweet puddings or rusk and milk for a handful of shelled peas or bit of banana.

In disposition she is boisterous and tempestuous. As an infant in arms she would curve her fingers and scratch if her wishes were not immediately understood and obeyed, and she strikes with her open hand when crossed. Neither trait is imitative. The child was never struck and certainly was never scratched. Her favorite play is rough-and-tumble with her older sister or with the dogs. She is fearless of animals, and will charge into her especial pet, a large Dobermann Pinscher, with regular war-whoops.

Although happier with her clothes off than in every-day dress, she shows inordinate pride in dressing up, and is proud of a new, frilly dress. When she first began to move about independently she would tuck bright-colored cloths, scraps, or rags under her chin and keep them there by pressure.

The baby began to talk at 6½ months, her first distinguishable words being "Susie" (the cat) and "kirry," an approximation of kitty. She now constructs simple sentences of a noun, without the article, and simple verb; in affectionate moments she calls her father "little daddy," a phrase of her own invention. "Daddy" is six feet tall and has never been termed "little" by anyone before. She has, however, no name for herself at all.

At nine months she taught herself to turn the pages of books and magazines, and was able to distinguish half-tone pictures of well-known objects. She could pick a horse, a dog or a man from a complex group in an illustration. She handles a pencil naturally, but cannot make recognizable drawings.

Her sister, born in 1920 and developing normally, was able to draw recognizable objects at two years.

The baby is very fond of music, and dances to records which have strongly accented rhythm. She will listen quietly to concert music, but dances to Chinese and Indian records and jazz.

The dance-steps are three in number. One movement is to remain on one spot, lifting the feet alternately in time to the music and planting them firmly. This for slow time.

FIG. 12.—W. K. baby, "crawling" position.

FIG. 13.—W. K. baby, nursing.

FIG. 14.—W. K. baby, sleeping "on all fours."

For quicker tempo she also remains standing, but sways her body at the waist with a pronounced out-thrust of the buttocks. Her neck is rigid, as are her legs from the knees down. I wonder if this does not contradict the sexual interpretation often placed on similar movements in African ritualistic dancing?

The third "step" consists of a stately pacing with arms outstretched parallel to the shoulders, alternated with rapid gyrations with the arms still in position.

She has never seen dancing in the home except the spontaneous leapings of her older sister, whose musical interpretation is more akin to the ballet.

The baby has never been taught "tricks" or "stunts," and the only variation from the usual in her rearing has been nude exposure to direct sunlight almost daily.

The child, even in warm weather, insists upon covering. The covering is always bunched over her *head*—even if it is a large blanket or, on the other hand, a pocket handkerchief. In view of the fact that she is fearless of the dark this trait may be only an idiosyncrasy.

If not too late for your purposes I shall try to get photographs of her poses when the weather is warm enough to permit her running about naked out of doors.

Faithfully yours,
W. K.,
Millburn, N. J.

March 20, 1930

Additional:

DEAR DR. HRDLIČKA:

Your letter of March 14th reached me here by devious routes. I am lingering in Laredo, Texas, after exploring Mexico, and now I am going to Santa Fé, a town I love for many things—its proximity to the cave dwellings at Frijoles Canyon among the foremost.

About our little monkey: She is now nearly three and a half years old, stands three feet two inches tall and weighs about thirty-eight pounds. She has never been ill.

No additional peculiarity has manifested itself. She still sleeps often on her elbows and knees, head on hands. She has no fear of high places, and has frequently electrified us by teetering on the edge of a chasm with no more concern than if she was on a street curb. She climbs like a squirrel. Ladders, trees, and fences are her favorite playgrounds. She delights in swinging from her hands; she will pull herself up to a straight bough or a horizontal bar and hang suspended by her hands, swinging and singing, at every opportunity.

She has a very good sense of rhythm, but her older sister has always possessed that, too. We have a collection of Indian music for the phonograph to which the youngster dances tirelessly—that, I remember, she did when just able to balance herself, as I wrote to you. The time shifts very often in some of the music, and she catches the new rhythm in a couple of beats.

She has marked strength in her hands, great tenacity of grip and a wide finger spread. Probably this is a development on account of her activities.

Mentally she is developing faster than her sister did at a comparable age. I think though, that association with older children—her sister and her school companions—accounts for this. The older girl had no such contacts at all. She draws very well.

A marked characteristic is her fearlessness of animals, except—and this we cannot explain—for cows and the like. The first time she saw an elephant she showed the same curiosity and delight as at her first teddy bear. Snakes, lizards, toads, dogs, cats, worms—and, until a recent unfortunate experience with giant roaches and centipedes in a primitive Mexican shelter—insects are to her animated playthings to be taken into the bosom of the family, a trait which, with reasonable precautions, we try to keep alive and cultivated.

At this moment she is wrestling with a goat outside my window. Not long ago she was kicking a donkey who had tried to kick her, until we separated the combatants.

Now, as to pictures, I am sorry that, what with combinations of bad weather, professional interruptions and probably an admixture of carelessness, I obtained only one rather poor snapshot of the baby swinging by her hands from a back-yard trapeze, and a photograph of her in the typical sleeping posture. I will send you the negative and a print of the latter as soon as I can get them. If there are any pictures you desire at this time to illustrate any phase of your treatise, I'll limber up the camera and have her perform. (See Fig. 3*b*, p. 41; also Figs. 12 to 14.)

I forgot to mention her distastes for clothing. I don't know if it is an acquired characteristic, due to her sun baths, or if she is an embryonic exhibitionist, but the young lady is apt to appear anywhere, at any time, with no clothing on. But on the other hand she has a passion for self adornment—a fluffy dress, a string of gaudy wooden beads, or the contents of a bottle of mercurochrome all rank alike.

Very truly yours,
W. K.,
Millburn, N. J.

April 23, 1928

Dear Sir:

Reading the enclosed newspaper clipping interested me. I wonder if you ever knew of a small child moving about as did my son. It was neither creeping or crawling but hitching in a way entirely his own so far as I have ever been able to find out.

He sat on the floor, crossed his legs, drew himself up to his heels, straightened out his legs, recrossed his legs—putting leg which had been under, on top. Pulled his body up to heels again. And repeated, recrossing and changing after every hitch. He did not walk until nearly twenty months of age. By that time he could change the crossing and hitch along as fast as any one could walk.

He is now nearly twenty years old, has a pair of good straight legs, loves to go on hikes but has never climbed. Is called lazy in that he does not easily take to carrying out other people's ideas, is of an artistic temperament. Animals or vegetation do not interest him. Instead, machinery, stage music, literature. He has a wonderful memory, but his writing is almost unreadable, after years and years of penmanship in school.

A young lady—same age—was a "crawler" on all fours. Outside of school appears very bright, but very lazy. Could not learn in school. Studies art and is a success, freehand drawing, pottery, etc. Is excellent in study of form, where a ruler is not required. She too, is considered lazy.

But both are very industrious in carrying out their own plans. Ancestry may figure. Each child came from a "lazy" family on one side and industrious family on the other. They are cousins by the industrious family. There are other children in both families, all of whom show the artistic traits but none are lazy. All of them were creepers: hands and knees.

Mrs. G. L. Kearns,
East Longmeadow, Mass.

July 12, 1929

Dear Doctor:

When our baby was about seven months old she started walking on all fours, with her feet flat on floor. She has a habit of climbing through chair rounds, steps, in fact anything she can. She has even gone as far as when, finding bread crumbs on the floor, instead of picking them up with her hands she gets down and eats them up like a little dog. I have noticed her doing this several times. She is large for her age and has the best of health. She is now one year old.

Our other baby of two years has the best health and is large for her age. When she was nine months old she could climb stairs but she was put in a kiddie car and never learned to creep so I do not know whether she would have had the same habit or not.

I am glad to know that our little baby is of such interest.

Details:

White; father, German; mother, German-French.

Female.

Excellent health, large for her age, great strength.

Second child.

Other cases in family?—Yes; father's uncle walked same way and has unusual strength.

Began on all fours about the age of seven months, continued until 12½ months, when she started walking. If in a hurry she would return to the former method even after walking.

Her feet were flat on floor; right foot moved forward with right hand.

Hands were fully open, head held down. Sometimes would run headlong into anything that was in her path. Always trying to climb up on chairs and through underneath chairs.

Also in habit of carrying objects in her mouth. If anything was dropped on the floor such as crumbs and she saw them, she ate them up with mouth instead of first picking them up with hands.

PLATE XI.—*a.* Keller, boy. *b.* Kidder, boy. *c.* Kidder, boy. *d.* Königsberg, boy. *e.* Gardner, girl, eleven months. *f.* Glenn, girl, fourteen and one-half months.

One time I spilled some water on floor and she lay down and drank it up from floor.

Our other child has unusual health and strength; never noticed her walking on all fours, but had the habit of climbing.

Yours very truly,
MRS. LEO KELLER,
Flat Rock, O.

First letter:

June 28, 1928

DR. HRDLIČKA:

I am reporting on the progress of my baby boy. My baby creeped on his hands and toes at five months and walked on all fours at five and one-half months and could pull himself erect on the furniture at the same age. Walked well at nine months. He is now eleven months and can run, climb up and down stairs. He does all of his crawling on all fours.

Yours sincerely,
MRS. I. W. KENNEY,
South Tacoma, Wash.

Second letter:

March 19, 1930

DEAR SIR:

Replying to your letter of March 14, relative to my boy, advise that he has developed into a very robust youngster; two snapshots of him are enclosed. He is the second child of a family of two, the older one being a girl. (See Fig. 4, p. 78.)

In case he is sitting on the floor or ground and desires to secure some object within a few feet he will most always walk on his hands and feet instead of crawling or walking upright and travels very rapidly and apparently comfortably in that position.

He is now twenty-seven months old, very alert mentally, has a remarkable memory and muscular control of his body, is fond of climbing and can climb any object that affords hand and foot holds. When he was nineteen months old I found him one day on the roof of a two story unfinished building. To get there he had to climb a ladder leaning against the eaves.

He possesses a faculty of self protection that is remarkable, since the age of six or seven months he could prevent a fall if there was anything within his reach that afforded a hand hold after he lost his balance. Since reaching this age he has been able to sustain his weight with his hands for long periods, and now in case he falls and is unable to grasp any object he will land feet first. He can carry one-half of his weight without any undue effort. Not sensitive to cuts, burns or bruises, very seldom complaining of the average childish injuries.

When he goes to bed he requires some object to put his arms around but after going to sleep he releases the object and assumes an ordinary sleeping posture.

His hearing is unusually good and any strange noise that he hears arouses his curiosity and he inquires what it is, not being always satisfied with the explanation of its origin.

Yours very truly,
Mrs. I. W. Kenney.

November 4, 1929

Report of a "bear-walker," by mother.

Her ancestry includes English, Scotch, Irish, Welsh, and American Indian (Cherokee on her mother's side, $\frac{1}{32}$, and a less degree of another tribe on her father's).

Born in Michigan, U. S. A.

Female, 3 years old, August 3, 1928; first child in family; superior in health, robustness, and mentality.

From nine months until she was twelve months old she traveled by walking on her hands and feet, never using any other method until she walked upright. To rest she squatted instead of sitting on the floor. She continues to squat when playing, and keeps that position for long periods while playing in the sand. (See Fig. 5, p. 86.)

Mrs. John C. Ketcham,
Hastings, Mich.

July 10, 1928

Dear Sir:

I was very interested in the recent account in the *New York Sunday Times* of your study of "quadruped progressors." The enclosed pictures are of my fourteen months' old son. He is the third child. Neither of the others thus progressed, nor did any other member of either my or my husband's family, as far as I know. I do not remember exactly how long he has walked on all fours, but think he has since he was about ten months old. And I remember he stood in the same position before he moved forward at all. He does not go on all fours exclusively but sometimes crawls in the accepted fashion for babies.

The only item in the description of "quadruped progressors" which my son does not follow is "the head slightly raised" one. As you will note in some of the pictures, he holds his head rather erect. (Plate XI, p. 245.)

Yours truly,
E. T. KIDDER,
South Strafford, Vt.

First letter:

January 29, 1928

It was with much interest that I read your letter in *The Journal of the A. M. A.* of January 21st. It was called to my attention by my husband, who is a physician.

We have six children, the oldest born in 1904, the youngest in 1917, all of whom ran about on all fours as you describe, never crawling on their hands and knees nor sliding along in a sitting position.

Four of the children are boys and two are girls. They were all normal, healthy babies; the oldest, a boy, and the youngest, a girl, were small, weighing 7½ and 7 pounds at birth; the others weighed from 10½ to 11½ pounds.

As far as I can remember they began running around on hands and feet at seven or eight months and were very active and rapid in their movements. They began to walk when about 16 months to 11 months of age. They ran with their hands flat on the floor and their heads slightly raised.

As to race and nationality both my husband and I are Americans of straight English or Scotch-Irish descent.

I am sorry not to have any pictures of the children taken while running about, and as all my careful records of the children's progress as babies were lost I am not able to be more exact in my information.

I do not know of any other children in the family connection who have crawled in this manner, but will let you know if I hear of any further instances.

Very truly yours,
Mrs. R. M. K.-S.
Sewanee, Tenn.

Second letter:

Feb. 3, 1928

I am so glad my six "monkeys" are of interest to you, for I always insisted that it was interesting for a whole family to run about like that, particularly as most of them were far enough apart in age not to have acquired the habit through imitation of their elders.

I am sure that the children all ran about on all fours even after they could walk. I feel sure that the oldest child could have walked much sooner than he did (at 16 months) but it was possible for him to get about with such ease and rapidity on all fours that he evidently did not see the necessity of adopting any other method of locomotion. He was born in the Philippine Islands, all the others here in Sewanee.

The girls, I believe, with the exception of the oldest boy, were slightly more agile than the others. The youngest child, a girl, was (and she is!) extremely active. She climbed steps, ladders, bars on doors, chairs, anything in fact, before she made any effort to walk. She has gone up small trees and posts by literally walking up them ever since she was a small child.

One of my boys (the 21-year-old one) is studying medicine at the University of Pennsylvania in Philadelphia, so if you want to see a six-foot-three "monkey" he is there for inspection!

I have heard lately of a child who crawled first, then ran on all fours before he walked.

M. K.-S.

Third letter:

February 15, 1928

My husband said, on reading your last note, tell him "the child climbs a tree as the Philippinos go up cocoanut trees"; but thinking a picture better than all descriptions I am enclosing two I took

. 249 .

of her as she climbed a tree in the yard, and one as she runs around now, which is as she did as a baby. Of course she doesn't run about now on all fours except intentionally.

Someone said you must be amused at having such anthropological information coming from Tennessee.

M. K.-S.

July 9, 1928

DEAR DR. HRDLIČKA:

A few months ago I saw in the *Literary Digest* an inquiry that was broadcast by you, I think, asking for information as to the behavior of children who have shown tendencies to start walking in some peculiar manner. At that time the matter did not impress me very much because I had no light to throw on the subject. However later on when our youngest baby, who is now fourteen months old, started attempting to walk, I remembered what I had read and am writing to you about this matter.

Our youngest baby is now fourteen months old and he has been walking upright during the last thirty-five days, to be exact. Previous to that time, for a couple of months, he walked like a dog on his hands and feet. He started when he was about ten months old and became quite proficient, indeed, in this mode of locomotion. He never crept on his knees. He always used his feet and often his clenched fists. He would use his hands either clenched, as I said before, or else spread half open like a monkey. His feet were always spread apart about twelve inches, with the soles firmly planted on the ground. In other words, he would not walk on his toes; he walked on his feet. He could run quite rapidly all around the house, and climb stairs.

When he was thirteen months and one day old he suddenly started walking, and after two or three attempts to walk upright, he learned to walk quite well. However, he still holds his legs spread apart in the same position as when he was running on all fours. He looks rather peculiar now when walking with his legs spread apart, his chest thrown out and his hands raised level with his head, so that the way he walks now looks just like a bear whereas before he walked like a dog.

The child is perfectly healthy. We have never had any need for a doctor. He eats, sleeps and plays wholeheartedly, and as far as we can judge there is nothing wrong with him.

Details:

Report by William Knight, father.

Child, white; American; male; second born; health, first class.

Started walking on all fours when he was ten months old. Never used his knees for this—could move around this way very rapidly and could mount chairs. At thirteen months started walking normally and has now given up the former mode of locomotion.

No other cases of walking on fours in families as far as known. But our first boy, who is now four years old, used to sleep in a kneeling down position, with his face resting on the pillow and he used to move about the bed by clapping his belly with both hands, at the same time that he supported his bended body on his head and feet and when he clapped his belly he would jump in the direction of his head, thus moving about on the bed.

> Yours very truly,
> WILLIAM KNIGHT,
> New York, N. Y.

June 18, 1928

DEAR DOCTOR:

Here is a picture of our son at age of 12 months showing his method of navigating. He always crawled on all fours, not on his knees, until he walked erect at 13 months. (Plate XI, p. 245.)

Hoping this will be of value to you in your research work, I am

> Sincerely yours,
> DR. C. W. KÖNIGSBERG,
> Santa Cruz, Calif.[1]

October 6, 1928

DEAR DOCTOR:

Concerning children running on all fours, our little granddaughter had this method of moving before she was nine months and at the age of nine months could walk. Has always been unusually strong, active and fearless. Her mother had the same method of getting about and one day she stood up in the middle of the floor, then took a step or two. She gradually became more confident

---

[1] Could not locate for further information.

and was walking at nine and one-half months. I know of no other cases.

Here are the details to the best of my ability in regard to both my daughter and granddaughter:

Daughter.

White; American born; mother, Irish-Scotch and English Yankee descent; father, English descendant from Ancient Briton.

Female.

Health, fine—Weight at birth 10½.

Second child.

Not to my knowledge (other cases of running on all fours).

Crept on all fours at 6 mo. 3 wks., walked fine at 10 mos.

No weakness; long before she walked she would stand up in the middle of the floor, finally took a couple of steps, and after that each time more until walking good.

Hand, fully opened, head straight out.

Nothing else peculiar.

Granddaughter.

White; American born; mother, English descent, Am. born; father, Welsh, Am. born.

Female.

Health, fine; unusually active and strong; weight 7¾ lb. at birth.

First child.

Mother "crept" on all fours (see above).

Ran on four at 7 mo., at 9 mo. walked upright all over. Photos enclosed.

Very fearless. Climbed to the top of a twenty-foot slide ladder when 1½ yrs. old. Is very quick and active. (Plate X, p. 189.)

> Yours very truly,
> Mrs. E. H. Kough,
> Austin, Minn.

May 20, 1929

Report of two boys:

Self—white, American; son—same.

Both male.

Health exceptionally good, both.

Self—10th of father, first of mother; son—first.

No other cases known of in family.

Time when started on all fours: Self—not known; son—began at seven months, continued to eleven or twelve months.

Method: Self—not known; son—progressed on hands and feet, knees nearly straight, palms on floor, hands fully open, head extended so that face was to the front.

No other peculiarities in either case.

Dr. F. W. Kuhlmann,
Hawthorne, Calif.

First letter:

June 25, 1928

Dear Sir:

I read your article "If your Baby walks like a Bear," with a great deal of interest. It recalled memories of my own little boy. He is now 4½ years of age. But at the age of twelve months we found him walking on all "fours." Actually he wears more holes into the knees of his stockings now than he did then. At the time he moved about on "all fours" we thought nothing of it. We thought there was nothing significant. Your article gives me the first information that there is something worth while in it. I am only too glad to give science any information possible.

I have no picture to send you, for at the time we did not think it uncommon for a child to move about that way. My boy is in robust health. Has been ill only with usual children's ills. As to his intellect, I believe he has a keen memory. I will give you one example. We travel quite a bit by automobile. In my home town he usually knows where we are going by turning in on various streets.

About a year ago we passed through a little town about 15 miles from home, and it required about one hour to get through because we met a convention parade which blocked traffic. We thought no more of the matter, but about six weeks later we happened to travel the same road again. Believe it or not, when coming to this town, the little fellow cried out, "Here's where we saw the big parade." I thought it very good for a boy 3½ years old (at the time) to recognize the place again so far from home and having only been through the town in an automobile. When I am giving a violin lesson he sits and listens, often for the entire lesson.

Yours very truly,
A. C. Kunze

Second letter:

July 30, 1928

DEAR SIR:

I have your letter of June 28 1928, which I had laid on my desk and neglected answering, before me now. I have been observing my boy very carefully in order to write to you and give details for the benefit of science.

I will endeavor to answer your list of questions as best I can.

He is white. Parents both born in Pennsylvania. On father's side, his grandparents were both born in Pennsylvania of German parentage; on his mothers side, the grandfather was born in Pennsylvania of German parents, and the grandmother immigrated from Germany.

His health is about the best that could be expected. He will be five years of age on February 25. I judge he weighs about 40 pounds. Quite a bit of strength in his muscles for his age. Good healthy color of his body at all times. Has had no illness thus far except natural child diseases. Very agile. Usually each day he does his exercises, such as "bend the crab," touching toes with hands while knees are straight, rolling or rocking on his abdomen, and others of such nature. He is also very quick and keen in his actions.

He is the first and only child thus far.

My mother gave birth to three boys, and we all are living, but she says she can not recall of us walking on all fours, nor has she heard of any of our relatives doing the same.

I believe he began to run on all fours at 8 months and continued until 14 months, when he walked erect. We did notice how strong he was in his limbs. Before he started walking he would be on all fours and then would stand erect without assistance or using a chair or such to help him stand.

I am sorry I have no photograph to send. At the time of his performance we took very little notice of his actions. Yet we had many laughs. When he walked on all fours he appeared as a young bear scampering over the floor. His knees were practically stiff when thus walking.

His hands were flat on floor and head usually erect. That is as far as we can recall. We had forgotten all about his childish actions until I read your article in a Pittsburgh paper. Then I recalled as much as I could and wrote to you.

As regards any other peculiarity of behavior, we note he is very quick and keen in mind action.

He throws a ball with ease and quite a distance and with accuracy in direction. When anyone plays with him they need barely move from their position in order to get the ball. It usually goes where he aims it.

We also compare our boy with three or four other boys of approximately the same age and note quite a difference. He seems to be the leader. What Albert does or says seems to satisfy the others.

He also has a small pool table and it is surprising to see him shoot with such accuracy, just like a person of older age.

When we go in the auto and turn in certain streets he can 9 times in 10 tell us where it will take us; such as a park, swimming pool, someone's home, etc.

About 2 months ago the *Pittsburgh Post-Gazette* had a picture, in their pictorial section, of a church. This church happens to be about one square from my brother's home in Pittsburgh. He lives over 20 miles from us. Now my boy has not seen this church more than 5 times at day time and that was only in passing in the machine. This church happens to be on the corner where we turn into the side street, where my brother lives, from the main highway. We do not attend this church nor have we ever been therein. As I stated he has only seen this church from the window of the auto as we passed by and that being only a half dozen times in daytime. My boy always likes to look at the pictures, so on this Sunday that the paper contained the picture he observed it, and immediately called his mother and told her that this is the church down at Aunt Thelma's place. My wife herself did not recognize the picture, and it was only after reading the words underneath that she could verify the boy's statement. Now the boy is unable to read a word so it is only by his observance and memory that he recognized it.

What could I do to help him along in a general development of his mind? I am desirous of having him become a violinist. Your comments will be greatly appreciated.

Yours truly,
ALBERT C. KUNZE,
McKeesport, Pa.

First letter:

March 4, 1928

DEAR DR. HRDLIČKA:

Have read with interest your article on quadrupedal babies.

My nephew, Richard J. Laurence, was such. He was born and raised in New York City. He is now four years of age.

At birth Richard was weak and sickly. At the age of one month his mother dropped her doctor's advice and brought him up according to her own ideas. He had a cold shower every day, followed by a sun-bath. He was out all day, every day, in all kinds of weather, rain or snow. He became a very healthy baby. Between the ages of nine and ten months he began to walk in the four-legged fashion. Never crept or crawled. Enclosed photos show his hands flat on the ground, his head held up. He ran so fast we caught only these three snaps of him in that position.

When he started to walk upright, he was a bit bow-legged, but soon outgrew that. At that time, and since, when he played on the floor, he would squat, sit on his heels, Indian fashion, and move around without rising to his feet.

His father and mother are both young, American, with a little English and French blood. Their ancestors were all physically and mentally normal.

Richard is an "only" child, fine, healthy, unusually bright. He is never ill.

I have never heard of another child walking in this manner.

Sincerely,

MURIEL R. LANGLEY.

Second letter:

DEAR DR. HRDLIČKA:

Was pleased to hear that my information was of help to you.

Aside from Richard's peculiar method of locomotion, he was in no wise different from other children. And at present, walking erect, he is simply a normal child, exceptional only in perfect health and unusual intelligence. The other members of the family have no striking peculiarities whatever.

Today Richard was "making believe" he was a cat, and was running about on all fours, but not as naturally and easily as when he was a baby. His legs seemed too long and his body turned from side to side. He looked very awkward, although he ran about quite fast. However, it soon tired him.

If ever Richard develops an unusual characteristic that might be of interest to you, I will let you know of it.

I hope some day to read more of your very interesting work.

Most sincerely,
MURIEL R. LANGLEY,
St. Albans, L. I., N. Y.

DEAR SIR:

Another case of child who runs on all fours. My own son had this characteristic. Second child, oldest son, four years next August. This child started this at creeping age of about 7th to 8th month. Kept it up until 11 months when he commenced to walk normally. Now 13 months old—entirely normal. Father, Swedish—mother, Scotch-Irish. Father's sister had a daughter, one of three, who had same trait; now past twenty years old and normal. Regret not having pictures. Boy ran with hands open and head in same position as tho creeping naturally. Rapid gait.

DR. E. V. LARSON,
Anoka, Minn.

July 2, 1928

DEAR SIR:

I have read with much interest your observations of children walking on all fours and am able to add to your collection of cases, as my grandson is one of that number. He is the first child. When about nine months old he began creeping by lying flat on the floor, crossing his hands under his chin, moving his elbows and dragging himself along. He soon gave that up and began to walk on all fours and when he was a year old had acquired a great deal of speed. We called him our little bear which greatly pleased him. He moved easily and seemed very happy running about that way.

I thought it very peculiar, never having seen or heard of a child getting about like that, and am especially interested in your research into the matter.

Even now when he is six years old, a bright healthy active child, he will at times run around that odd way.

His parents are both college graduates and his father, Dr. L. P. Wehrle, is an instructor in Entomology at Cornell U.

There is a baby girl of six months in the family now and we are wondering what her method of creeping will be.

Very truly yours,
MRS. MARY E. LASON,
Washington, D. C.

First letter:

June 23, 1928

MY DEAR DR. HRDLIČKA:

It was with great interest that we read in this weeks *Literary Digest* your contribution regarding the infant who walks on all fours.

Our ten months old daughter has afforded us unbounded amusement from this peculiar type of locomotion, but little did we realize it was an uncommon method. She goes like a streak, pad, pad, all over the house and climbs like a young squirrel.

If I can furnish you with any data from personal observations up to date or make directed ones from now on I shall be very glad to do so.

At the risk of being entirely irrelevant I want to state that the one and only toy that has so far brought real joy to this youngster is a most life like stuffed monkey. She loves it, talks to it and plays with it in a most amazing fashion.

Very truly yours,
MRS. J. M. LEAR.

Second letter:

July 26, 1928

MY DEAR DR. HRDLIČKA:

In accordance with your request of June 25 I am sending you pictures of our baby walking on all fours. Though the pictures were snapped under forced and unnatural conditions the position is fairly normal. I should say that usually the legs are slightly straighter and hips elevated more. The position of head and hands is the same. The picture was made at the age of eleven months. (Plate XV, p. 333.)

The following will be an attempt to answer your questions in order:

Child, white—American.

Girl, first and only child.

Excellent health and considered unusually strong and active.

If the phenomenon has existed among relatives I do not know of it.

Began at age of nine months. Is now a year old and uses it constantly with some attempt to walk.

The performance varies in speed. Out of doors on grass or gravel walk she picks her way cautiously. Indoors she runs like a streak.

She often uses her feet to reach for things and has climbed ever since I can remember, it seems. Two months ago she climbed entirely unaided up the back of the car seat in order to get a small can. And she can climb it and throw her leg over the top and get into a sitting position where she often rides—Ford Coupe—she will grasp a finger of her father or me in either hand and allow herself to be lifted shoulder height.

For two months she has gone up a few steps holding on with hands and stepping up with feet rather than knees. At the age of five weeks when laid on her stomach she held her head up turtle fashion. When she learned to sit erect and alone at the age of six months she held her back very straight and her position while standing is erect.

Trusting that I have given you a clear description of her, I am

Interestedly yours,

Mrs. J. M. Lear,

Chapel Hill, N. C.

April 1, 1928

Dear Sir:

I noticed the item in the *Literary Digest* for March 10 regarding children who run on all fours.

I am enclosing kodak prints of my little girl who used that method instead of creeping. She started walking at fourteen months of age but still went on all fours when in a hurry. She is a strong child and normal, now 4½ years old.

Details:

Race and nationality: American on both sides for several generations.

Sex: Female.

What child in numerical order: First.

Health and robustness: Always a very active and strong child. Never any serious illness.

So far as I know, the phenomenon has not been observed before among relatives.

Child began to run on all fours about 11 months of age and continued until 15 months old when she began walking.

She could move very rapidly on all fours. She would look up to get her direction and then lower her head and "scamper." Often bumped into objects if she did not look up often enough. The position of her hands and feet is shown in kodak picture sent previously. She is now four and one-half years old and is strong and healthy and has no marked peculiarity of behavior that I know of. She seems very bright for her age. She still has a tendency to stand with her weight on the outside of both feet, turning the ankles a little, but is not "bow-legged."

Mrs. M. L. Leffingwell,
Neenah, Wis.

May 2, 1928

Dear Dr. Hrdlička:

We, too, have a "bear walker."

I am attaching several photographs of "Jimmie" in action and otherwise. They are not the clearest in the world and if you need better ones we will take some more. Am sending the other pictures thinking you might like to see him when he is right side up. He still crawls when he is in a hurry.

Details:

White, American, English-Scotch extraction.

Male.

Unusually well and large for his age. Never has been sick except cross cutting teeth and with one cold.

Second child.

No other case of walking on all fours in children of same parents or in family, so far as known.

Began at about seven months of age; kept it up until he learned to walk at one year.

Hands open and walked flat on soles of feet and palms of hands and carried his head up and back. He liked to carry toys or most anything in his mouth. The back end of his anatomy was high up in the air. A strange thing he could do almost from the first when he was traveling by this process was to stand up in the middle of the floor or wherever he chose without the least trouble or touching anything. He could be walking on all fours and immediately stand up where most babies would have to go to a piece of furniture or the wall to help themselves up. He learned to walk easily and from the

Fig. 15.—Master Jimmie, fifteen months.

first walked so strongly and balanced well and walked over door sills without paying attention to them. When he gets in a hurry he still goes on all fours at 15 months. (Will get picture to illustrate his walking on all fours.)

As stated above—hands wide open and flat on the floor and flat on his feet, head up and back. He sleeps on his face with his knees up. When he has a little piece of ice and it makes his hands cold he lays it on the floor, sits down and picks it up off the floor with his mouth. Instead of talking he squeals most expressively. He can say words when he wants to but he insists on making his wants known by different kinds of squealing. He is extremely good natured and affectionate. He has never kept a person in the house or his mother awake at night since he was born, not even when he was weaned. Has never cried hard in his life, except for a minute or two if hurt or startled. He is very bright and normal in every way except trying to act like a little bear.

There is one other little girl cousin of this little boy who slept like this one, on her face with her knees under her chest.

When this baby was progressing on all fours on the floor, it was nearly impossible to upset him, he never seemed to get bumped and he was like a "loaded" toy, he wouldn't tip over.

I have tried to get a picture such as you wish but it has been too cool outside and we cannot take a fast enough one inside. Will send one as soon as possible.

Mrs. Edith B. Leonard,
Jackson, Miss.

October 15, 1928

Dr. Hrdlička:

Patricia LeSourd, born November 4, 1927, has been moving on all fours since she was a little over five months old. Our doctor said that she was advanced, but I have made no study of this tendency.

She is not walking yet, though she does get up in the middle of the floor by herself and takes a few steps. We are not encouraging her to walk.

She plays ball rather well, will run after a ball and then throw it rather hard with great accuracy. Many times she raises herself on both knees to give added strength to her throw.

For some time she has been saying "ma, ma; da, da; and by, by." She waves by-by with great vim.

She is most determined, and will do only the things she wants to do. Our baby doctor tried for two weeks at the hospital by starvation and every other means to put her on lactic acid milk, but had to give it up. Thumping or slapping her hands will not deter her from touching anything she wants to touch, and no matter how hard we hit, she only smiles, and sometimes slaps her own hands to mock us. She seems very strong, and will hold her weight on a rod for some time.

Very truly yours,
Prof. Howard M. LeSourd,
Duke University,
Durham, N. C.

March 19, 1928

Dear Sir:

Replying to your note in the *J. A. M. A.* for January 21, 1928, I have the following data to offer.

J. H. L., white, American, of mixed ancestry, well developed and well nourished, male, born January 4, 1927. The first child was born October 22, 1923. There was a miscarriage in June or July, 1926. Therefore, this is the third child.

The first child walked on all fours to some extent, though not as much as this one. A maternal aunt of this child also walked on all fours as a baby. She was one of five children and none of the others walked in this manner.

J. H. L. began to walk on all fours at six months. Most of his creeping was done in this way, *i.e.*, not much on his knees, mostly on feet and hands. At fourteen months he still makes use of the method to insure speed and safe footing, apparently, upon various occasions. He sometimes drops from the upright position to all fours, but more often starts for some desired object from a sitting position.

The hands and feet are flat upon the floor, except as the heel is raised when in motion. The hands are open. The order is right hand, left foot; and left hand, right foot. The resulting direction is somewhat sidling, often going slightly to one side, perhaps more often to the left. He locates an object toward which he proposed to go and then travels with his head practically in line with his back, until near the object, when he lifts his head. Snaps are enclosed and we have a small portion of movie film which shows some phases of this performance. The snaps are at six months and the movie at about ten months.

He climbs stairs and goes down without assistance, since the age of eight months. He carries a little footstool about and climbs upon chairs, thence to tables and other heights. He also recently climbs chairs without the stool. He "hauls himself up," much in the manner of the seal. He will start off the edge of the table, as if to drop to the floor on his feet, then, finding nothing beneath, will draw himself back to safety. He chooses spots where there are chairs when he finally comes down, of course.

Sincerely yours,
Mrs. John U. Leversee,
Minneapolis, Minn.

July 14, 1928

DEAR SIR:

I read an article in the *Literary Digest* of March 10, 1928, to the effect of children walking on all fours instead of crawling.

We have one son and three daughters and will say for your information that our youngest girl, who will be three next November 28, did not crawl but walked on all fours rather than any other way of getting about. When she desired to go somewhere she simply raised up on all fours, got her balance and started out. My wife first called my attention to it, and we thought it real fun to watch her mode of getting about. She even resorted to this after she learned to walk.

She walked with her hands flat, began at about 11 months old and walked this way until about 14 months old. Mother is a Norwegian and I, the father, born of Danish parents.

Yours truly,
WM. S. LINNETT,
Pierre, S. D.

October 25, 1927

DEAR DR. HRDLIČKA:

I was much interested in an account of your article on babies that run on all fours, because that is the way my own baby daughter moved about previous to walking. I am enclosing a small photograph. You will notice that one foot is flat on the ground. I never thought of this trait as being unusual until I read of your paper. The photograph is one of a series of snapshots I was taking. The baby was constantly moving and hard to pose, so I just shot at random, hoping to get some good pictures. This is one of the results.

The baby at first propelled herself by sliding on her stomach, pushing with her hands and feet. She began this at the age of 9 months.

At the age of 10½, she began walking on her hands and feet, with her knees off the ground. At times, when moving slowly, or when still, she had her knees on the floor. Most of the time, though, she moved at her utmost speed, on hands and feet.

At the age of 10 months, she began pulling herself up and walking by leaning against the wall, or by holding on to furniture. At 1 year and 2 weeks, she started walking by herself. She had good control, no fear, and stepped right off. Unlike many babies who are wobbly and fall after walking a short distance, this baby walked steadily, could stop and stand still, or turn around and walk in a different direction at will. She could raise and lower herself at will without help.

> Yours very truly,
> HOWARD LIVINGSTON,
> Los Angeles, Calif.

June 19, 1928

DEAR SIR:

Having just recently read of your research work for traces of animal characteristics among children, I am writing to tell you about our oldest boy, Russell A. Lovell, Jr. From seven months to one year old he walked on his hands and feet. We thought it odd at the time as we had never seen it done by anyone before and have never since seen it. Our second child, a girl, crept in a somewhat similar manner, using her right hand and right foot, and left hand and left knee. After some time she changed to both knees, before learning to walk at 14 months.

Russell is now nine years old, and is, and has been strong, active and healthy all his life, especially in infanthood. He weighed 9 lb. 5 oz. at birth, and at one year was 21 lb. 14 oz. He was nursed until nine months old.

At 4½ mos. rolled over each direction;

At 5 mos. first attempt at creeping on hands and knees;

At 6 mos. crept swiftly about in the same manner;

At 7 mos. changed to walking on palms of hands and bottom of feet. Barefoot or stocking footed until about a year old. At about this same time he began to stand upright holding on to couches and chairs.

At 9 mos. went up and down stairs. At 10 months stood alone. At three days before one year he walked unaided. That following week after he could walk around, he seemed to forget he could; and would occasionally drop down on his hands and knees, but always finding it slow going, would return to upright position and trudge off. This didn't last but a day or two. We have snapshots of all these various stages.

The heritage in our children is of old Colonial stock in three grandparents lines and the fourth English-Irish coming to the U. S. A. in 1850.

One great grandfather was 96 yrs. at death.

One great grandfather was 85 yrs. at death.

One great grandmother was 92 yrs. at death.

One great grandmother was 84 yrs. at death.

One great uncle now 80, also two great aunts now 78 and 79. All these are active and husky.

Russell is above average mentally, having accomplished his first year's school work in one-half year; and also his fourth grade work in one-half year; a record which was never before attained in this particular city school building. He averages 96–100 per cent in all subjects at present.

He is long bodied and short legged.

I shall be pleased if this is of interest to you.

Very sincerely yours,
Mrs. R. A. Lovell,
Worcester, Mass.

March 25, 1928

Dear Sir:

Seeing an article in a recent issue of the *Literary Digest* regarding children who creep or run on all fours, may I send you data in connection with two such cases in the same house at the same time. Both boys were healthy normal babies with only nine days difference in their age.

George: Canadian 3 generations, of Penn-Dutch and Eng.-Irish extraction. The oldest of two boys and the only one who ran on all fours. Rolled all over the floor at four months, crept on all fours at six months, upstairs at eight months and walked a week before he was eleven months old.

Ran with hands and feet flat on the floor which caused a swaying motion of the body. Eyes mostly fixed on the object he was traveling to, grew through a healthy boyhood, is now 21 years old. Short, stocky and strong, a great walker and a good swimmer with above the average staying powers.

Stuart: Canadian 3 generations, of English-Scotch extraction. The fifth of a family of seven boys and the only one who ran on all fours. Ran thus at seven months, hands and feet flat on the floor, ran upstairs at eight months and walked at thirteen months. Grew through healthy boyhood. Is now 21 years of age—good at Rugby, and perfectly well.

I am sorry we have no snapshots of them but we had no idea it was such a rarity and any pictures we have are in a sitting position.

Trusting the enclosed notes may be of some use to you in your work.

Yours sincerely,
MRS. E. LOWRY,
Toronto, Ont.,
Canada.

First letter:

March 5, 1928

MY DEAR SIR:

It was an odd coincidence that the day our baby developed the tendency of walking on all fours that Mrs. Lund should read an article in the N. Y. *Evening Journal,* presumably by you, stating that this was a rare occurrence in children.

Joan is a baby girl born April 3, 1927. It was last Saturday (March 3) that she first attempted to walk on all fours. She has been creeping in the ordinary way for some time and is unusually active, creeping as fast as her limbs will carry her. She only adopts this mode of traveling when she is in a hurry, otherwise she is contented with ordinary creeping.

Details:

First child.

No other child among relatives has shown the same phenomenon.

She began on March 3, when she was exactly eleven months old.

She still continues to run in this manner.

Palms flat on the floor; fingers extended straight in front; on her toes; knees bent; feet set well apart.

She holds her head up to see where she is going.

Have noticed no other peculiarities but should any develop will be pleased to advise you.

At present, we have no photographs, but will try to take some for you.

Yours very truly,
L. H. LUND,
New York, N. Y.

Second letter:

March 19, 1930

DEAR DR. HRDLIČKA:

No further peculiarities have developed in our little daughter. She will be three years old next month and is a normal healthy child.

The only thing that occurs to me that might be of interest to you is the fact that she continued running on all fours until the day before her first birthday when suddenly she picked herself up, stood erect and proceeded to walk without any support whatever, not holding on chairs or such, as is the usual procedure with children. Since that day on she continued to walk in the normal position.

Very truly yours,
L. H. LUND,
New York, N. Y.

March 17, 1928

DEAR SIR:

We have a daughter who runs on all fours.

Details:

Race and nationality—American, of Scotch-English, Scotch-Irish stock.

Sex—Female.

Health and robustness—Excellent.

What child in numerical order—Second.

Has the phenomenon been observed in any other child of the same parents or among relatives?—Not as far as I know.

At what age has the child begun to run on all fours, and how long has it continued?—Ninth month; still continuing, now about end of eleventh month.

The position of the hands, etc.—Hands open; head, rather high; sometimes at right angles when looking about; feet are straight, slightly bent perhaps; she can get about the home quite deftly.

Details as to any other peculiarity of behavior of the child, or any other children in the family—Has a strong inclination to thumb sucking.

MRS. L. G. MACKAYE,
Ann Arbor, Mich.

June 2, 1928

DEAR DR. HRDLIČKA:

A few days ago I showed the enclosed snapshots to Mr. Matthew Stirling and he suggested that you might find them interesting in connection with your studies of the type of locomotion represented. (See Plate XV, p. 333.)

The girl was 15 months old when the photos were taken. She is the youngest of a family of three girls. As I recall, she never crawled but adopted the means of moving on all fours quite naturally. The older girls crawled in the usual manner.

You will notice that there is quite a slope down to the river bank. Her speed and sureness of foot were quite remarkable either going to or coming from the water.

The young lady is quite normal and healthy. I should surmise that her greatest joy comes from playing in the water with her dog —a beautiful pointer.

> Very truly,
> K. A. MacLachlan,
> San Francisco, Calif.

July 3, 1928

MY DEAR DR. HRDLIČKA:

Having learned of your interest in quadruped progression in infants I believe that you may be interested in another case.

My youngest son, of a family of seven children, has traveled that way consistently from the time he first started to move about, having shown no tendency to creep. He was born on February 12, 1927, and has been remarkably strong and vigorous from birth. He learned to walk during his eleventh month and rapidly gave up his former mode of locomotion. He shows an unusual interest and ability in climbing. None of his relatives so far as I know have employed this method of progression although his oldest brother and an uncle used an intermediate form, employing both hands and one foot with the other leg bent under and assisting somewhat with the locomotion by pushing from the knee. My son's ancestry is all old American stock of British and German extraction. I am a member of the faculty of the University of Pennsylvania and his mother is a college graduate.

> Sincerely yours,
> W. H. Magill,
> Philadelphia, Pa.

January 6, 1929

DEAR DR. HRDLIČKA:

Indirectly I have heard that you are interested in babies that "creep on all fours." If there are any questions you wish answered in connection with our baby I shall gladly answer them. These pictures were taken the day after he took his first steps.

Details:

Child, white; American; male; first born.
Health, excellent.
No other "on fours" known of in family or relatives.
Began at twelve months, continued two months.
Have sent a set of pictures to show this.
Hands open, flat, feet flat, knees bent, head held up.
No other peculiarity of behavior.

Yours truly,
MRS. K. V. MANNING,
Williamstown, Mass.

March 14, 1928

DEAR SIR:

In an article in the issue of *The Literary Digest* for March 10, I see that you want information in regard to children who run on all fours instead of creeping on hands and knees. My two children both ran on all fours before they walked.

My son was born May 14, 1913. At the age of eight months he crept with ease and then began going on all fours, especially when he was in haste. He held his hands open and his head well up. He was a large and very active baby. As soon as he walked alone, 13½ months, he abandoned creeping and running on all fours entirely. When he first began going on all fours I wrote home to my parents, of course, about it. My father immediately replied that I had done the same thing. So far as I know, no one else in the family did it.

My daughter, born February 17, 1916, did exactly the same thing, except that she began a trifle earlier and walked alone at 11½ months. She was small and very active. Both children are bright, normal youngsters.

FIG. 16.—Robert E. Manning.

My ancestry is English on both sides of the family. Both my paternal and my maternal forbears were pre-Revolutionary colonists in New England. My husband, who is of English and German descent, is Professor of History at the Pennsylvania State College. I am a college graduate.

Details:

MILTON MARTIN:	MARION MARTIN:

White, American. Maternal ancestry: Chiefly English, settled in America before the Revolution; paternal ancestry: Chiefly English with a little German.

Male.	Female.
Very well and strong. Unusually large baby. Very active.	Very well. Plump but small. Very active.
First born.	Second born.
These two are the only children in the family.	The mother went on all fours.
Began to run on all fours at about eight months, continued till he walked alone at 13½ months.	Between seven and eight months, continued till she walked alone at 11½ months.

Both children began creeping on hands and knees but soon adopted the running on all fours, especially when they desired speed. Both used the hands open flat, kept the feet a little apart from each other, toeing out slightly, and held the head well up. They traveled thus much faster than on hands and knees.

Both children, before they could creep, moved by "swimming" on their stomachs; but they soon found out how to use their knees.

Before she could creep, Marion always raised herself to a sitting position by placing her hands, palm down, under her chest, raising her shoulders by straightening her arms, and at the same time describing outward circles with her feet extended. As she brought her feet front, she pushed her body back till she was sitting upright. This perfect "split" was done with rapidity and ease.

Yours sincerely,
MRS. A. E. MARTIN,
State College, Pa.

July 30, 1928

DEAR SIR:

My little girl will be 19 months old on July 31, 1928, and she has not walked alone yet, only on all fours. She just creeped for about two weeks and she has been going on all fours for about five months. She will put her hands and feet flat on the ground with her fingers wide open and she will sometimes put her head on the ground and try to see behind her. Today she stood alone for five minutes.

She has not been sick one day since she was born and she talks very plainly and has nineteen teeth. I have a little boy 3½ months old and he is in just as good health as she was. I was reading in the paper where you would like to hear from all parents whose children walk on all fours.

Yours truly,
MRS. KENNETH S. MASLEN,
San Anselmo, Calif.

August 27, 1928

DEAR DR. HRDLIČKA:

Alan called to your attention by Mrs. Engelmann [*q. v.*], is a very sturdy child. He weighs now 42 pounds, is 43 inches tall, and measures 24 inches around the chest, which is one and three-fourth inches more than the average child of like proportions. He is very alert mentally, understanding and absorbing books that are usually reserved for children from eight to ten years. He, in common with other children, is fond of climbing, but I do not think that he displays any unusual ability along this line.

I was always pleased, rather than annoyed, that he took to the four-footed manner of getting about, because it seemed to me to be cleaner than creeping. He still enjoys running on all fours at play, and even as a baby could work up exceptional speed. The only other peculiarity that I can recall is the position in which he used to sleep. We were almost driven frantic endeavoring to break him of the habit of sleeping on knees and chest—rather like the attitude of a Moslem at prayer.

I was very much interested in your idea that this was an atavism. Such a possibility never occurred to me.

Details:

Report by Mrs. Francis W. Mason (mother of child).
Child, white; American.

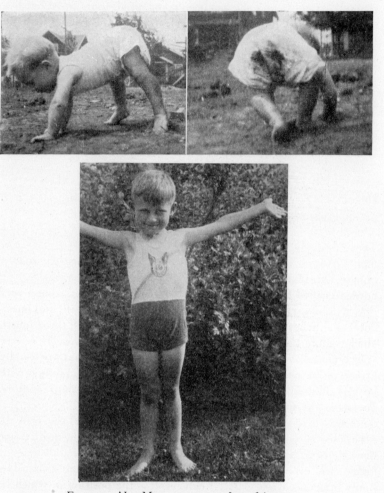

Fig. 17.—Alan Mason, near 1 and at 4½ years.

Male; first child.
Born June 21, 1923, started walking on all fours at nine months.
Health above average.

Walked on all fours until 13 months old. Even after that he dropped now and then to this position for running. Continued this until almost two.

No other anomalies.

Yours very truly,
MRS. FRANCIS W. MASON,
Portland, Ore.

July 1, 1928

DEAR DR. HRDLIČKA:

Our baby also walks on "all fours." He was a year old on the sixteenth of June, 1928, and has quite a history, which I would like to state briefly.

He was born in Vanderbilt Hospital at Nashville, Tenn. A normal delivery in every way and baby weighed eight pounds. He was black, but instantly the blackness disappeared and upon examination was found to be perfectly normal.

Five hours later he turned black again and was given oxygen. They discovered he had been injured at birth and for five days and nights he breathed oxygen and was watched constantly by trained nurses. The sixth day they stopped the oxygen and he has been normal ever since.

When he was nine months old he rode through an open cellar door on a "walker" and fell twelve feet and fractured his skull with no ill effects from that. Three weeks later he had pneumonia.

At eight months he moved around on the floor on his stomach. A little later he crawled on his hands and knees. At about ten months he started on all fours. At twelve months he walks everywhere, but seems to prefer the "all fours method" because it is much quicker.

He says a great many words, and understands what we say to him. He is a perfect specimen of babyhood and we are so proud of him.

We have a little girl who is three and a half. She is very intelligent for a child of her age. She sat on the floor and pushed herself along with her feet and never crawled.

Yours truly,
MRS. R. C. H. MATHEWS,
York, Pa.

July 22, 1928

DEAR SIR:

My knowledge of my odd physical characteristics is so slight that I never linked them with my strange mental twists until I read the article in the *Digest*. I ran on all fours as an infant. But there were other peculiarities.

If there is such a thing possible, I would say I did not understand spoken speech until I was quite a child. I remember my babyhood vividly much more so than most children, I think, and I can affirm that I obtained my first knowledge what seems telepathically. I used to wonder why people made their mouths go and made sounds, then for a time I understood both people's thoughts and their words, losing the power to understand what they meant and understanding only words about the time I first went to school.

I do not remember when I learned to read and my parents say they never knew how or when I did. I know I could read almost everything when I went to school and I remember sitting a wee child among the big boys and girls reading out of the fifth reader. On the other hand I could not learn to spell. I can not spell now, if I stop to think. I spell automatically but if you asked me to spell a word, I would have to stop and think how I would write it, then how it would look, before I could answer you.

I do not observe readily. I can pass an object fifty times and would not see it but if I touch it, even if only with my clothes, I know exactly where it is and can remember years just exactly where an object is, if I put it away. In my school work, anything I could memorize I could have perfectly, like history for instance, mathematics I would not do, I was too indolent, but anything in which sound entered like foreign languages was beyond me. I simply could not learn.

I had "spells" from my earliest memories. Trances probably. I seemed to leave my body and roam the world far and wide and could tell of wonderful adventures when I returned, or could have if I had not been forbidden. I was told they were dreams. I knew my parents considered these a disgrace and that other people thought I was "not right." I used all of the will power I had to keep from having them and although I have always "seen things" occasionally, I have not had the spells since I was twelve.

In such "dreaming," if I wanted to get away from some terrible indefinable menace which has always beset me asleep and often awake, I took to all fours. If in my dreams tonight I was beset by this threat I would get down and run on my hands and feet, but I do not run as animals do; my arms do more of the work than my legs. I pull myself forward in an unexplainable way and several times in my life when running to catch a car or hastening to keep an appointment I have had a momentary impulse to get down on all fours. I have always had this fear. Have it now although I have never known what fear is as most persons mean it. I have been in two cyclones and enjoyed them. I love thunder and lightning; am never afraid of burglars or drunks, of dogs or anything like that.
Details:

Report by M. E. M.: White; American; mother "Yankee," father Scotch-Irish.

Female, now 57; first of twins.

Health poor but good vitality. Mentality, peculiar.

I know little except that I ran on all fours. I must have slept curled up because they told me that they would have to bury me in a cheese box if I died in my sleep.

My people considered me "strange," and I was thought "not quite right" by some people. I early grew clever enough to conceal my oddity and so have always passed in a crowd, but I realized I was handicapped by not acting normally.

Yours very truly,
M. E. M.,
Oberlin, O.

Sept. 13, 1928

Dear Sir:

Some time ago I saw your article in the *American Journal of Physical Anthropology* on "Quadruped Progression in Human Child," and would appreciate a reprint.

It may be of interest to you to know that my baby girl who is beginning to walk began to move about first on her hands and feet and has never crawled. She is now just passed 11 months, having been born October 7th last year at the Johns Hopkins Hospital. She is our second child, we having lost our first girl at birth. This child is rather precocious, as under intelligence testing she shows herself to have a mental age of about 18 months, or an IQ of about

· 277 ·

1.6. In her quadruped progression she always goes forward and moves along very rapidly. As yet she has only taken one or two steps alone, although she can stand up alone without support and will raise herself up on her feet without support. She began to wiggle along on her abdomen first, but did this for only about a week, and then spontaneously began to go along on all fours about two months ago.

> Yours very truly,
> J. L. McCARTNEY, M. D.,
> Institute for Child Guidance,
> New York, N. Y.

June 29, 1928

DEAR SIR:

My youngest baby, a girl, 21 months the sixteenth of this month, at about the age of seven months began walking on all fours and surely did get there. Never crawled any other way but this. She was walking by the time she was ten months old and without the least bit of trouble. She never fell around like the other children did. I have four and she is the only one who crawled in this way.

When in a hurry or playing she walks on all fours yet occasionally.

> Yours truly,
> Mrs. CARL McCREEDY,
> Corning, Ia.

June 26, 1928

DR. HRDLIČKA:

Both of our boys ran on all fours when they were learning to walk and we had not considered it anything at all remarkable. They both crept for a while and then went on hands and feet until they could walk. The older one walked at thirteen months and the younger at fifteen months.

Last summer when the younger was just past a year old, the two of them used to race around on all fours; and they could make some speed too. The older one was a bit inclined to be flat footed so it made an excellent foot exercise for him. They have always been healthy youngsters.

Details:

Robert Holder McNichol, 4 yrs.
Paul Fullerton McNichol, 2 yrs. 4 mos.
White; Canadian of Scotch extraction.
Male.
They are both well and sturdy.
They are our only two children.
No other cases in relation.

Robert began to run on all fours when he was about 12 months old and continued till he learned to walk at about 13 months. Paul started to run on all fours when he was about 13 months and learned to walk when he was about 15 months. Even after they learned to walk the two boys used to get down on all fours and race around the house for fun. Sometimes I see one of them now get down on all fours and then kick one or both feet up in the air.

They both learned to creep first. They could go very quickly on all fours. They ran with hands fully open and on tip toes, knees straight so that their buttocks were much higher than their shoulders; and their heads raised just enough so that they could see a short distance ahead.

They are lively noisy boys and full of capers but I don't know that I could name any special peculiarities. We have no snapshots of them in action.

Yours very truly,
Mrs. Hazel H. McNichol,
Halifax, N. S., Canada.

June 19, 1928

Dear Sir:

I have four children, three girls and one boy, aged 11, 9, 4, and 2 years, all of whom had the trait of running on all fours. As I remember they crept at first in the ordinary manner, on their hands and knees, but after a time started to go on their hands and feet and almost entirely discarded the other method. The eldest in particular I remember as being able to run quite fast, and in all cases they got about much more rapidly than by ordinary crawling. The three girls started doing this somewhere around nine or ten months, I should say, and continued until they could walk alone, which in all three cases was about at one year.

The boy who is now four years of age did not start creeping until nearly a year old, and did not walk until about fifteen months. This was partly due, I think, to the fact that he had a "baby walker" in which he could go all through the house at a great rate. He had no incentive to creep or walk until I took the walker away entirely.

I enclose a rather poor snapshot of the boy, just before he started walking. This shows fairly well about the way he went, and as I remember, the others had practically the same gait.

All four children seem to be healthy normal children, at least as intelligent as the average and seemed no different from the ordinary child. They were quite large healthy babies—one (the first) weighing $7\frac{1}{2}$ lbs. at birth, the others 8 lbs. 2 oz., 9 lbs. and $8\frac{1}{12}$ lbs., respectively.

This method of progression always reminded me of either a dog or a bear cub.

> Respectfully yours,
> MRS. A. K. MCGOWAN,
> Ilion, N. Y.

November 4, 1928

DEAR DR. HRDLIČKA:

Your letter received, concerning my child walking on all fours and I shall endeavor to give you what few details I have. At the time of his running on all fours, other than being funny to look at, we really thought little of it and would be interested to hear what you will find out.

I have heard of a child who at eight years is still running in that manner, mind affected and unable to walk at all, so I am wondering if it is a healthy trait. Am answering according to the questions.

White—American.

Male; second child.

Very normal until he had whooping-cough at two years which developed throat and ear trouble until his tonsils were taken out at three years and since has been normal again. However, had German measles at six months and chicken-pox at 22 mos., but has an older brother in school who brought it home.

The habit was known of in no other child in our families.

This is copied from his baby book: When first put on floor nearly nine months old (was a June baby) in about a week moved four feet [distance]; 10 mos., crawled everywhere; 11 mos., crawled upstairs; 11½ mos., started using "all fours," reminds one of a little animal; 12 mos., stands up to chairs; 13 mos., walks all around furniture; 14 mos., stands alone and gets up unassisted; 15 mos., started off walking although had taken a few steps now and then before. But even at 3 years when pushing a plaything on floor will use all fours in preference to other mode of locomotion.

Did not notice at the time but recently when out in the woods he got down on the grass and ran on four with his head up and hands open, fingers spread out. He is now three and one-half years old.

Don't think of anything else peculiar about him except that he has been slow in talking, not really carrying on any real conversation until nearly three, but seemed lazy as he understood everything.

The running on fours must have developed him well as in his kindergarten physical examination he was the only child of about thirty-five who had no mark against him; everything perfect, well built.

The older boy began to crawl at five and one-half months and crawled until he walked at fifteen months, on his knees, however.

Very sincerely,
MRS. A. R. MELLOR,
Des Moines, Ia.

January 14, 1929
DR. HRDLIČKA:

Permit me to add to your cases of children who walked on all fours.

Gordon Wilmot Metcalf, born March 6, 1924, at Oberlin, Ohio.

White, American; father's family of English descent; came to America in 1640; mother's family of old English stock.

Male; second child; other child is a son, born April 30, 1920.

Excellent health, average height and weight. Unusually active and well developed muscularly. Very quick in his movements. Excellent sense of balance.

No other case in family or among relatives, so far as known.

Started to run on all fours when 11 months old. Still does so occasionally. Moves along very rapidly. His hands are flat to the floor with fingers outspread. Legs are spread rather widely apart. Runs on the balls of the feet with toes widely spread.

Is perfectly normal and very keen mentally.

The child has been ignored when he ran on all fours. He has neither been encouraged nor discouraged in this trait, being left entirely to his own devices. He has always been unusually quick and active. At two years of age he would climb 10-foot ladders by himself. He taught himself how to turn somersaults when two years old. When three and one-half years old, I would lift him up to a wire clothesline, where he would chin himself three or four times. He could also "skin the cat" at that age, without assistance, until he had a bad fall which somewhat dampened his ardor for this sport. When Gordon started to walk, he still preferred to run on his hands and feet because he could reach the desired point so much more rapidly than by walking; the rapidness and smoothness of movement has always been very noticeable. He has never crawled or used his knees. We have had no household pets until a few weeks ago, so his case is not one of imitation, but rather one of instinct.

Yours very truly,
NORMAN W. METCALF,
Chevy Chase,
Washington, D. C.

May 12, 1928

DEAR DOCTOR:

I understand that you are interested in receiving accounts of children who have spontaneously developed the habit of running effectively on all fours before learning to walk upright.

Both of my children by my second marriage have had this experience. My boy, aged now 6½ years, always of a healthy and robust nature, walked on all fours—"bear walk" with stiff knees and straight arms—for a short time, after learning to creep and before learning to walk upright. The position of his hands were usually wide open, walking on the palms; however, sometimes he was noticed to walk with the fingers clenched, putting the weight on the knuckles. As we remember, the head was usually held in a line with the body; but when he would become angry, he would hold the head up, and cry lustily.

The younger child, a girl, also developed the same habit, after she had crawled for a long time (about 2 months) on her hands and knees. Then for about a month she would walk on all fours, gaining quite a good speed in traveling. Her hands were always open, walking on the palms of the hands, with the elbows stiff; however, the knees were sometimes slightly bent; and at other times, straight. She now walks quite normally, and is now seventeen months old, well developed and in good health. Her head was held in a line with the body, while walking or running on all fours. She was about nine or ten months old, as we remember, when she commenced. She commenced walking alone at the age of 11½ months. She now has most of her teeth, and is commencing to talk.

Father is Canadian; of Canadian parents, of English-Irish stock. Mother is American, of American parents, of Irish-German stock.

We regret we have no pictures of them, in this position.

> Sincerely,
> FRANK C. MIGHTON,
> San Pedro, Calif.

June 24, 1928

DEAR SIR:

Referring to an interesting article in the current *Literary Digest*, I know of two cases of children walking on hands and feet. Mr. and Mrs. N. Conant Webb, Montclair, N. J., have a fine baby boy born last August, a strong, hearty child, normal in every way. I saw him when he was about eight months old. His efforts at locomotion were all on hands and feet, knees not touching the floor at all. He is a great nephew of mine.

The other instance was the case of a great nephew of my wife, an unusually active, agile child and very bright mentally. He visited us when he was about six years of age and it was wonderfully interesting to see him walk, trot and gallop as the dog does. Apparently with as much ease as walking on his feet alone, or with as much ease as a dog. To the great grief of the entire family he has since died. He was the most active child I have ever seen, accomplishing feats in climbing that were phenomenal.

> Yours very truly,
> CALEB S. MILLER,
> Washington, D. C.

March 24, 1928

MY DEAR DR. HRDLIČKA:

Shortly after reading your note in *Science* for March 9, 1928, on "Children Who Run on All Fours," such a child was brought to my attention and I have obtained from the mother as complete a history as possible, as follows:

White, American, male, present age 6 years, the first of two children, always in good health and of somewhat above the average mental development.

There is a history of a paternal uncle exhibiting the same phenomenon.

This child began to run on all fours at the age of 11 months, continuing this method of progression until the age of 15 months, at which time began to walk. Until 18 months of age there was frequent lapse into running on all fours in spite of ability to walk. In running on all fours the child used the flat of the hands fully open with the head up. Unfortunately there are no photographs of the child in the act and no other peculiarities of behavior could be elicited from the mother.

I hope that this data may be of help to you.

Very truly yours,
DR. HYMAN MILLER,
Los Angeles, Calif.

May 21, 1928

DEAR SIR:

In answer to your article in the *Pathfinder* of April 14th, 1928, you will find enclosed some pictures of Miss Nannette King Millisor.

We are very much interested and want to be of as much assistance as possible and want to hear more about it from you.

Race, white; sex, female.

She has always been very active, has been flopping over on her tummy since the age of five months. Her first crawling motion was flat on the stomach and she pulled herself forward with her arms as if she were swimming. She next went to hands and knees at the age of nine months and then to the all fours habit within the next month, and kept this habit until she started to walk at the age of one year and twenty-three days. Since that time there has been very few times that she goes on all fours, however is still doing it at times. She went on all fours with remarkable speed, hands and feet flat, head up and went running. Around the house flying.

I am sorry I was unable to get pictures in the nude or without her coat and bonnet on. However if you would like them very much, I will try to get some other pictures—although it may be impossible since she is walking so well. She is not very large, but plump and healthy looking at birth, weight six pounds. At one year, 19½ pounds, 27½ inches tall. Eight teeth, cut her first two teeth at 6½ months and so on every two months, 2 teeth more, etc. She has always been of a very pleasant disposition, started laughing at the age of 5 days (not colic) and has been very pleasant and laughing ever since. She has big blue eyes like her mother and a deep, deep dimple in her chin like her daddy.

I could write on and on about all of her good qualities. She is considered an exceptional child by all. Talks some, has several little tricks.

Seems to understand anything we tell her. Is very observing. In entering a strange place, she takes everything in—scarcely anything she does not see, but this isn't all due to the all fours habit, I guess. We hope you will find something of interest in this letter and would like very much to hear from you.

We are,
Yours truly,
MR. AND MRS. ARDEN J. MILLISOR,
Marion, O.

July 31, 1928

MY DEAR DR. HRDLIČKA:

It is with pleasure that I send the name of my twelve months old son for you to add to your list of "little bears." Little Clifford began at eight months to walk on all fours, with palms flat and knees at a slight angle. He could run that way with uncommon speed, and though he has walked upright for the last month, he often resorts to the swifter, surer method of the animal in emergencies, particularly if he is fleeing from danger.

My older boy, age two and one-half, although he crawled in the usual manner, is remarkably agile in climbing and although he does not "walk up trees," he is unusually sure footed.

. 285 .

They are from pure American stock, dating from the seventeenth century, and have superior health and intelligence. Both parents are college graduates.

Yours sincerely,
MRS. EMERY F. MITCHELL,
San Francisco, Calif.

First letter:

June 24, 1928

DEAR SIR:

From an article in a recent *Literary Digest* I learn that you are interested in receiving information about infants who walk on all fours instead of creeping. I do not know whether your appeal for such information has been answered to such an extent that you have been able to already satisfy yourself as to whether this is really a form of atavism, but in case you are still interested in the subject I am writing to tell you that my little son has crept upon all fours ever since the age of about 9½ months. He is now a little over a year and has just recently learned to walk, but he still relies upon his "quadruped progression" when he wants to get anywhere in a hurry. He is a very healthy baby, has never been sick a day, never had any sign of a cold, and I think is normal mentally as well.

Very truly yours,
MRS. JOE ALEX MORRIS,
Austin, Minn.

P. S. The baby also is a "climber" and climbs everything possible to climb—climbed up steep stairs at age of ten months.

Second letter:

July 3, 1928

DEAR DR. HRDLIČKA:

It is hard for me to tell in what ways, if any, my child exhibits peculiarities as he is my first baby and I have not had many opportunities to observe other children of the same age. Lately he has showed a tendency when playing with any object, to get up on all fours and circle around it, moving his hands hardly at all, but making the circle entirely with his feet. Also I have noticed that when walking upstairs, when holding on to someone's hand he does not put both feet on one step as most children do, but goes up the steps in the same way an adult would. When going upstairs by himself he also goes up on his hands and feet instead of on his hands and knees. He began to climb stairs at the age of about ten months when one day we were very surprised to find him half way up a steep flight. He also climbed up on a couch alone at about the same age. I am enclosing as good a photograph as we could get, for as usual when we wanted him to creep he walked, and when we want him to walk he creeps. I am sorry the picture does not show the feet clearly; I will try and get a better one for you, but I think you can see his position fairly well. His head is sometimes down, sometimes up and his hands usually wide open I believe.

Details:

White; American; Scotch, Irish, English descent.

Male, first child.

Very active; never been ill since birth.

No other cases in relatives known of.

Began at 10 months, still continuing at 13 months although not so frequently as child now walks.

Hands open, head down or up, both ways.

Shows strong climbing inclination.

> Very truly yours,
> Mrs. J. A. Morris.

First letter:

May 14, 1918

Dear Sir:

In the Sunday edition of the *Berliner Morgenpost* I have just read with great interest that in a lecture before a medical association you have asked for reports of cases of children running on all fours.

A girl named Elfriede, born on the fourteenth of November, 1921, in Wilmersdorf has done this when small. She scurried over the room on all fours with wonderful rapidity. Later on she learned the ordinary walk. Enclosed is her picture from that time.

> Respectfully yours,
> Hugo Mossner,
> Charlottenburg, Germany.

Second letter:

July 18, 1928

In answer to your request I send you here some further notes on the child in question.

Whoever saw the child as she ran about like a little dog laughed heartily and so did we all.

The child likes to do all sorts of gymnastics, to climb and to jump. She sits with preference in a squatting position, as shown in the accompanying picture. She loves best to sleep on her stomach with the limbs drawn under her, like a dog.

The father is a German, the mother from Baltic Russia but of German ancestry; both live in Berlin. The little girl was the first and only child of the family and is now six and one-half years old.

She is sound, strong, plucky, mentally very alert. Good observer, and has always had much liking for animals especially dogs and horses.

She plays a great deal alone, and makes designs especially of dogs which she represents in all possible postures. Other children she just tolerates; when irritated will strike them. Is at her best when she plays alone or with grown-ups. To us, her grandparents, and also to the brother of her father (my oldest son) she shows a great tenderness. Grown people with whom she comes in contact regard her as bright and smart.

Respectfully,
H. M.

July 16, 1928

Dear Sir:

In view of the statement in the article "Does your Baby Walk like a Bear?" in the July 7 issue of *Science News Letter* I am enclosing some old snaps of my boy and giving some particulars about him. He is now twelve years old and has long since abandoned that method of locomotion so that I cannot give you any further particulars as to his gait than you can ascertain from the pictures.

His name is Albert G. Mowbray and he was born in Winchester, Mass., June 23, 1916. My mother's family was of old New England stock, my father's Scotch-Irish. My wife's father's family was also old New England, though we were both born in California. Her mother's father was of Scotch extraction and his wife an

Alsatian. His closest physical resemblance is to his mother's family.

When he was born the doctor and nurses commented on what a strong baby he was and particularly how broad and strong his back was. He has been a generally healthy child though inheriting astigmatism characteristic of his mother's family which, I think, accounts for his seeming lack of activity. He prefers a long hike to an active game. Neither my wife nor I can recall when he first began to go on all fours. He was very slow about walking. As my wife recalls he was nearly 23 months old before he did so. My own recollection is that he got over the ground on all fours very rapidly.

In school he rates high in all intelligence tests. He has a decided flare for natural science and I think has a fair understanding of what he reads.

He is decidedly lacking in manual dexterity. He is not adept with tools, is poor in drawing and in writing; in the latter case I think it is because he was pushed along too rapidly in school when they were being taught to write and never learned to form his letters with care. Now he writes very rapidly but irregularly.

Very truly yours,
ALBERT H. MOWBRAY,
Berkeley, Calif.

P. S. The woman in one picture is not my wife but a maid we had at the time. My wife also suggests that I add that his sister, 2½ years older was equally slow about walking though she crept in the usual way.

March 10, 1928

DEAR SIR:

I have just finished reading your article on "Children who Run on All Fours," and we note that it corresponds exactly to the walking of our baby. He started to creep when he was seven months old, and has never put his knees to the floor; he holds his hands palms down on the floor and his feet are flat on the floor, while his head is held low and he either walks or runs on all fours.

If he is in a hurry he can run as fast as a man walking at a good stiff gait. He is almost fourteen months old and is just learning to walk, if he gets in a hurry, however he starts to run on all fours. He is an intelligent baby, and is strong and healthy. We will try and take a picture of him while running and if you wish, the picture can be taken at the moving picture studio here.

We should appreciate knowing what this peculiarity indicates.

Very truly yours,
Mr. and Mrs. D. G. Myers,
Seattle, Wash.

August 26, 1929

Dear Dr. Hrdlička:

The all fours habit appeared in the boy whom this concerns at the age of ten months and now at twelve months he is still going on all fours like a dog or a monkey. Hands held open when running and feet flat on ground. Head mostly held up. Enclosing two photographs, one in act of getting on feet and the other while running. This is the first case I have seen in my twenty-three years of practice. Rather interesting. The name of this child is Harvey Fred Crozier.

Details:

White; American.

Male, second child.

Health, perfect.

No other cases known in relations.

Began at eight months; now thirteen months and still going on all fours.

Hands fully open when running, head up mostly, but also goes with it on level with body.

Yours very truly,
J. Niess, M.D.
Carmi, Ill.

At fourteen months my boy started to go about on all fours, and how he could travel. We thought this a strange way for him to go about; he walked at eighteen months.

He was born a premature twin with small hopes of being kept alive; is now four years old and unusually well developed. Even now he often travels on all fours.

Yours truly,
Mrs. Joseph O'Donnell,
Apponaug, R. I.

July 2, 1928

DEAR SIR:

Having read an article in the *Literary Digest* about babies "who walk like bears," I wish to call your attention to a case in my family. My son, born in 1910, never crept, but ran about on all fours from the age of about five months till he was about a year old, when he began to walk. Also, when he was a few weeks old he tried to swim. At least, that is what it looked like. When placed on his stomach in the bath basin or tub, he moved arms and legs in a perfect swimming manner; and he enjoyed it so much that he screamed when we took him from the water. The neighbors used to come in to watch him—it was quite a sight. He has always been strong and healthy. He raised his head the day he was born. He has never been sick, with the exception of colds.

I am greatly interested in Anthropology, Biology, and other Sciences; and I hope the foregoing will be of interest to you.

Details:

The father is American, son of a Norwegian father and Irish-American mother. The mother is American whose ancestors were German and English.

Male; the first and only child; except a son still-born in 1925.

Health always perfect. Was never fat, but strong. At present time very muscular.

An aunt, who is dead, spoke of someone else in the family who ran on all fours; do not recall who it was; but probably my father, uncle or cousin.

He began to run on all fours at about eight or nine months, or it may be a little earlier, and continued to do so until a year old, when he walked.

He ran about swiftly, and not awkwardly. The feet and hands alternated, as a dog runs.

His hands were fully opened. The legs were straight, not bent at the knees, making him stick up in the back. But his head was level, that is, he looked forward, and sometimes up, when running.

He always smelled of any article given him. That trait was not outgrown till he was about fourteen years old. He has always had a pleasant disposition—cried very little when a baby. He always liked raw vegetables, and cares very little for meat. The only "oddity" he has physically, is that his great toes are extra long and large compared with the rest of the foot. He is a great walker.

Yours truly,

Mrs. Oscar O. Olsen,
Providence, R. I.

July 16, 1928

Dear Sir:

Possibly you may be interested in hearing of our son who "crawled" on all fours, placing his hands flat down on the floor. Being a large well developed child he looked like a big white bug making its way over the floor.

He is the youngest of three, neither of the others taking this means of locomotion. I found it an advantage, as his little dresses did not get so soiled as the usual method. He crawled less than two months, for at nine months he suddenly found that he could stand up and walk, and he forsook his four legged method. I remember that, before he reached the tenth month, he walked with me down the sidewalk to a neighbor's house to call. Undoubtedly his legs were strengthened by his running on all fours. The other two children, both girls, walked at eleven and twelve months respectively.

He is now twenty-three years old, in his last year at the Theological Seminary at Louisville, Kentucky. He was always a good student, that is, he learned readily, but in his grade school days would spend but little time in study. Until he acquired his growth he was somewhat lazy physically; due perhaps to his rapid growth. He entered college at sixteen and worked his way through as he has through the seminary. There are few branches of work at which he has not worked to acquire the necessary funds for his education, though much of it has been earned through mental labor.

At present he is preaching in a country church, conducting citizenship classes for foreigners at the Y. M. C. A., writing for newspapers and furnishing a front page article for a religious weekly, in addition to his seminary work.

He is about five feet ten, weighing perhaps 145 or 150 pounds.

I have written thus fully, as I understood you wished information about such cases. His mental development was in advance of most of his school mates and at present his reasoning powers and powers of expression both orally and in writing are beyond the average young man of his age.

Yours very truly,
Mrs. S. C. Osborne,
New York, N. Y.

April 2, 1928

Dear Sir:

I was much interested in an article appearing in the *Evening Star* of March 31, relative to children who walk like bears when young.

My second child, a boy now ten years old, normal in every way and who has always been so, never crawled a foot in his babyhood days. I do not recall just how old he was when he started to move on all fours, but that was his only way of getting about. We were stationed in the Canal Zone at the time and he was often referred to as a "Honey Bear," which is a native animal there.

As a baby he had a strong liking for going up and down stairs on his all fours. I was post commander and lived in a big house at the top of a hill overlooking Culebra Cut. A long winding road came up to the front of my quarters, but I had a short cut made down the back way which consisted of some 208 steps. This boy, when less than a year old, would start at the bottom of these steps and go clear to the top on his all fours and seemed to get quite a "kick" out of it, although he would stop to rest once or twice at first. We were very thankful that he did not crawl as other children for it kept him off the damp ground in the rainy season.

Very truly yours,
H. E. Pace,
Major, War Department,
General Staff,
Washington, D. C.

April 4, 1928

Dear Sir:

The enclosed picture was made when our girl "Ann" was one year old. She was just beginning to walk. She had been crawling in this "all fours" style for two months. She used this method when she was in a hurry—and could scoot. Even now at thirteen months, while she raises up anywhere and walks easily, yet if in a big hurry she runs on her four "legs" with eyes to the front—on her objective.

· 293 ·

While this picture is blurred (moving), yet it clearly shows all essentials needed to illustrate her movements. Only today I noticed that she will stop, back up a few inches so as to balance on her "hind" feet, and then raise upright, seeming to use her hands very little—kangaroo style.

Since she was an infant I have given her exercises, resulting in a muscular body and perfect balance. Her legs, back and arm muscles are especially strong. She was taught to sleep on her belly. Even now when she is put on her back, when she gets drowsy she will literally whirl over on her stomach and drop off to sleep.

Her heredity is known for many generations. On both sides and back for three generations they were total "drys" and lived extremely clean and simple lives. Excepting for one "wet" great-grandfather, this record goes back much further. The longevity of these people was great—over 90 is not unusual. My mother is hale and hearty at 78—does all her housework and cooking. Father, same age, is judged to be about 55. He is very active with only partially gray hair. His teeth are almost without fault. Only yesterday he drove 105 miles and back, just on business.

She likes to play by herself. Her only sickness was a mean cold developed at 8 months, contracted from her father. She was put on a bottle at 6 months. She is warm blooded—requiring light covering.

Almost every one is astonished at her "evident" intelligence. She is a close observer, and pays rapt attention to all strangers and to any one who will talk to her. She jabbers freely when alone. She is very fond of "rough house" playing. She has missed the usual thousand falls, as to our knowledge she has never been hurt by her own fault excepting once when she climbed out of the Kiddy Coop and once out of the carriage.

Her memory and tenacity of an idea is remarkable. For an hour she will complain at a disappointment in spite of attempts to divert her mind. She can stand much pain without crying. She will work quietly for half an hour in trying to extricate herself from an entanglement.

Some of her physical doings have been astonishing.

> Very sincerely,
> FRANK PARKER,
> U. S. Department of Agriculture, Bureau of Agricultural Economics,
> Raleigh, N. C.

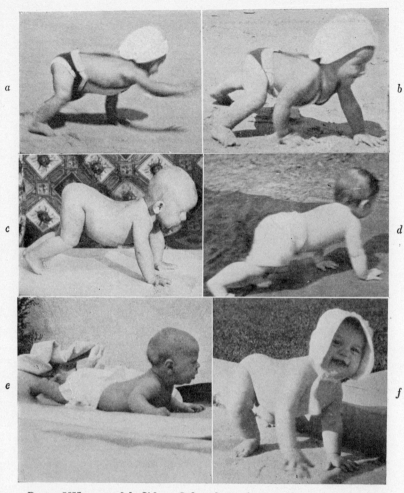

PLATE XII.—*a* and *b*. Sidney Oakes, boy, nine months. *c*. Libuška, girl, seven months. *d*. Ann Parker, twelve months. *e*. H. W. Smith, boy, at seven weeks. *f*. H. W. Smith, boy, at seven months.

First letter:

March 22, 1928

My dear Dr. Hrdlička:

Your notes in *Science* with regard to children that run on all fours have interested me because my first born child, a girl, now 4 yr. 3 mo. old, so ran.

She never crept as most children do but began moving about by wriggling on her stomach and moving her arms like one swimming. Next she raised herself on her hands a little, and then she began running on all fours. She would raise her hand high with fingers distended and arm straight out in front. She loved to bring her hand to the floor with a smack. From the first she ran quickly and confidently and ultimately acquired amazing speed. I am a fast walker and she could easily outstrip me. I never have seen anyone enjoy locomotion as she did. She used to chase herself about the room for the fun of it. Possibly her proficiency in running on all fours made her a little slow about learning to walk—why learn the clumsy way of grown ups?

My daughter is a fine husky child, at all times rather large for her age, and has had no serious sickness. Besides she is well muscled and strong.

Her brother, our second child, is 13½ months younger and we hoped he would run on all fours too. In fact we thought that he might learn the trick from his sister who was still running on all fours when he learned to creep at seven months but he never did. He too is a sturdy healthy child.

I should say that my daughter began to run on all fours at nine months and kept it up till she was seventeen months. After that she gradually gave it up but even now in a moment of fun she will run on all fours for a minute or so. She learned to walk at fourteen months.

I have never seen any other baby run on all fours. Certainly my two half brothers and two half sisters—who had the same ancestry as I, did not run so. My wife tells me that neither she nor her mother ever saw a baby run on all fours until they saw my daughter do it, and there are plenty of Evans babies.

As for ancestry I am a New Englander of the old stock—my ancestry I believe is pure English, or at least British for nearly 300 years.

My wife's ancestry is more mixed but I believe it is Celtic. My daughter has the quick Celtic mind of her mother, Horatio Jr., my son, has the slower mind of my people. I have a second daughter who should be creeping or running by Xmas and I will report on her if you wish.

I enclose photographs all of which I think are self explanatory except the one marked with a cross on the back. It shows the child in the act of raising herself to walk or perhaps sitting down at the end of a run. Note the legs.

> Very truly yours,
> HORATIO NEWTON PARKER,
> Jacksonville, Fla.

Second letter:

March 23, 1930

MY DEAR DR. HRDLIČKA:

In response to your letter of March 15, I would say that my second child, Horatio Newton Parker, Jr., never went on all fours; as most children do, he creeped till he walked.

My third child, Margaret Irwin, began by creeping but soon began traveling on all fours. However, she did not keep it up long for she began to walk at eleven months of age.

Should your records be available to the public I would be glad if you would refer me to the place of publication for I am much interested in your research.

> Very truly yours,
> HORATIO NEWTON PARKER.

October 29, 1929

DR. HRDLIČKA:

I observed my son and noticed his habits when he began to run on all fours. It is rather interesting to note, however, that although he could run quite rapidly this way, he did so only when he was on the lawn. When in the house he used a different method. In the house he would keep his left leg doubled back under so that whenever he wished to stop and sit up he could so do without difficulty.

His right foot he placed on the floor after the manner of walking on all fours and his manner of locomotion could more properly be described as walking on "all threes." I was never able to get a picture of the "all threes" method.

He is a very vigorous youngster, having been strong and healthy since birth.

> Yours very truly,
> LEROY T. PATTON,
> Head of Department of
> Geology,
> Texas Technological College,
> Lubbock, Tex.

May 16, 1928

MY DEAR DR. HRDLIČKA:

I am sending you a snapshot of my boy Thomas Paull showing his way of going about. I do not remember just how old he was as Thomas is now nearly fourteen years of age, but I thought the picture might be of interest to you.

Details:

Race and nationality—White, American.
Sex—Male.
What child in numerical order—Second.
Health and robustness—Good.
Has the phenomenon been observed in any other child of the same parents or among relatives?—No.
At what age has the child begun to run on all fours, and how long has it continued?—From creeping to walking, or from one and three-fourths to two years.
Add description, as detailed as possible, of the performance itself, supplemented when this can be done, by a photograph of the child in the act—See picture.
Details as to any other peculiarity of behavior of the child, or any other children in the family—Very imitative, a good mimic. Sometimes climbs trees with hands and toes instead of "shinnying."

> MRS. M. H. PAULL,
> Barre, Mass.

June 29, 1928

Dr. Hrdlička:

When my baby was about nine months old he started to hitch along while sitting down, using his feet and right hand to propel himself. He did this for about two weeks.

Then he started walking on his hands and feet and by the time he was ten and one-half months old he was running around with great ease and attaining quite a high speed.

He did not try to stand erect very much until just before he started to walk. He started to walk just a week after he was twelve months old.

He walked easily and steadily but for a long time after learning to walk whenever he wanted to hurry he would drop down on all fours and run fast. He is now four years old and has always been perfectly normal.

Details:

White, American born; also parents; French and Irish ancestry. Male, first child.

Health very good; was a large fat baby; has had no children's diseases as yet.

No other cases of running on all fours known in the families.

Began about nine and one-half months and continued until about fifteen or sixteen months, although he walked at about one year old erectly.

He ran just like a puppy but kept his knees almost stiff.

Fully open hands and head slightly raised.

He has always been very shy and now at the age of four years does not "mix" easily with other children.

My second baby is now eight months old and should there be any peculiarity about his creeping I will advise you of it.

Yours very truly,
Mrs. Jack Pedenboy, Jr.,
San Francisco, Calif.

First letter:

June 30, 1928

Dr. Hrdlička:

My boy Donald started to crawl when he was five and a half months old and he walked on all fours like a little bear. People used to remark how strange it was but being a young mother I felt proud to think he was so strong.

· 299 ·

He stood up alone when he was six and a half months old and at the age of nine and a half months he walked.

Very sincerely,
Mrs. Oscar Peterson,
St. Paul, Minn.

Second letter:

March 20, 1930

Report—by mother, Mrs. O. Peterson.
Race and nationality—White, Norwegian.
Locality—St. Paul, Minn.
Sex—male.
What child in family—First and only.
Health and robustness—Very good.
Age—Four years old (now).
Has the phenomenon been observed in any other child or among relatives—No.
Nature of peculiar behavior—He was five and one-half months old when he started to walk on all fours; but did not continue it very long because we got a walker for him when he was six and one-half months and then he ran around in that.
What did people think of it—Thought it was strange.
No other peculiarities.

Mrs. O. Peterson.

March 26, 1928

Dear Sir:

Reading in the *Denver Post* under date of March 25, 1928, that you desire reports from parents who had children crawling on all fours, I am moved to write you in regard to our son.

Richard Wm. Philleo was born March 16, 1924, the first child of his mother who was aged 20 years at the date of his birth. Father was aged near 29 years. Weight of child at birth 8½ pounds.

From the first he seemed possessed of unusual strength in his arms and legs and could raise himself on this bearing when he was between four and one-half and five months of age.

At the approximate age of six months he began to walk and run on his hands and feet, with these members flat on the floor, and the knees bent forward, and moved in this manner until he was about a year old.

At seven months he was capable of making considerable speed on all fours. We lived in a flat, third floor, and our entrance was at the rear, the flat was approximately one hundred feet in length, and the doors were in line. He soon became aware that the door bell was a summons, and as the front room of the flat was the one in which we spent most of our time, on account of light and air, when the bell was rung, he was up and away to the rear on all fours, and neither my wife nor myself, walking rapidly, were able to beat him to the door. He seemed capable of making considerable distances in this manner, both on the floor and ground, without it apparently tiring him.

At one year he began to walk upright but up until 16 months, if he were in a hurry, he would resort to all fours again.

We never made any effort to discourage this means of locomotion, as I, the father, was of the opinion it would, and I believe it did, give him a wonderful chest development.

He has always been healthy, and we have never had occasion to have the doctor for him in his four years.

I am endeavoring to write without prejudice, but I have noted what to my mind seems an extraordinary vivid imagination, and as several disinterested outsiders have commented on this, I mention it merely for what it may be worth.

Our second child, a little girl, born two years and five months after his birth, was, as one might say, just a common garden variety of baby.

Details:

Race and nationality—White, Irish American.

Sex—Male.

What child in numerical order—First.

Health and robustness—Excellent.

Has the phenomenon been observed in any other child of the same parents or among relatives?—No.

At what age has the child begun to run on all fours, and how long has it continued?—Seven months to a year.

The position of hands, etc.—Hands fully open, head up in order to see.

Details as to any other peculiarity of behavior of the child, or any other children in the family—No other peculiarity.

Very truly yours,

A. W. PHILLEO,

Casper, Wyo.

March 19, 1928

DEAR SIR:

I was very much interested in the enclosed clipping from yester-day's *New York Herald Tribune*, because my grandson, now sixteen months old, who has now learned to walk, was never known to even touch his knee to the ground during what is ordinarily the baby's creeping period, but ran around on all fours as described in this article of yours, and even yet, although he walks very nicely, when he gets in a hurry chasing a ball or something of that sort, he drops down and runs on all fours.

We had noticed it and talked about it considerably and were therefore very much interested to see that apparently this is just what we thought, a very unusual proceeding for the infant human.

Very truly yours,
NOBLE E. PIERCE,
Hartford, Conn.

Report of a Case:

July 6, 1928

Race and nationality—White, American.
Sex—Male.
Health and robustness—Normal.
What child in numerical order—First.
Has the phenomenon been observed in any other child of the same parents or among relatives?—No.
At what age has the child begun to run on all fours, and how long has it continued?—Began thus at 10 months; six weeks later started to walk.
Add description, as detailed as possible, of the performance itself, supplemented when this can be done, by a photograph of the child in the act—Photo sent. (See Plate XV*b*, p. 333.)
The position of the hands (whether fully open or partly closed) and of the head, while running on all fours, as well as any other peculiarities of the child's behavior—Hands fully open, head well up.
Details as to any other peculiarity of behavior of the child, or any other children in the family—When running on all fours carries toys in mouth; will try to get a photo of this.

FRED. R. PITTS JR.,
rep. by JOHN D. AXTON,
Washington, D. C.

September 24, 1928

DEAR DR. HRDLIČKA:

Our baby is one of those who goes on all fours. At the age of eight months he started to creep, but in just a few days he was going on all fours, which got to be rather speedy. I think he would have crept sooner but the floors were cold so I could not put him down.

Almost as soon as he started to creep he started to climb up to things and walk around them. Now we can say he walked when he was a year old. A few days before he took a few steps alone and they have increased rapidly.

He is a very large baby, not fat, but just large. He weighs twenty-eight pounds at one year, eats all vegetables and fruit and is a "pig" for milk. Has eight very nice teeth.

Yours truly,
MRS. H. E. PRUEITE,
Glidden, Ia.

June 29, 1928

DR. HRDLIČKA:

My son, at the age of ten months, began to walk on all fours and at the age of fourteen months is still doing it. He stands perfectly alone and takes an odd step occasionally alone. He can walk all over with a little support but finds he can get along faster on all fours and has obtained great speed this way. He has been in perfect health since birth.

Sincerely,
MRS. WALTER RAPP,
Jersey City, N. J.

June 17, 1928

MY DEAR DR. HRDLIČKA:

I was greatly interested in the account in the *New York Times* today of your study of children who "go on all fours instead of creeping." The article states that you wish information about other "quadruped progressors."

My second child, Philip, born January 7, 1923, used this form of locomotion, much to my amazement, as I had never seen or heard of this substitute for creeping.

Philip never crept in the ordinary way, and did not move about at all until he was rather older than most babies are when they begin to creep. His physical development was somewhat retarded by illness during his first year. He did not sit alone until he was nearly ten months old. He began to go on "all fours" about two weeks before his first birthday. He walked late in March, 1924, when he was a little more than fourteen months old. But until he was about twenty months old he would drop to the old position when he was tired or in a hurry. On hands and feet he had little trouble in keeping up with his sister, two and a half years his senior.

People were always amused and surprised by his way of getting about and we used to call him "the little grizzly bear," for his gait suggested a bear's fat, clumsy but surprisingly rapid gait. Philip put his hands down flat on the palms, with his fingers spread out, his arms were straight, but his legs were a little bowed at the knee. When he was in a great hurry he did not put his heels down, going on hands and toes. Usually, however, he put his feet down flat on the soles. He was shorter than the average boy baby (he still is) and about eight per cent above the average weight in relation to height, as he still is.

In other respects, he has always been a normal boy, except that his school now considers him above the average mentally. Their mental tests give him as I. Q. *155.*

At my home in New York City I have a kodak picture of Philip "bear walking," taken just before he began to walk, but after he was able to stand alone. When I return to the city I can send you a print of this picture if it would be of any use to you in your study. I shall also be glad to furnish any further details that would be helpful.

I shall be much interested in the results of your study, and should like to know where they will probably be published.

Details:

Child—Caucasian; American; male; second born.
Health—Good.
No other case like his known of among relatives.
Keeps head raised a little when going on all fours.

Child has always been rather precocious mentally. Physical development "normal."

Mrs. Beulah A. Ratliff,
New York City.

July 20, 1928

Dear Dr. Hrdlička:

I am enclosing a snapshot of the baby daughter of one of my friends.

The baby ran everywhere (as quickly as a kitten) on all fours. The enclosed picture is not very good. She was running after a ball, and had just stopped to roll it back and the picture looks as though she were just getting up.

The baby is not sixteen months old, and is walking. The mother's name is Mrs. John Rayley, Oakland, Calif.

I think one of our friends took some moving pictures of Elizabeth running on all fours. Everyone always was greatly interested in her method of getting about, and I think Dr. Robert Newell (Stanford University Hospital) took some moving pictures of her.

Very sincerely,
Mrs. J. B. Rex,
Berkeley, Calif.

March 7, 1928

My Dear Dr. Hrdlička:

This week's *Digest* (Mar. 10) publishes for request, four reports on children who run on "all fours." I knew of a case such as you cite some 25 years back. At Woodbury, Long Island, New York, where I was teacher in the little local school, there was directly across the street an old home, in rather run down state, inhabited by two maiden ladies of refinement, the last of their family. They were impecunious, trying to hold the old home and its lonely old contents intact. I had known them for a long period of time and boarded with them during my year in their town. Their household consisted of "James"—an erstwhile tramp, and "Ellen," rather a slatternly, slow-moving, slow-witted woman of middle age, who had the child Harold. My impression is that he was illegitimate. Ellen was apparently Irish but spoke with a cockney accent, when she did speak, which was not often nor much. She never went anywhere to my knowledge.

The child Harold was about five when I lived there. There were no other children anywhere near for playmates, though he frequently sat and watched the children in the school yard across the way. I do not believe any of them ever showed him any friendliness. There were the two dogs belonging to the menage (and a great number of cats, I never knew how many), both old and not at all playful, but it always seemed that the child felt a fraternal feeling for them and shaped his existence by them. He went about out-of-doors on all fours, at times imitating the dogs in lifting his leg quite expertly at the trees and bushes in simulation of urinating. He would run about on all fours with a large bone in his mouth and seemed particularly to do these things before observers. In the house I seldom saw him, as the kitchen and sleeping quarters for himself and mother were in a wing, but occasionally the door to the sitting room would fly open and he would come in on hands and feet and dash round the center table and out again before one could recover from surprise. It seems to my memory that he was as agile as a monkey.

He seemed excessively shy, never would say anything. I cannot recall ever having heard him speak, although I lived there five or six months. One of the ladies told me she had tried to teach him a few simple things—colors, counting, etc., but he seemed not at all responsive although attentive.

He was not a particularly unattractive type of child, very little color, brown eyes slightly crossed and light hair. He ran with end joints of his fingers bent back and under.

I was interested in knowing how he developed and was told that he went to school for a few years anyway. And was grown the last time I heard of him and working on a farm somewhere in the vicinity.

If this jumble of remembered data interests you, I think I could on a visit to my home town, Cold Spring Harbor, near Woodbury, dig out something more explicit about him and perhaps his antecedents. The old ladies are dead and the house in other hands but friends of them, in fact any of the townspeople would remember the peculiar child. It was a subject for universal discussion.

Very truly yours,
(Mrs.) Lotta W. Rees,
New Haven, Conn.

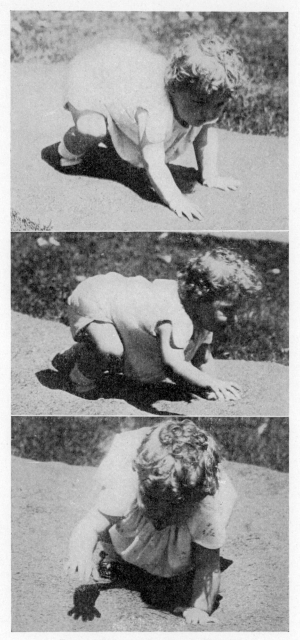

PLATE XIII.—Barbara Louise Rhodes.

· 307 ·

May 9, 1928

DEAR SIR:

In a recent issue of *The Literary Digest* we noticed an article regarding children "going about on all fours" and suggested any-one knowing of a case either writing you or sending photographs.

Under separate cover I am mailing you photographs of my granddaughter whose father is of English descent and her mother from the Latin races mixed with Irish. The baby was born January 22, 1927, and these photographs were taken April 29, 1928. She has never crawled on her knees although we tried to teach her, but goes from a sitting position to her feet with hands flat on the floor, and moves very rapidly, even more so than our own children who crawled on hands and knees.

The photographs show her in five positions and I have also sent you one standing so that you may judge her physical and mental development.

Physically she has never been ill, except a slight fever in cutting her teeth. She has ten teeth, two in front above, four in front below and two first molars on each side.

Mentally she is very quick. When asked questions will point to herself for Bobbie, her shoes, teeth, will comb her hair if given comb and also knows the different members of the family.

Yours very truly,
BAYARD C. RHODES,
San José, Calif.

June 22, 1928

MY DEAR DOCTOR:

I have been extremely interested in the articles in *The Literary Digest* regarding your views of children who walk like a bear. My daughter is seventeen months old now. She never crawled. She immediately started action on "All fours" and kept it up to our great amusement until she was a year old and then she walked on her feet alone, dropping very seldom back on all fours.

She is extremely healthy, climbs everything like a boy, is mentally very keen, very sunny disposition and her name is Dorothy Clare Roach. She is slightly bow-legged and that is our only worry. She is quite chubby and walked too soon, I think. She tries to say anything I tell her.

My father and brother and husband are doctors—so that is one side of our history. My mother's people were lawyers. I was thirty-three when she was born and she is my only child so far.

I should love to hear anything interesting from your research work and contribute anything that I can.

Very sincerely,
MRS. CHARLES ROACH,
Zanesville, O.

First letter:

June 27, 1928

DEAR DR. HRDLIČKA:

This morning I noticed the accompanying articles in our local paper, the *Daily Mining Journal,* and after quite a search I succeeded in finding unmounted prints of our eldest son who walked on all fours from about nine to fourteen months, walked, and climbed stairs, descending backward (of course), and ran so fast down the concrete sidewalk in front of the house I had to run to keep up with him. He was a big, strong child weighing ten pounds at birth, and although he took every contact disease in the catalogue, from whooping cough at ten months to scarlet fever at ten years, he was always healthy in his own right.

He is now nearly nineteen, a Junior at Harvard Engineering School, and rowed on his Freshman 150-lb. crew. He is six feet two inches tall, slender, but strongly built, and passes such an intelligence test he can't live up to it in class. He is the oldest of five children, but the others crept normally, so I shall not send you any pictures of them.

Yours very truly,
MRS. ALTON T. ROBERTS,
Marquette, Mich.

Second letter:

July 6, 1928

Subject—White; ancestors English, Welsh, German-Dutch, in America from 1620–1650.

Male, first born.

Very strong child, weighed ten pounds at birth, large frame and sturdy build. No trouble, but took every contact disease, had it violently and recovered promptly and completely with no after-effects. Is now eighteen years and ten months old, six feet 2 inches tall, weighs 155 lbs., mostly bone and muscle, rows on the 1930 class crew at Harvard.

None of my other four children went on all fours, and none of my sisters or brothers or their children, that I know of, did so either.

He began to move on all fours at about nine or nine and a half months, and kept it up until nearly fifteen months. He could go so fast and so easily there was no incentive for him to walk upright.

Fig. 18.—Master Horace N. Roberts, at about twelve months and at four years.

Photograph in first letter. You can see the back was straight, the legs straight, the feet and hands flat on the ground. He moved freely and easily, without bending his knees very much more than anyone would in walking upright. He went upstairs freely, but I carefully taught him to come down backward. His first efforts at locomotion were going upstairs, and I would sit on the stairs watching him climb and helping him down for an hour at a time. He was a gay and jolly baby and so proud of his athletic prowess. He would run down the walk like a little dog beside me, to the corner to meet his father at noon, both of us running and laughing until we were breathless. He could run faster than I could walk, and he loved to be chased. It was odd his soft little hands were never calloused by running on the concrete. He walked readily once he began, but he was slow to begin because the other way was so quick and easy. He carried his head up, his face forward, as in the photograph, although on account of his straight legs, his spine sloped decidedly toward the front.

My children, probably because I have not a very extended experience, seem to me normal, healthy humans, good tempered, well, intelligent and amusing persons. They all have a very marked mechanical ability, and good bodily control, except the youngest who does not swim well (but that is probably indifference). They pass amazing intelligence tests and flunk cheerfully whatever studies do not interest them. They are all over average height for their age, but both my husband and I are, too. My oldest son went to Phillips Exeter Academy when he was twelve and graduated at sixteen, entered Harvard Engineering School that fall and has just finished his second year there. He is very fond of dance music and jazz, playing a banjo in a dance orchestra two summers. He was in the Freshman Musical Clubs at college.

That seems to be about all, doesn't it?

Very truly yours,
Mrs. Alton T. Roberts,
Marquette, Mich.

March 16, 1928

My Dear Doctor:

I am enclosing a photograph of my daughter in answer to a quotation in *Literary Digest* of March 10th, trusting it may be of interest to you.

The child never crept but at the age of 10¾ months started walking on all fours as shown in illustration and walked and ran in this manner. She started to walk on her feet alone at 1 yr. 20 days.

Apparently she had no fear of walking on her feet alone but it appeared to be more convenient on all fours. She would sight the object of her destination and then without further observation would take off in the direction desired.

Her parentage is principally Anglo Saxon with a mixture of northern Europe including German, Russian, Swedish and Scotch. As to the heredity of the child no record of any such tendency has been recorded in her parents, although a younger sister showed the same tendency to walk on all fours for a short period of time.

The child is now sixteen years old and is a Junior in the Germantown High School.

The photograph may be retained.

Yours very truly,
HENRY C. ROBINSON,
Philadelphia, Pa.

March 13, 1928

DEAR SIR:

I read with great interest your note on: "Children who run on all Fours" in *Science* of March 9, 1928, and wish to send you some notes on my oldest son Paul who had this habit to a marked degree. He could run so fast on all fours that people came to see him. I believe I had the same habit, because I remember having been able to outrun other children on all fours in our plays. The points on which you desire information are answered as follows:

White and German; male (one of twins).

Very healthy, though not of heavy build.

First child.

No other child of seven had this habit. Probably his father; none of the other relatives as far as known.

Began in the tenth month, began to walk upright in the twelfth, but continued for a long time to run on all fours when excited or in a hurry.

As we remember he had his hands open and his head a little downward. He began moving about by creeping on the knees.

He grew up to become a very efficient and successful scientist (oil geologist) now in Tulsa, Oklahoma.

Sincerely yours,
RUDOLF RUEDEMANN,
State Paleontologist,
New York State Museum,
Albany, N. Y.

April 25, 1928

DEAR SIR:

Enclosed are photos of our young son. I read the statement of your request in the *Literary Digest* of March 10. We shall be pleased to answer any questions you may ask.

Respectfully,
MRS. HENRY RUSSELL,
Roswell, N. M.

March 9, 1928

DEAR DOCTOR HRDLIČKA:

During the war, while stationed at Camp Upton, N. Y., we were frequently entertained at the various recreational centers by a young chap whose specialty was the imitation of various animals. He ran, jumped, and propelled himself through hoops over tables and climaxed his exhibition by jumping through a barrel. Later on, I came to know him intimately, and he always assured me that it was a natural endowment, that he had learned to walk that way and never to this day had he suffered any discomfort in that position, his arms and legs being almost equal in length. He was, I believe, of Pennsylvania Dutch stock of ordinary intelligence. He later capitalized all his abilities by entering vaudeville in an act known as Selbini and Nagle, The Butterfly and the Cat. His imitation of the cat is a truly remarkable life-like presentation, and is given on what troupers vainly call "big time." His name is Albert Nagle, and he could be addressed I suppose, at the offices of The National Vaudeville Association, New York. It is quite possible that he could furnish you with some valuable data.

Sincerely yours,
LOUIS B. SAMMS,
Richmond, Ind.

A letter was sent to Mr. Nagle and resulted in his not only replying, but on his next visit to Washington inviting Dr. Hrdlička to see his performance and wholeheartedly assisting him in every way. With some guidance he wrote the following remarkable account of his case:

Report to Dr. Hrdlička by Adalbert Nagle, and his examination:

"When a baby I was undernourished through faulty diet (bad cow's milk); but later caught up and became a 'fat' child.

"At about one year, as told by my people, I began to move on hands and knees, and kept this up until nearly three years, when I began to run on all fours. Soon after that I began also to leap on things like a cat or a dog. Began to walk upright about four, but used to run a good deal on all fours even then, from preference and because I could move faster.

"The habit was of course discovered by my parents and I was 'knocked all about the house' for it as well as laughed at; but kept on because I 'liked it.' Later became so proficient on all fours that I could outrun a pony for a short distance (a block)."

The family is that of Pennsylvania Dutch. Both father and mother around seventy, still living. There were eleven children in the family, the subject being the sixth. None of his brothers or sisters and no one among the relatives showed anything such as he did, so far as can be found out. One younger brother became an acrobat, but of just the ordinary kind.

"As a child, but well after I started to run on all fours, I had a pet Shepherd dog that I liked very much, and I remember imitating the actions of this dog. Was always and am still very fond of animals—had many as pets—all sorts of animals. Will pick up stray or sick dogs, attend to them and then place them with good people.

"I became so quick in jumping that if I could approach pigeons or other birds to within a few feet I would catch them by a quick jump before they could fly away; but did this only for fun, never hurting."

Also as a child, used to take wooden blocks in his hands and imitate by running on all fours the horse's trot and gallop, both in gait and noise.

Never cared much for school, though finished grammar. Liked geography, later physiology; did not get on very well in arithmetic, and only just enough to pass in spelling.

Used to run on all fours between school hours just for his enjoyment. Out of school liked very much to see all sorts of constructive work and building; never hated anything.

When about seven ran once from their porch on all fours after a big dog, when the dog turned on him growling and as if to bite him, frightened him so much that he got St. Vitus dance; but recovered.

Is single but nothing abnormal sexually or any other way as far as he knows.

As he was growing up he appreciated that his special "abilities" could be capitalized, and so he endeavored to develop them as much as possible to make a living with them as he does now.

Was never seriously sick. No traces of any epileptic condition. Is strong, and except for his special talent much like other people. Has dreamt during his life a great deal of flying through the air, on wings or in planes. He still does so fairly frequently.

No phobias, or traces of any other mental abnormalities. No nystagmus, tremors, or disturbances of sensation. Markedly developed musculature of the hand, particularly the radial half.

In running or jumping on all fours alights first on the tips of the fingers and then in the same motion on the balls of the metacarpus, the thumbs being held at more or less an angle from the palm.

Measurements show moderate stature (161.3 cm.), good head (C. I. 80.0), fairly normal length of legs (H. sit.-Stat. index 53.5) long arms (arm spread 109.4 pc. of stature), well developed chest (29.7 × 22.8 cm. at nipple height), relatively somewhat large (esp. broad) hands (19.0 × 9.9), relatively broad feet (24.3 × 10.0); strength somewhat above average for one of his size.

March 24, 1928

DEAR SIR:

I noted with interest an article in the *Literary Digest* on Children Who Run on All Fours, and am enclosing some pictures of my daughter, age one year and eighteen days. She began running in this manner when she was about ten months old. She now walks quite well, having begun to walk a few days before she was a year old.

Additional information:

White—Father's parents born in United States; grandparents in Germany; mother's mother born in U. S., father, in Switzerland.

Female; second child—first child also a girl.

Child is very healthy; weighed 7 pounds 12 ounces at birth—at fifteen months weighs 24 pounds. Has never had any trouble but slight colds.

The older child learned to run on all fours from the baby and both still do so chiefly for amusement.

Walked a few days before she was a year old and practically discarded the all four method at once.

For posture, see pictures.

Both children are very limber and enjoy rough handling. The baby who ran on all fours seems to be very bright and seems to learn very quickly. Father and mother are both college graduates. Mother was for two years a physical director in a St. Paul, Minnesota, high school.

> Yours truly,
> MRS. HUGO SCHLENK, JR.,
> New Orleans, La.

May 23, 1928

DR. HRDLIČKA:

Having read in a Vienna paper your desire for information concerning children running on all fours, I respond herewith to your wish and send you at the same time some snapshots of my youngster who, as you will see, runs on all fours like a little bear.

The boy was born April 14, 1927, is very strongly built, in every way well developed. At birth he weighed Kg. 4.48.

He proceeds from healthy parents whose ancestors on both sides are marked by considerable longevity. I, his father, am 54 years old, 184 cm. tall; his mother is 26 years old, and 170 cm. tall.

We have two other children, the oldest a very strong girl, 3 years 8 months old; the other a strong young boy of 2 years and 8 months. Neither of these children have shown anything peculiar in learning to walk. As to little Erich, who is the subject of this letter, I should like to add that he also is able to hold all sorts of articles with his feet, respectively his toes and is capable of grasping objects with his toes as well as he is with his fingers.

> Respectfully yours,
> JOH. F. SCHMIDT,
> Appiano (Bolzano), Italy.

July 19, 1928

DEAR DR. HRDLIČKA:

I presume that by now you have discovered that babies who go on all fours like dogs are not so rare as at first indicated in the first article in the *Literary Digest* which mentioned your investigations on this subject. I find that among my friends on the staff of the University of California there have been several cases.

I am enclosing several photographs of my daughter, now a year old, who has travelled on all fours for about five months. She does crawl occasionally and at present is beginning to walk, but trotting on all fours is her chief mode of locomotion. At first when a little over seven months of age she would rise up and stand in that position without being able to take a step forward but would lift first one foot and then the other for a brief period. A little later she would make one lunge forward and then fall flat. Within a few weeks, however, she was making excellent progress and now makes remarkable speed, although she really prefers to walk upright at the present time unless she is in a great hurry. (Plate XV.)

You will be interested in knowing that I, myself, did not creep in the usual manner but walked on all fours. My first mode of locomotion which I used for some time, was rolling and later I ran on all fours. I of course do not know much about the details of my performances.

I do not know that this case indicates that the tendency to this style of locomotion is hereditary but perhaps you may find on further investigation that it is.

> Very truly yours,
> DR. WARREN R. SCHOONOVER,
> College of Agriculture,
> University of California,
> Riverside, Calif.

May 8, 1929

Report of a Case:

White; American (French, Scotch, English and Dutch; all known ancestors crossed to this side before the Revolution).

Female, first child.

Health, fine. Slightly built, small bones and head, not fat but weight normal considering build. Active. Good at climbing.

Phenomenon has not to our knowledge been observed among children of our relatives.

Began all fours walk at 9 months of age. Took first unsupported step in an erect attitude on her first birthday and abandoned the all fours method as fast as she perfected regular walking, in about 2 weeks.

At the age of 7½ months, after weeks of attempts to progress by means of swimming motions executed on her stomach with hips and shoulders in the air, she raised herself onto her hands and knees. As her knees presently slipped out from under her she moved backwards, retrogressing about a yard in several repetitions of this operation before she lost her patience and resumed the swimming motions, whereby she at least lost no more ground. She was extremely anxious to go forward, and would regularly become angry after her attempt to do so had failed a number of times.

At 8 months and one week she rolled from a position flat on her back to her stomach and then was sitting up. By this time she was crawling backward for some distance.

In another week she began to crawl forward in the proper manner, going only a few steps at first. At 8 months and 3 weeks began to go on one knee and one foot. Before 9 months she had taken a step or two with both feet and both hands on the ground.

Her hands were fully open, we believe.

As a small baby she had a great preference for holding her legs straight up. Very limber. Very observant.

EWING C. SCOTT,
Sweet Briar, Va.

August 29, 1928

DEAR SIR:

You may be interested to know that my little girl for several months has walked on all fours. She is now fourteen months old and can walk upright but more often than not still walks on her hands and feet and does so very quickly, much quicker than walking. She has never crept on her knees at all—people have remarked how unusual it was—in fact it was a friend who remarked, "Did you read 'Why Babies go on All Fours'?" Adding, "If I were you I should write to the Professor."

Her father by trade is a rigger which involves a great deal of climbing about so perhaps this accounts for baby's instinct to walk on all fours.

I also have two boys, both of which crept on their knees as most babies do. My baby girl is the only child I have had to "go on all fours."

Yours truly,
MRS. E. SEALY,
Billingham, England.

Apr. 15, 1929

Dr. Hrdlička:

Our boy has run on all fours.

Details:

Norwegian, English.

Male, fourth child.

Excellent health.

Not observed in relatives.

Began on all fours at the age of 9 months, kept on until 11 months when he walked erect.

Hands and feet flat on floor, knees slightly bent.

Hands fully open; head slightly lifted. His progress was very swift.

He climbs on everything he sees. Can stand on rocking chair, rock, and balance perfectly without holding on. He very seldom falls. Very fond of animals, but afraid of feathers or small chickens. Is very good natured. One day he was left alone downstairs while I was working upstairs. He pushed a chair to the library table, climbed on the table, threw everything off on the floor and when he decided to climb down he evidently missed the chair. I heard him crying in a peculiar manner so decided to come down and see what was wrong. He was hanging over the edge of the table, his hands pressed flat against the table top, holding himself in that manner. Nothing there to grasp a hold of at all. He seemed to have an unusual strength in his fingers to hold his weight in that manner.

Yours truly,

Mrs. Leonard Seaman,
Bradgate, Ia.

May 9, 1928

My Dear Doctor:

A *Boston Transcript* Editorial states that you are desirous of knowing about children who run around on all fours like a dog. Neither of my sons ever crept, their first method of locomotion being that described. I have photos of the first one in this position, but none of the second. Both are normal boys mentally. They placed the open hand on the floor.

Details:

Race, white; nationality—American; British ancestry.

Sex—Males.

Health and robustness—Eldest has heart lesion, otherwise healthy; younger, robust.

What children in numerical order—First and third.

Has the phenomenon been observed in any other child of the same parents or among relatives?—No.

At what age has the child begun to run on all fours, and how long has it continued?—Hubert began at 8 months, discontinued at 14 months; Theron began at 8 months, discontinued at 14 months.

These boys ran on all fours with much greater speed than children generally creep. The younger sometimes crept but the elder never did. We used to compare the performance to the gait of a turtle. Just at present I have no photos of either available but I have films somewhere of the elder which I will find and from which I will have prints made. There are no abnormalities in the family, otherwise, that I know anything about. Hubert is five and one-half years old; Theron 22 months. Between them there was a boy who died at 4 months of diphtheria or influenza (the doctors disagreed).

Position of the hands, etc.—Hands fully open, heads up like a turtle.

Details as to any other peculiarity of behavior of the child, or any other children in the family—None. Normal in conduct. Both above normal in intelligence.

Yours very truly,
IRA H. SEFTON,
Colfax, Calif.

March 29, 1928

MY DEAR DOCTOR HRDLIČKA:

I have noted your brief mention in the March 9, 1928 *Science* of the "children who run on all fours." I am submitting a report on another child for your series. This is my son, born February 20, 1927, the third child. He has been a healthy baby, very vigorous, of good disposition, well developed and a little larger than the average for his age. His grandparents are all American born— maternal grandparents are English in descent and paternal grandparents are German. The creeping or running on the hands and feet has excited the interest of his grandparents who apparently have not seen but one similar case in the family (see details).

Quite certainly the older brother and sister and the one cousin on the maternal side did not show this phenomenon.

The child began to run on all fours about the first week of December 1927 at which time he was in his tenth month. At this time we had moved into a new home with tile floor in the dining room where he was allowed to play on the floor. He had previously been in a home with oak floors and the usual rugs. In the new house all other floors were oak with rugs. The mother assumed that this tendency to get up on all fours was due to the hardness of the tile floor. No further explanation for it was thought of. The child has, however, showed this style of running about on rugs and oak floors equally as much as on the tile floor. He has been able to crawl on his hands and knees as the other children have done but has apparently discovered the superior speed he can make on all fours.

The position he assumes is one with the arms approximately parallel and the palms of the hands extended in front, flat on the floor. The legs are separated so that the feet are about as far apart as the length from the breech to the heel. The head is sometimes carried in the ordinary posture so that the child cannot see very far beyond his hands. Often the neck is extended so that the child can look directly forward.

Other than this peculiar method of locomotion the boy has shown no peculiarities and has been considered a very normal child of happy disposition. Unfortunately it has not been practicable to secure a picture of him in this position. He has just learned how to walk at the age of thirteen months and does not frequently attempt to creep or run on all fours since that time.

Details:

American born; two grandparents English; two grandparents German by extraction.

Male, third child.

Always healthy and very robust.

The phenomenon has been observed only in a maternal uncle who ran on all fours until about eleven months when he began to walk.

The boy began to run on all fours at about nine and one-half months. He almost stopped it at thirteen months, when he began to walk, but infrequently he still does it at thirteen and one-half months.

The child will run with the arms roughly parallel and the palms of the hands flat on the floor, fingers pointing forward. The feet are separated by a distance approximately equal to the length from the breech to the heel. The foot is placed flat on the floor except toward the end of the stride when he is up on his toes. The feet move alternately, the hips are held higher than the shoulders by a matter of possibly two inches and the head is carried in either the normal posture so that the eyes are directly toward the floor or the neck is extended so that the child can look forward. A photograph has been impossible because the climate has not permitted us to let him try it out of doors and we have not been able to do any indoor photography with his speed of motion.

There are no other peculiarities in the child's actions or in those of his brother or sister.

Very truly yours,
ELMER L. SEVRINGHAUS, M.D.,
State General Hospital,
Madison, Wis.

July 20, 1928

MY DEAR SIR:

Having read in the *Literary Digest* that you are collecting data relative to atavistic traits in children such as walking on all fours, I write to give you the facts about my daughter. She was a normal healthy beautiful nine pound baby, never a day of sickness. At ten months she "hitched" sitting down and the next month began to "scuttle" sideways on all fours. She would "reverse" rather than turn around, as I have seen cub bears do, to reach an article in back of her. She climbed stairs almost at once, in the same position and no slope but held its fascination for her exploring habits. She endeavored to climb vertically but was too heavy to get very far. She is now fifteen and physically and mentally a fine specimen of development. She walked at fourteen months.

I enclose picture.

Her ancestry is Puritan and she has data of a race of men and women who have always borne a responsible part back as far as 1600 in England.

Details:

Report by Ruth F. Sherry, mother, on daughter Virginia, fifteen years old now, second child.

Slight heart lesion from infected tonsils, otherwise above normal. Mentality very good, has poise and sagacity.

She "hitched" in upright position at eight months, at ten months walked on all fours with hands perfectly flat and toes and hands inward very rapidly; always "backed up" when anything was to be reached in back of her instead of turning around (like bear cub). Climbed stairs incessantly and came down backward, always on all fours, also walked sideways, sometimes wheeling with incredible rapidity. Climbed chairs, etc., but too heavy to climb trees or vertical objects.

No other bear walkers in either family or relatives (as far as known). We have two fine sons, above normal in every way. (I judge from school records and Binet tests); they did not walk on fours, however.

This child, Virginia Sherry, had a high temper and would lie on her back and kick a wall or door. Very violent, now controlled. Thumbsucker, contented, not nervous, very active, strong willed.

I would say she almost loped like a dog when in a hurry, using the left hand and foot alternating with the right hand and foot and sometimes singlefooted but not using first hands and then feet which I suppose is a gallop. She always had weight on one foot. Very robust. Slept with knees up often.

Very cordially,
RUTH F. SHERRY,
Evanston, Ill.

April 22, 1928

MY DEAR DR. HRDLIČKA:

Since returning home from Florida I have been able to make some observations on my little grandson's method of progression— of which you have some strips of film—(John Allen Sherzer, Ann Arbor, Michigan). He has never crept in any other way than on his hands and feet, beginning at about ten months. He is now eighteen months of age and is slowly giving up this method, rising onto his feet and walking unsteadily. Up to a few weeks ago he used the all fours style for distance and speed, but now to cross the room he prefers to walk. He started on all fours either from a sitting or standing posture, applied his entire hands and feet to the floor, with his head raised enough to see for what he was aiming. His hands ordinarily showed a tendency to turn in, *i.e.*, the lines of the middle fingers would meet ahead.

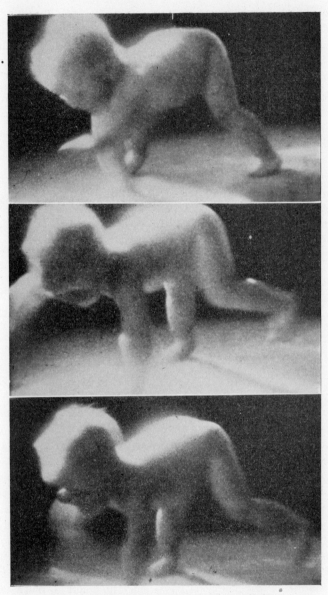

PLATE XIV.—Master Sherzer (*from a film*).

His hands are moved alternately—and also the feet and legs—the right hand and left foot—then the left hand and right foot. There is very little flexing at the knee joint, giving a stiff legged effect and a humping up of the hips as shown in the photo enclosed. Here the right hand and left foot are in the forward position, the left hand (and presumably the right foot) is being sent forward to take its position ahead of the right hand. Up to a few weeks ago the movements were made so rapidly that it was difficult to get the order, but now he is slowing up his movements as though he was wondering whether walking might not be better. He has shown a peculiar tendency to veer off to one side with his hips while his head was being steered to its goal, as though his steps were not equally spaced. This may be only an individual characteristic. He has one brother, about eight years old, who showed nothing of all this.

Sincerely yours,
WILLIAM H. SHERZER,
Michigan State Normal College,
Ypsilanti, Mich.

July 3, 1928

DEAR SIR:

I see by the current issue of the *Science News Letter* that you are collecting reports of instances of children who walk on all fours, like an animal, instead of the more usual method of creeping on hands and knees.

Our older boy, now fifteen years old, used that form of locomotion, but not until he had learned to walk, at the age of about thirteen months. Previous to that he never crept, but moved over the floor in a sitting position. As soon as he had more control of his legs, he began to walk on all fours, and continued to use that method of getting about indoors until he was four years old, or more. The continuation of this animal-like behavior so late may have had some psychological basis, since he could go much more rapidly and with no danger of falling, as in running; and to this day he is over-cautious in any matter involving physical risk. I am sure, however, that his first adoption of the quadruped method of progression was instinctive, as we had no dog or cat or any animal about the flat where we then lived.

His brother, two years younger, even with the monkey-like example of John constantly before him, never attempted quadruped walking, so far as my memory now serves. I remember our commenting on his failure to imitate John at the time, and then I explained it by the fact that Scott (the younger boy) was more thick-set and a plump baby, and consequently could not be so comfortable in that position as John, who was more slender and spidery; but perhaps you have another explanation.

John's subsequent history contains a bad case of chorea from about the age of four to eight or nine years, with traces yet remaining in the form of unpleasant nervous mannerisms. But with the removal of his tonsils when he was about eight years old he has improved, is now normal in weight and height, and has just completed the tenth grade in school with very high standing.

It may be worth remarking that the order in which he moved his arms and legs differed from that of the child reported in detail in the News Letter. That is, if his manner of moving them in a private demonstration this morning was the same as in childhood days. His order is: left foot, left hand, right foot, right hand, touching the floor at approximately equal intervals, instead of hand and opposite foot synchronizing.

I should like also to report the peculiar behavior of a baby who was at our house two days ago. This child is eleven and one-half months old, and has for two months been standing with a support. But she prefers to stand on tiptoe. There is no deformity of her feet, and she can place her foot flat on the floor with no discomfort, but her mother says she will go around and around the play pen on tiptoe very rapidly, and it is only when she is tired enough to sit down that she will drop her entire foot to the floor. She is a perfectly healthy and apparently normal child mentally, of native American parentage. I should have said that our boy's racial inheritance is American also. New England for many generations on one side of the house and Pennsylvania German for at least five generations on the other.

Very sincerely yours,
Mrs. J. W. Shive,
New Brunswick, N. J.

DEAR DOCTOR:

Having read in the *Berliner Morgenpost* of your interest in children who run on all fours, I permit myself to inform you that I also have a little girl of that nature. Before she learned to walk she ran on all fours, and that with astonishing swiftness. On August 23 of this year she will be two years old. She is a healthy and strong little girl, runs already upright quite nicely, but frequently after she becomes absorbed in her play on the floor she suddenly gets up on all fours and runs that way to get some objects that she wants for her play. I shall be glad if this information will be of some use to you.

> Respectfully yours,
> MRS. ANNA SIKORSKI,
> Berlin, Germany.

First letter:

> March 15, 1928

MY DEAR DR. HRDLIČKA:

"As a result of the item which we recently released concerning your inquiry about children who run on all fours, I have a letter from Mrs. Helen Hamilton Sims, of Philadelphia, wife of Captain John C. Sims, who was associated with me during the war, with which letter Mrs. Sims sends me the two enclosed photographs. She also writes as follows, remarking that the child was born in the summer of 1917.

"Here are," she writes, "two pictures of him 'in action' and I have never seen anything like the speed he made. He looked just like a small bear—and did it long after he could walk because he could go so much more quickly on the flat of his feet and his hands.

"As to his race—well Jack (Capt. Sims) is all Scotch Irish—and I am Scotch, Irish, English and Welsh. The photos were taken at just a year old and he continued the practice till nearly two.

"If your friend Dr. Hrdlička wants any more data I shall gladly give what I can, for I really love to talk about my children."

> With best regards,
> MRS. H. H. SIMS,
> (through E. E. FREE),
> Philadelphia, Pa.

Second letter:

March 21, 1928

MY DEAR DR. HRDLIČKA:

I have no other photographs of my small brown bear at an early age. The ones Dr. Free forwarded were taken to send to my husband while he was in France.

His race is more mixed than I thought, as I quite forgot a completely Dutch great grandmother—otherwise, as I wrote Dr. Free, he is all a product of the British Isles though "Made in America."

He preferred to go on all fours long after he could walk.

Mr. Sims says his nephew, now grown, also did this, but I never saw him.

Details:

Race and nationality—American.

Sex—Male.

What child in numerical order—Second.

Health and robustness—Excellent; very strong straight back.

Has the phenomenon been observed in any other child of the same parents or among relatives—First cousin.

At what age has the child begun to run on all fours, and how long has it continued—Seven or eight months till nearly three years.

Held head back so as to see.

Extremely normal child, sunny, thoughtful. No peculiarities. Very slow at books, but very intuitive and observant. Oldest and youngest children much "quicker" than he.

Sincerely yours,
MRS. H. H. SIMS,
Chestnut Hill, Pa.

July 18, 1928

DEAR SIR:

Some time ago, in a London, Ontario, paper I noticed a piece concerning "Children Who Run on All Fours." In this article one is asked to send to you pictures and statements of children who do this.

I have a baby boy, now almost fifteen months old. He began creeping on his hands and feet at the age of nine months and until he was a year old (when he began to walk upright) he went around this way. In the pictures I am enclosing you will observe that he holds his head erect and his hands are spread open.

As far as we know he is the only one on either side who has gone in this manner. He is a very healthy happy child and always has been.

As to race, my husband is a descendant of parents of German origin while I am of English descent.

Is there anything you can tell us about your observations that would be interesting for us to know? We would be glad if you would tell us if it is not too much to ask.

Additional details:

Child, white, Canadian; male; first child; now 15 mos. old.
Health, perfect.

> I remain,
> Yours sincerely,
> MRS. CARL E. SMITH,
> Guelph, Ont.

June 29, 1928

DEAR DOCTOR:

I would like to report to you that my baby walked on all fours instead of crawling or sliding. He is my fifth child and the only one to creep by this method. He began at about eleven months of age and now at sixteen months he can go thus upstairs, downstairs and even climb up on the table if there is a chair handy. He is rather small in size but I have never seen a healthier baby and think he can take care of himself.

> Yours respectfully,
> MRS. J. O. SMITH,
> Redding, Ia.

First letter:

April 18, 1928

DEAR SIR:

I have read your article on infants who run on all fours. I am from Scotland and my husband from Canada. We have three children and the youngest, a boy, ran on all fours until he walked. He is our brightest child, having sat up when four months, took steps at eight and walked well when ten months.

I have also seen him get up in his bassinet without touching anything with his hands and without getting first on his knees, and I have never yet seen another child do it.

I am enclosing a snap of my niece taken when on all fours. We took the picture to send to her grandfather in Scotland as we all thought her method of getting around so odd and amusing.

> Yours truly,
> Mrs. J. Willard Smith,
> Hyattsville, Md.

Second letter:

May 1, 1928

Dear Sir:

I am enclosing the information you desired.

Child—White; American (father Canadian, mother Scottish).

Male, third child. (My sister's child who crawled on all fours was also her third.)

Health very good and quite robust. People remark on him being so fine a child and so big for his age.

Not in either of our children. My sister has one girl who used that same method.

Began on all fours around six months. Walked well when ten months. Occasionally even yet I see him on all fours but he only resorts to that when vexed over something. For instance today he had a knife which I took from him. He was quite peeved, lay down on the floor, then got up on hands and feet, and ran over the floor to lie down again.

I could not describe the performance more accurately than just by saying he moves exactly as a monkey does. I believe, though, his head is mostly down, especially when grieved.

Hands on floor are open and the head more down than up.

I have seen him when he was six months old get upon his feet in his bassinet without touching anything with his hands or elbows and not even getting on his knees. I never could understand how he accomplished the rising up so nicely as he arose too quickly for me to see the position of his feet. He has no other peculiarity and my two girls are quite normal in every way. I am sure you could not see three healthier children anywhere. (Plate XII.)

> Mrs. J. Willard Smith.

Aug. 1, 1928

DEAR DOCTOR:

Here is a report on our little son.

Child, Anglo-Saxon-American.

Male, first child.

Very well, unusually large and strong for his age.

No other case known in family or among relations.

Ran on all fours from the tenth to the sixteenth month.

When Jeremy started to crawl at 7 months he used his whole body, pushing backward on his abdomen and digging in with toes and hands but not raising his body. During the eighth month he began raising one knee, creeping with hands, one foot and one knee, a sort of hitch, went forward, backward and sideways. This continued for about two weeks. Then he began walking on hands and feet. From his tenth to his sixteenth month this was his only mode of locomotion and he became very proficient. Walked with great ease and rapidity, almost running at times. Very often he stopped, balanced on feet and one hand and waved his free hand, while he shouted or babbled.

During his first year and up to his eighteenth month when he was actually on his feet he did not wear shoes and stockings. When he first began to crawl it was warm enough for him to be on the grass and during the months when he was learning to get around he was on the grass or a sandy walk most of the time.

While running on all fours his hands were partly closed in gripping position and actually gripped the ground, so that his nails were often broken and full of dirt after an hour of running in this way.

From the third month he was unusually active though it was difficult for him to sit up or pull himself up because of his size. At birth he was 22 inches long and weighed eight and three-fourths pounds. He continued to gain and grow all through his first year at such a rate that the physician, under whose care he is, watched very carefully for symptoms of a pituitary disturbance. Now at two years the rate of growth is not so abnormal and the physician thinks that while he is undoubtedly a pituitary type the disturbance is not a serious one probably and seems to be taking care of itself. He is mentally normal, somewhat backward in talking, says only words, with no sentences yet but does some of the motor and mechanical tests of children older than he.

At three months there was a decided increase in his motor activity and from then on until his tenth month he was active most

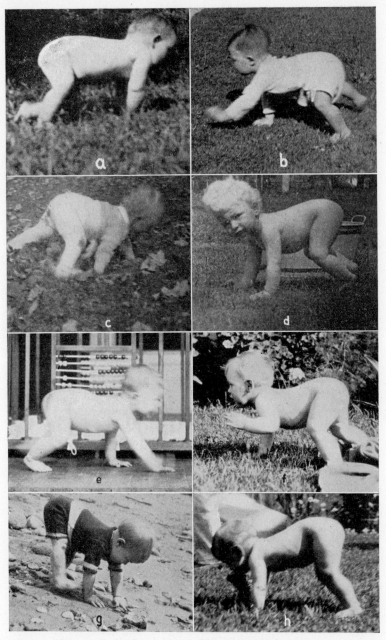

PLATE XV.—*a.* J. R. Smith, boy, eleven months. *b.* Van Cott, boy. *c.* Younger, boy. *d.* Walter, boy. *e.* Lear, girl, eleven months. *f.* Betty J. Schoonover, ten months. *g.* MacLachlan, girl, fifteen months. *b.* Fred. R. Pitts, Jr., boy.

of his waking time. He was never happy when placed in his carriage even when it was in motion, but bounced around, tried to get up and when taken out showed great satisfaction.

Additional note:

JEREMY ROGERS SMITH—born August 3, 1926.

From tenth to sixteenth month, regular method of locomotion was walking on hands and feet. When he first began to crawl, hitched along on one foot, one knee and both hands for about two weeks, then began walking on both feet and hands.

> Yours very truly,
> MRS. PHILIP L. SMITH,
> New York, N. Y.

February 9, 1928

DEAR DOCTOR:

In answer to your letter in the *J. A. M. A.*, Jan. 21, 1928, I am sending you a picture of a baby who walked on all fours for several months.

This child is the third in the family. The parents know of no other case of the kind in either family. The families are all of average intelligence, American born for many generations. The little girl commenced to walk in this manner at about 7 or 8 months, and kept it up until beginning to walk at about fourteen months. Was always strong and well, though bothered by adenoids and tonsil trouble; was operated for both at about one year of age.

She walked with both hands flat on the floor with fingers extended and the feet flat also. The picture would say opposite limbs moved together, and the right foot and leg seemed to swing around somewhat, though not enough to look awkward. She held the head thrown up face forward most of the time. She has been fairly strong all her life, excepting some throat trouble and her voice rather coarse and low pitch. She is now married, and she has one baby girl about eight months. The baby does not show any peculiarities of any kind.

The mother is now 28 years of age, good form, graceful, handsome. A very positive blond, blue eyes, average height and weight. This is all I can tell you about this case.

> Yours sincerely,
> FRANK S. SMITH,
> Nevada, Ia.

July 19, 1928

DEAR SIR:

I notice in the *Literary Digest* of June 23, 1928, you are interested in babies that learned to go about on all fours before learning to walk.

My baby, now 18 months old, learned to get about like that when she was seven months old. She learned to run on her hands and feet so fast that I would have to run to catch her. By the age of one year she had quit that means of walking almost altogether as she began to walk naturally when she was ten months old. At infrequent intervals she runs about on her hands and feet even yet.

Yours sincerely,
MRS. H. C. SMITH,
Richard City, Tenn.

DEAR SIR:

I am interested in the enclosed clipping taken from my copy of the *Literary Digest* for March 10, and although not a physician I take the liberty of writing to you.

I am the mother of a baby boy who went around on all fours for some five months. This baby is white and born of English parents who belong to the mass of common working people. The baby was between eight and nine months of age when he first started going on all fours.

Palms flat on the floor, knees stiff, feet slightly raised and head well up. The speed attained while running in this position used to amaze us constantly.

The baby began to stand erect at thirteen months and at fourteen months was walking. For a time he would drop back to the all fours position even then, but it wasn't long before he forgot about it altogether.

I enclose an imperfect snapshot which I tried to take last summer while the baby was in this position.

At the present age, twenty months, we have a healthy, sturdy limbed child with a beautifully shaped head. Which we hope is a promise of a wider destiny than we, his parents, have experienced.

Very truly yours,
MRS. ERNEST STANSFIELD,
Sanford, Me.

First letter:

March 6, 1928

DEAR SIR:

In the March 10th 1928 issue of *The Literary Digest* occurs mention of children who run on all fours and an invitation is extended to physicians to make report of such cases coming under their observation. I am not a physician but am interested in the subject on account of our little granddaughter.

Child's name, Patty-Lou Stark.

At about 9 months she began running on all fours instead of creeping. Feet squarely on floor, palms open, left arm and right leg moving in unison. For slower movement and shorter distance uses hands and knees at her choice. Holds head squarely ahead and about level with back. Race—white. No known similar cases in the family on either side. Child is now past twelve months, stands alone, has taken a step or two but does not walk; has used a walker car since she was about 7 months. Is a little overweight but healthy, strong, vigorous and normal in all respects. At three months she had two teeth.

We have no photos of child in such posture but will try for a Kodak picture, and if successful and it is desired, we will send you one.

> Respectfully yours,
> JOHN G. STARK, the girl's grandfather,
> Elmwood, Neb.

Second letter:

March 27, 1928

DEAR SIR:

Referring to yours of the 10th inst. we have the following to say as to your additional questions regarding the unusual creeping attitude of Patty-Lou Stark, daughter of Mr. and Mrs. E. N. Stark of Elmwood, Nebraska.

The first child (only child).

We have the table of genealogy of the Stark name to 1650 and other branches of the family for several generations and there is no mention of any similar case. This of course would not prove that some such case has not happened. But we never heard of any.

We are enclosing two kodak photos, the best we could do, which indicate quite well and accurately the performance of Patty-Lou. Patty now at 13 months, walks freely and naturally and is erect and straight of limbs.

Climbing appears natural with her but not so exceptional that we would take special note of it; it would seem to us that she is

FIG. 19.—Miss Patty-Lou Stark.

too young to judge as to this. Her favorite pet is her dog, Rover, which name she says distinctly and applies the name to anything that has fur.

Respectfully yours,
JOHN G. STARK.

March 11, 1928

DEAR SIR:

I have just noticed in the *Literary Digest* that you want information concerning children who walk on all fours. If our little girl is not one of the eleven already reported you may call it the twelfth.

My father was a Frenchman, mother's parents came "across" from Germany while young. Wife is of Irish derivation with a trace of American (Indian). We have four children, ages 6, 4, 2 yr., 5 months.

The youngest girl commenced to walk on hands and feet at about seven months and continued for some three months. She went palms down, head up and traveled rapidly. We have no picture of her in action. If there is anything out of the ordinary about this kid now it is the way she dances around on her toes, claps her hands, etc., as an expression of delight . . .

Let me add, with pardonable pride, that a week ago we had the kids examined by an "expert" at a free health clinic and he said we had a fine family.

Respectfully yours,
F. W. STENGER,
Houston, Mo.

April 2, 1928

MY DEAR DR. HRDLIČKA:

In the *Literary Digest* for March 10, 1928, I saw your article on children who run on all fours.

Our oldest child used to move about this way, but we had no idea it was so "unusual" or such an "interesting abnormality." The data I can give you must be from memory only.

From about fifteen months of age Charles went on all fours whenever he wished to make speed. Otherwise he wriggled along on his stomach. He was slow at creeping and did not really make much progress before thirteen and a half months.

At eighteen months he learned to walk and never returned to the "all fours" method.

My husband took some moving pictures of Charles on the run; and I enclose a snapshot taken from this film.

Mr. St. John and I are Americans chiefly of English stock for about eight generations in this country. My husband is professor of botany at the Washington State College at Pullman.

Our second son, now a year old, creeps everywhere on his hands and knees, but has never attempted to go on all fours.

Details:

Child and family; American on both sides as far back as the Mayflower and the thirteenth generation. Chiefly English stock, with a tiny addition of Scotch Irish and Swiss.

Male, first child.

Health, excellent.

Cannot recall any other instances of this phenomenon in either side of the family.

Ran on fours from about 15 months until he learned to walk at 18 months, when the habit was discontinued.

Hands fully open. Head varied, sometimes held up to see what was ahead, sometimes dropped a little forward.

No other peculiarity.

> Sincerely yours,
> Mrs. Harold St. John,
> Pullman, Wash.

January 3, 1928

Dear Dr. Hrdlička:

In *Science* Oct. 7 supplement, under "Quadruped Method of Locomotion" you are reported to say that it is rare for children to move on all fours, like a bear. I pulled these photos out of our first child's album but have delayed sending them until you should return from Europe.

These pictures are of our daughter, made at our home about 1916, and show her preferred and fastest way of getting over the ground.

On remarking the subject others have told me of knowing children who used that method of locomotion. Perhaps it is not so rare.

Desired details follow:

Mary Elizabeth, the main subject of this note, was born March 24, 1915, and is our first child.

Our second child, Samuel, born October 24, 1917, did creep like other children but at the age of three or four it was a very distinct personal peculiarity that in his play, whether indoors or out of doors, he ran, of his own will, on all fours, both hands and feet flat, and travelled at a very considerable speed that way.

Mary Elizabeth began to travel on all fours at about the age of 10 months and never did creep. As shown by the photograph her hands and feet were flat on the ground and there was no intermediate movement at elbows and knees.

As closely as we can remember she stopped running on all fours at about the age of 1½ years, after learning to walk upright.

As mentioned above, her hands and feet were flat and she moved as a beast does normally, and not by racking.

Her head was held up as shown in the photographs.

· 339 ·

The child was peculiar in no other way but is, at the age of 13, overlarge and is a leader in school work.

Sincerely yours,
R. W. STONE,
Harrisburg, Pa.

February 1, 1928

DEAR SIR:

I am sending you a picture of a young friend of mine, which, I think, shows the mode of progression although it is rather hazy in one or two details.

The following in answer to your specific inquiries: White; chiefly English; male; fair health; more robust as an infant than at present age, 5 years; first child; began at about 12 months and kept the habit until at least 18 months; used exceptionally thereafter. As an accompaniment to this habit the child used to slap the floor with his hands when proceeding rapidly.

Sincerely yours,
TRACY I. STORER,
Davis, Calif.

October 1, 1928

DEAR DR. HRDLIČKA:

I have a little boy who is nineteen months old who also used the peculiar method of locomotion on all fours. He never crept like the average child, but started at the age of eight months walking on his all fours. The day after he was ten months old he walked alone on two. He seemed exceptionally steady on his feet in spite of the fact that he walked on his tiptoes until very recently. He is a husky little chap and I am inclined to think that this method he used is the reason he has such hard and strong muscles in his arms and legs.

Child, white; American; male; my first born.

A number one health and quite robust, with a figure that makes us wonder if some day he might not challenge Gene Tunney or his equal.

This, to my knowledge, is the only time this mode of locomotion has occurred in either Mr. Stretch's family or my own.

He began on fours at the age of seven and one-half months and continued until ten months old when he walked. After which he did very little running on hands and feet.

Used to get down on his hands and toes. Was never known to put his heels down and this was very noticeable as he was always barefoot until he walked. His hands as I remember were always open. As to his head, he generally held it so that he could see the object he was going for or the place to which he was going. During the period of walking on his all fours he used to amuse us greatly by climbing up the corner of his pen; but instead of, perhaps, wrapping his legs around the rungs, he used to wrap his toes and feet. At that time his grandmother remarked that she had never believed in Darwinism until Sonny came.

You will no doubt think I have a little monkey, for sure, only he really doesn't look like one. He climbs everywhere even out of his high chair and he is not quite two years old. His sense of balance seems to be very keen. When he first began to walk, he walked on his toes, holding his hands parallel with his head for balance. He still shows a tendency to walk on his toes and his instep and foot are very well developed. I have a sister who has a baby that walked on her toes so I did not think this was so extraordinary. I am mighty sorry now that I didn't take a picture of him while in the act of walking on his all fours.

I am greatly interested in your subject, Dr. Hrdlička. I now have a little daughter but she is only six months old. I am waiting now to see what method of locomotion she will use. If by any chance she should use this same method or have any little similar peculiarities I will let you know about them even if it should prove that we are a bunch of monkeys.

If there is any report you would care to send me I will give you my new address. I am

> Yours very sincerely,
> Mrs. E. N. Stretch,
> Meriden, Conn.

July 3, 1928

Dear Dr. Hrdlička:

An article in *Science News Letter* of June 30 has just come to my attention. In this article it is said that you are seeking information about babies that walk on all fours. It never occurred to me that this was at all abnormal. I thought that it merely indicated a strong, vigorous child. I have had four children, three boys and one girl. The boys all walked in this fashion and I have snapshots of all of them in action. I can find in my collection no record of the little girl on all fours so can not be positive that she did so. I think, however, that she did.

It was such a common thing among my babies that I gave it no thought. I remember noticing that my sister's babies never did so but thought it because they were not so vigorous as mine. Mine all started by creeping on hands and knees in the regular fashion but as they gained in strength they would run very rapidly with hands and feet all flat on floor and bodies raised high. The oldest boy died at three years from diphtheria. The others are well and normal in every respect—all above average size for age.

The pictures are only small snapshots.

Sincerely yours,
Mrs. David Sturrock,
Aguacate, Prov. Havana, Cuba.

June 17, 1928

Dear Sir:

I have just read a newspaper article concerning your investigations, relative to children who walk like quadrupeds and am writing to tell you about my two year old son.

He has been walking in this manner for several months but has taken very few steps alone. He now rises from the floor and stands upright without assistance. He says some words quite plainly but makes many queer sounds.

For the first eleven months of his life he was undernourished and grew very little. If there is any literature on the subject available we shall be glad to know of it.

Yours truly,
Mrs. O. G. Stutler,
Parkersburg, W. Va.

October 20, 1928

Dr. Hrdlička:

My youngest baby never crept but ran on all fours like a puppy at a little less than a year. Enclosed is a snapshot of her. I tried to get one from the side but she moved with such rapidity that it was impossible to get her. She is now eighteen months old and handles herself as well as her brother who is nearly three.

Details:

Mother of child of English and German descent. Father Irish. All born in America.

Child, female; age 22 months, weight 30 pounds; third child.

No other case of walking on all fours known in the families.

Started around nine months and continued for about six or eight weeks. Even after she walked upright for some time whenever she required speed would drop on all fours and run.

Hands were flat on ground. Feet usually on toes. Head on level with shoulders, and how she could travel!

She is unusually quick to grasp things. Talks clearly and well. Very active. The oldest boy is unusually bright, overactive and of a nervous high strung temperament. The second child (a boy) is just the opposite. Timid, slow to walk and talk. Does not talk as well as the baby. Slow in every way.

Both the first and third child have unusually good sense of balance. The boy could hang from anything, he could get a toe hold on before he could walk. Both of them are forever climbing. The middle child is always afraid of falling and loses his balance at the slightest provocation.

Sincerely yours,
MRS. J. A. SULLIVAN,
Meriden, Conn.

March 30, 1928

DEAR DOCTOR HRDLIČKA:

I have noted your appeals for photographs showing quadrupedal locomotion in children, and send you herewith a film taken by Dr. W. L. Schmitt, of the National Museum, whom you doubtless know. The subject is my own son, Herbert, the picture being taken at the age of approximately one year. (Born June 27, 1917 —Dr. Schmitt may be able to give approximate date of film, if worth while.)

It is worth mentioning, in connection with this picture, that Herbert's great toes, for the first two years or more of his life, extended at a decided angle with the others, giving to his feet a decidedly simian appearance. The condition persisted so long that we became worried and consulted an orthopedic specialist. His feet are now perfectly normal, and he displays no peculiarly pithecoid propensities.

Race and nationality—White, mainly of English descent.

Sex—Male.

What child in numerical order—Third.

Health and robustness—Good.

FIG. 20.—Herbert Sumner, one year.

Has the phenomenon been observed in any other child of the same parents or among relatives?—No.

Peculiar position of great toes; see letter.

Sincerely yours,

F. B. SUMNER,

The Scripps Institution of

Oceonography,

La Jolla, Calif.

March 28, 1928

DEAR DR. HRDLIČKA:

I am much interested in an abstract in the *Literary Digest* for March 10 in regard to children who run on all fours, as I have a son who moved about in this manner before he began to walk.

The enclosed snapshot shows the characteristic manner of his moving about. It will be noticed that the hands are held flat and quite far apart, that the legs are kept near together, the back straight and horizontal, and the head on a level with the back.

This was the first and only means of "creeping," the child starting in at the age of seven months and continuing until he began to walk at the age of fourteen months. He traveled at considerable speed in this manner.

Following are some of the details asked for regarding the child:
Race—White.
Nationality—American.
Position of hands while running—Open and fingers spread.

In addition, I might say that the boy comes from long-lived ancestry, and that he is of the twelfth generation in the United States from English stock. He has always been unusually healthy, and I might say that his I. Q. is far above normal.

I will be interested to know what conclusions will be drawn after a study has been made of this phenomenon of walking on all fours.

> Yours very truly,
> S. L. Swasey,
> La Tuque, Que., Canada.

First letter:

July 4, 1928

Dear Dr. Hrdlička:

I had often wondered whether many babies went on all fours as my little girl did.

She was born at Sloane Hospital in New York City, Dec. 16, 1924. She did most things just a little sooner than my books on babies specified, such as laughing, holding up her head at three months, reaching for and holding her own rattles at four months. She had a rope across her "kiddycoop" and pulled herself up to sitting position by this at six months. Then she started using her feet just like hands—would pick up a talcum powder box or a rubber doll with her two feet and place it in her hands and the most piercing shrieks usually went with these accomplishments. Now, neither my husband nor I have ever had much faith in this "monkey business," at least not any more than thinking people are forced to have in spite of religion; but to watch her juggle those toys with her feet and further stunts of swinging on her rope would almost convince anyone.

She was a fat baby too, not wiry, and very pretty. In the seventh month she started to creep on hands and knees and at eight and one-half months pulled up by a chair to a standing position. Just about this time some of my husband's business friends came to call and one of them called my attention to the baby. Said he had never seen a child "get a high behind" like that before. There she was on all fours just standing still and twisting her head all around, apparently enjoying everyone's amusement. She continued this, sometimes creeping, but when in a hurry—up and on all fours and go like the wind. She took her first steps in upright position at twelve and one-half months and walked well at fourteen months but always fell back to all fours when tired or in a hurry. And now at three and one-half years when she wants a real hilarious time she says, "Mama, let's play bear" and this means a chase with her on all fours.

She is in perfect health according to an examination last month. Is large for her age—forty-three inches tall—forty-four and one-half pounds; and is considered very smart, I mean bright.

Our four months old boy is trying to move himself around and am interested to see if he will take to all fours naturally, too.

Very sincerely,
MRS. LEE TALBOT,
Tulsa, Okla.

July 18, 1930

Second letter:
DEAR DR. HRDLIČKA:

We appreciate your interest in our children and if what had seemed mostly amusing to us has any scientific significance I am very glad to give you the information.

Making allowances for the fact that most of us parents are proud of our offspring for one reason or another, physicians of good standing and several others who should know assure us our children are above the average in health, general appearance and intelligence. But personally I thought all these qualities were quite natural since they were born healthy and I took good care of them. We did think our daughter's performance on all fours not alone amusing but very unusual to say the least. All in fun we used to call her our little monkey for this and the fact that when she was just a few months old she would pick things up with her feet and place them in her hands and screech and shriek piercingly.

Also perform on a thick cord we had across her crib. But I believe I wrote you of all this in detail before. She still gets a great "kick" out of going on all fours although she is now 5½ years.

The little boy did not take to this method of locomotion naturally but she taught him. However he had a method all his own quite as amusing to watch. He started it just after he was learning to walk between 12 and 13 months. He always had a way of dropping on his knees, then sitting back on his heels and would play this way by the hour. From this position he would fall forward on his hands with his head high and hop forward quickly. This looked just like a little frog hopping. He still does it. It is just as funny looking as the little girl but doubt if it is as interesting to you. He is undoubtedly bright and very healthy and strong. He got his first tooth when 4 months old and the full set by 1½ years. He is now 2 years and 5 months, just short of 36 inches and weighs 31 lbs. He spoke sentences of 6 and 7 words at 2 years very distinctly. I never made any special effort to really teach either of the children to talk. And he says things that shows he really thinks. One amusing thing he told me just after he was two. I was having some difficulty in cleaning his little nose so he just said, "Mother, better get the vac-cuum." A long word for him but the idea was good. When the trees started to get green in spring he ran and told us one bright morning that "Santa Claus had been trimming the trees up so pretty."

The little girl is big and strong and although I have not sent her to school have taught her myself and read to her a great deal. Also play a lot with both of them. She's interested in stories and has worlds of imagination. She loves to hear about far away places and people and has times of pretending she's all kinds of things. Last summer I was studying Russian and she was picking it up with the greatest of ease. She is not a musical genius but when we sent her to take piano lessons at 4½ she took to it naturally and just after her fifth birthday played a couple of short pieces in a recital. She took these lessons ½ hour daily from a musical friend of ours but did not practice any at home. Since moving we've had to discontinue the lessons. We also sent her to a class in "natural" dancing at the Y. W. C. A. and her teacher praised her ability in this.

Naturally she has faults like most but we are very proud of both of them. The little girl sometimes has a way when speaking to strangers of trying to speak too fast and ends up in stuttering. This is not so pronounced as a year ago. She has also times of dreaming or whatever it is and pays no attention or seems quite dumb about the matter in hand. But we try to help her over it and am sure she'll get over it in school as it certainly does not amount to a serious fault.

These children have a great conglomeration of ancestry.

> Mrs. Lee Talbot,
> Oklahoma City.

April 21, 1928

Dear Sir:

In the *Pathfinder* of the 14th inst. I read the article on "The all-fours habit," in which it mentions that you would like to hear "from physicians who observe children running on all fours instead of creeping" and although I am not a physician, but a rancher, a case has just come to my notice. In fact we were just remarking about it when I noticed the article in the paper.

One of the partners in the Ranch, who lives about half a mile from me, has a little boy who was born last June and he does not creep but runs around at considerable speed on all fours with his hands and feet flat on the floor and his knees straight. When spoken to or his attention attracted he looks up without changing position.

The father is Mr. George Neis who is of German parents and the mother is French Canadian.

Trusting this information will be of some help in your research, I remain

> Very truly yours,
> Fred H. Temple,
> Christopher Lake, Sask.

June 22, 1928

Dear Sir:

I have a daughter, aged one year, who for about 2 months previous to her first birthday amused us by walking about on her hands and feet in the curious fashion described in this week's *Literary Digest*. Her legs being longer than arms she would tend to incline somewhat forward, thus apparently affording, as it were, an impetus or incentive to keep moving.

She is an unusually beautiful and perfectly formed child and was able to walk just previous to her first birthday.

Ancestry is American from Colonial days on both sides.

Details:

Child, white; ancestry, pre-revolutionary American.

Female, second in the family.

Health, perfect.

No other such case known of in family or among relatives.

Moved on all fours from tenth to twelfth month of her age when started walking.

Active, running about with the legs stiff and hips higher than the head, producing a swaying of the body when in motion. Legs wide apart.

Head parallel with the body but child inclined to turn head sidewise and look up at parents to see if being watched. Child apparently pleased at her performance. Hands fairly open.

Both the little girl and her brother are especially bright and intelligent above the average. Girl is brown eyed with brown hair like both her parents while the boy is blue eyed blond unlike any immediate progenitor, though the facial characteristics are alike.

Yours very truly,

REV. I. M. TERWILLIGER,
Carmel, Calif.

July 18, 1928

DEAR DOCTOR:

My daughter in Hollywood, Cal., asks me to write reporting her son Smith Thompson, 2½ years old now, who traveled on hands and feet. He was breast fed, after 6 months given supplementary feeding of "Dryco" and orange juice, juice of parsnips, carrots, etc. She, my daughter, wants me to impress on your mind that he is a "wonderful child" in all particulars. He started going on "all fours" at seven months, and at nine months could move by this means very rapidly. He began walking at one year and one week but if he got in a hurry or his nurse wanted to catch him to prevent an accident or mischief, he would drop to hands and feet and get up more speed. Dr. Nixon of Hollywood, a child specialist, says his leg and shoulder muscles are especially well developed. At 2½ years he weighs 38½ pounds and Dr. Nixon says he has measurements of a child (in length, chest, etc.) of 3½ to four years old. So far as I know he is the only child in our family to adopt this form of locomotion.

Fraternally yours,

Dr. H. W. Smith,

Roodhouse, Ill.

for Smith Thompson.

April 1, 1928

Dear Sir:

I am responding to your article in the *Literary Digest*, for March 10, 1928, concerning children who walk on all fours.

Our first child, a boy, born December 23, 1926, crawled on hands and knees from six months to one year. He crawled before sitting up alone, the latter taking place at about seven months. At one year we noticed him walking on hands and feet, soles flat on the floor, hands spread out flat, legs stiff; left hand and right foot, right hand and left foot alternating; head down. We supposed this was the beginning of his learning to walk. At thirteen months he began to walk alone. At fourteen and one-half months he got up from the floor by himself and walked. He rises to a standing position from one of all fours. He practices this several times in succession, dropping to hands and feet, straightening up with an effort, gaining his balance, then moving forward. At fifteen and one-half months he still walks on all fours about half the time, especially when in a hurry to reach something. We have a dog with whom he plays almost constantly. There might be a possibility of influence there.

His health, mental and physical, seems fine. Ten pounds at birth, he weighs twenty-five to thirty pounds at fifteen months. He has always been physically very active. One spell of diarrhea at seven months is his only illness. During that sick spell a peculiar habit was formed, of banging his head against the end of the bed, hard enough to cause a discolored bruise. He still persists in this habit, especially when sleepy, angry, or disturbed in any way. He will stand up and bang his head on the side of the crib, or on the fence of his pen. He also rocks in his crib on hands and knees, always before going to sleep; often rocks and bangs his head in his sleep at night or during a nap. He stands up and shakes the side of the crib so violently that he moves it all over the room; also shakes fence of pen, or high chair, always with a rhythmical motion; often emits peculiar cries during this proceeding, rather like a monkey in his cage.

He sucked his thumb from six months to one year. Stopped entirely all at once. His teeth are slow to develop. The first lower appeared at about eleven months, second lower at twelve months, two uppers during the fifteenth month.

His race is Caucasian, nationality American. I have no information yet about other children of the family. Our second child, a boy, is only three months old.

I shall be glad to give any further information that would be of assistance in your study. I am very much interested in the findings of your research.

The pictures do not show his gait very well, which is a rocking motion, legs unbent, buttocks high in the air, forming a downward slope to the head, which is very close to the ground.

Sincerely,
MRS. WARREN O. THOMPSON,
Boulder, Colo.

First letter:

June 1, 1928

DEAR DR. HRDLIČKA:

In a conversation with my mother last night, I discovered that there is a history of at least partial quadrupedism in my own family. My younger sister, Margaret Thone, never crept when she was an infant. Her usual method of progression was to assume a sitting posture and then hitch herself forward with her heels; but when she was in a hurry she would turn over and walk on all fours.

My mother informs me that I never used this method, so far as she can remember, but was a normal creeper. However, I do recall that as a child of seven or eight I used to "go quadruped" as a stunt to amuse my younger cousins, and used to carry them on my back in that way. I discontinued this at the age of about thirteen, and thought I had lost the ability completely; but this morning I tried it and find that I can still walk on all fours, though somewhat slowly. I have a little difficulty in getting my heels down to the floor now. I am surprised that I can do it at all, however, considering the great length of my legs. I "toe in" with my fingers, and I also found myself doubling the distal joints under and obtaining "purchase" on the carpet with my knuckles instead of with my finger tips.

My mother states that she has practised quadrupedism ever since she was a child, at first as a stunt and then as a part of setting-up exercises. She is still able to do this, at the age of 55. She does not know whether she was a naturally quadruped infant, and since her parents are dead there is presumably no way of determining this.

She has another trick, which may be an atavism. With her knees perfectly straight, she can turn her feet inward and set their plantar surfaces squarely against each other. This also is a childhood stunt continued as a bit of physical exercise. Perhaps these bits may be worth adding to your record.

> Very sincerely yours,
> FRANK THONE,
> Des Moines, Ia.
> (Science Service)

Second letter:

September 4, 1928

DEAR DR. HRDLIČKA:

I am now recording here the peculiar type of dream which we discussed.

I used to have these dreams rather frequently during adolescence, and still have them, although they have now become somewhat rare. In my dream I find myself fleeing in terror from some unknown pursuer, running as fast as I am able, bending my body somewhat forward. My arms must be a good deal longer than normal, although if this is the case I have never taken notice of it. At any rate, in my haste and anxiety to get away I find myself frequently placing my hands on the ground and vaulting forward on them, very much as I have seen long-armed apes do in running about the floors of their cages. This terrified flight of which I dream usually takes place through a rather open woodland, and sometimes on the side of a hill. But whether I am running up hill or down, I assist my feet with my hands.

As I have informed you in another communication, I was not as an infant a natural "quadruped," although in my childhood I practiced the trick as an amusement, and am still able to go about on a level surface in this way.

Very sincerely yours,
FRANK THONE,
Science Service,
Washington, D. C.

June 23, 1928

DEAR SIR:

With reference to your interest in children who walk on all fours, as referred to in this week's *Literary Digest*, some information as to my son, now ten years old, may be of interest to you.

I attach hereto a small schedule, giving accurate information regarding the two generations preceding him; also general information as to their forebears.

My boy weighed 9½ pounds at birth; I was twenty-four, and he was my first (and only) child, as I have been a widow for seven years.

At three months he weighed 20 pounds; was above the average in length and weight, for his age; and has continued so. At six months he had eight teeth; at one year, sixteen. From seven to eight months of age he began crawling, as we termed it, on all fours, hands and flat footed. This continued until about thirteen months, when he walked very well erect, but really lasted until about sixteen months, as he reverted to crawling when in a hurry. I do not know that I could now cite a single specific instance of a child using this same mode of locomotion, but I have seen it enough to know that it is really not excessively unusual, and I considered it of little moment. His feet are sound and shapely, with good arches.

He has had very little illness. His tonsils were removed at two years, as he had suffered from birth, almost, with tonsillitis and had a bad inheritance as to throat—both parents and one grandparent on each side. His teeth have been very soft, and decayed easily, even with good dental care; and I have been advised part of this is due to the fact that he was a bottle baby.

He is now ten and a half; is 57 inches high; weighs 85 pounds; is broad shouldered and erect; becoming a little more slender.

He is in the sixth grade at school; reads everything he can but lacks concentration, although he learns readily when he properly applies himself. He has always been agile in climbing, balancing, etc., shoots accurately (probably due to far-sightedness); but is almost noticeably slow in games which require running. Is a good swimmer and dives fairly well. *He does not choose to fight.* He will put on boxing gloves for a friendly scramble, but when it begins to be a real fight, he is through. I believe this is largely a physical disinclination, rather than cowardice, for he is reckless in many other ways. However, I also have always had a distinct dislike for physical touch, let alone encounter, which latter always gave me a semi-delirious, smothering sensation.

His father was termed "bookish" as a child; had a good education and started early in the banking business; I have been a business woman for fifteen years, interested in the same lines; a constant reader. And my boy can learn most anything except arithmetic.

Very truly yours,
Mrs. M. H. Thornton,
Memphis, Tenn.

March 30, 1928

My Dear Doctor Hrdlička:

In response to your desire for information concerning children who before walking acquire the habit of running upon all fours, as expressed in *Science* for March ninth, I submit the following:

All the six children of my father used the "all fours" method of locomotion previous to an adoption of the erect method of walking. The family is now grown, but because of the prevalence of the method used in the family I thought you might be interested in knowing of the family trait. The characteristic has not so far been handed down to the next generation. The eldest son only has children, a son and a daughter, neither of whom exhibits the trait. To tabulate the case:

Race and nationality: German and French; in this country previous to the Revolution.

Sex: Three males and three females.

Health: All normal.

What child? All six.

Phenomenon noted among children of relatives? No.

Age limits for performance: Six months to one year.

The method employed was identical in all six cases. The open palms were placed flatly upon the supporting surface, as were the feet.

Very truly yours,
Mrs. Loel Z. Tiffany,
Columbus, O.

Chicago, October 8, 1928

Dear Sir:

Quite by accident I noticed an account in the *Literary Digest* about babies walking on all fours. I was very much interested because I, too, had a "little bear." She is now five and a half years old.

When she was just a year old, my father was brought to my house sick. Evelyn had always been an unusually strong, healthy baby. She is very pretty and very bright and lovable in addition. She was then going about on all fours just like a little bear. One day my father remarked, "You used to do that too."

My legs below my knees are not perfectly straight and I toe in slightly. Her legs are shaped exactly like mine and she walks just as I do. I wondered if that had anything to do with it.

She finally got so that she was running on all fours without making any attempt at walking erect. I don't remember that she ever crept. I used to put her out on the sidewalk to play with her older sister and other children and it certainly became embarrassing to me to see her running on all fours. I think the neighbors must have wondered what kind of a little animal I had. I did not have time to help her walk.

My father died just before she was fifteen months old. I then started to help her and she walked in no time, never going back to her strange manner of locomotion.

Her sister never crept, but pulled herself up by a chair and then around the wall and walked by herself at fifteen months.

All of my relatives were very early pioneers to the New England coast.

I have always been very healthy but could never do hard physical work as I never weigh over one hundred pounds. I passed with a score of "B" at a eugenics test at the State Fair and scored "A" in intelligence. Evelyn scored 97½ at the Better Babies. She is of a sturdier build than I and has never had a doctor.

Their father is descended from a very musical millionaire family back in Germany although he is three-fourths French now.

Hoping that this is of as much interest to you as the article was to me, I am

Sincerely yours,
Mrs. Rachel Whitcomb Treidel,
Detroit, Mich.

April 27, 1928

My Dear Sir:

The enclosed is a snapshot taken of my son, Bryce, at the age of ten and one-half months and before he learned to walk erect. From my position as an artist I have been keenly interested in the unusual fact that he never crawled or crept, or even "hunched himself along" as do so many infants, but always has traveled as shown in the enclosed, on all fours. And learning of the investigations you are conducting it is satisfying to be able to send this and to offer you any further assistance which my keen recollection of the manner in which his ability developed may give. (Plate XV*b*, p. 333.)

This snap was taken with the speed set at 100, which I have assumed means 1/100 second; yet you will notice that the forward hand is somewhat blurred. This was because he moved so fast. Indeed he was able to cover ground at a rate that astonished all of us. And in the transition from four feet to two he learned to stand, balanced, almost a week before ever taking his first step; raising himself up from the floor in the middle of the room (unaided by any support), much as I have observed bears to do, looking about, swaying, and then dropping back on all fours to travel again.

While on all fours, with the foot farthest forward (about parallel with the navel) the whole surface of the foot touched the floor. But from close study I doubt that any weight was placed on more than the balls of the feet. The head was always carried just as caught in this snap. The feet spread widely to allow the legs to swing well forward.

The lad walked in this way, I should say, nearly two months. It may have been longer. The picture was taken in August of 1924. I regret that I have no others.

As regards his physical condition now I should say (with a serious attempt to discount my judgment in the interest of scientific accuracy) that I have never seen a lad of four years and eight months with a finer physique, with greater strength, with a quicker wit, nor with so great a fund of apparently inexhaustible energy. My father, himself grandfather of eight and father of seven as well as having been a schoolmaster for some forty years, has made the same statement.

Both Mrs. Van Cott and myself I should regard as merely average healthy specimens with no unusual developments or history. Neither of us learned to walk in the fashion of our son. *Details:*

Race and nationality—White, U. S. A.; early New York Dutch ancestry.

Sex—Male.

Health— Absolutely healthy and robust.

What child in numerical order—First and only.

Has the phenomenon been observed in any other child of the same parents or among relatives?—No.

The position of the hands—Partly closed while in contact with ground.

Details as to any other peculiarity, etc.—None other. All the rest are "garden variety."

> Cordially,
> DEWEY VAN COTT,
> School Department,
> New Britain, Conn.

First letter:

April 17, 1928

DEAR SIR:

Although I am only a nurse, I want to tell you about a child I saw on a ranch near San Antonio, Texas. It could run on all fours faster than a grown person could pursue without running also. It was a girl, nine months old. The hands were held flat, palms down, the head well up. Its father was American, born of German parents, its mother a southern girl, native of Texas, ancestry unknown to me. The baby had never crept, could stand upright beside a support but not walk. When it wanted to go anywhere its movements were so swift as to be fairly startling. This was in 1916.

This is the only case of locomotion on all fours I have ever seen.

Yours very sincerely,
Clara M. Van Dorn,
Arroyo Grande, Calif.

Second letter:

May 1, 1928

Dear Dr. Hrdlička:

I will answer your questions so far as I can. I was only in the family as a nurse. It is several years since so a snapshot is not possible.

The child's father was of German parentage but born in the United States. The mother, a southern girl, descended from early settlers, nationality unknown to me.

Child, female.

Very strong, well and robust.

She was the third child, two boys preceding.

No other child of the family had run on all fours.

The baby was nine months old and had run on all fours for nearly two months. I have no report of her afterwards.

I most vividly remember seeing her run down the lawn, over the not very smooth sod. Her mother in pursuing her, must have run seventy or eighty feet at least, before she caught up with her. The child could stand by a chair, I think she probably could have walked, but she always dropped to all fours and ran, looking for all the world like an animal.

She spread her hands flat and held her head well up.

Otherwise the child acted in a normal manner.

Since writing about this case, I remember of a nurse in the P. & S. Hospital, in San Antonio, Texas, who told me she had seen four half-witted children of a German family, on a ranch in Texas, who habitually ran on all fours. I do not know anything about them personally.

Yours very sincerely,
Clara M. Van Dorn.

June 27, 1928

DEAR DOCTOR:

I am citing the case of my baby boy, almost eleven months, who propels himself around like a cub bear on his hands and feet.

He is an exceptionally husky boy, weighing almost 24 pounds and won a blue ribbon at the annual baby show when he was eight months old.

He started to walk a little on his hands and feet when he was seven months and by the time he was eight months he was going all over the house on all fours, his knees never touching the floor. The remarkable part of it all is how fast he travels, just runs across the room, particularly when there is something he is after, and so many people have noticed him scooting along this way. He has stood now for some time and shoves a chair along and walks that way but makes much better time the other way. Our other boy sat on his little "bottom" and managed to get there, but so much slower.

Details (written later than the above):

White; American parentage and grandparents Scotch, English, Irish and Holland Dutch extraction.

Male; second child.

One hundred per cent perfect. Blue ribbon baby at eight months.

No other bear walkers known of in family or relations.

Began on all fours between seventh and eighth month, continued until he started to walk at eleven months and short time thereafter.

He started to travel around this way from the beginning, his knees never touching the floor, and looked like a cub bear, but made such speed.

His hands were fully opened and his head raised and sometimes he would run around this way with something in his mouth.

He is now fourteen and one-half months old and although he has been walking a few months he occasionally reverts to his former method of getting around when he is in a hurry. He seems to be an unusually strong child, his legs being so straight and strong and he has enormous strength in his hands and arms. I can truthfully say that he has such strength that he can hold his own with his older brother aged four years and it is a difficult task for me to handle him myself. We have no photograph of him "in action."

When he started to walk he simply raised himself from the floor and started out with a great deal of confidence, of course, just going a few steps at a time.

Sincerely,
Mrs. Beatrice F. Van Kirk,
San Francisco, Calif.

July 23, 1928

Dear Sir:

My baby started to creep on all fours when he was nine months old; he is just one year old now and can walk from one thing to another and stand alone a little. He seems utterly fearless, has climbed the stairs on all fours since he was ten months old. He has always been an extremely happy and lively baby. He has always seemed healthy but he is not very fat. He weighs twenty-three pounds now, and weighed eight and one-half pounds at birth. I have a good photo of him on all fours.

Sincerely yours,
Mrs. P. Versfelt,
Caldwell, N. J.

April 18, 1928

Dear Sir:

We read of your inquiry of children who walk or run on all fours.

Our son David Porteous Walker, born October 9, 1926, a member of the Caucasian race, 18 months old now, walked and ran that way from about the age of 11 months until he walked erectly at the age of 15 and ½ months and then intermittently and at odd times now. When he wishes to get to a place more quickly than he can run, or if there is an obstruction in his way on the level such as a two by four on the ground in the yard, he will get down and go on all fours over it as he might fall walking over it. He used to make as much speed as a dog or cat.

He runs with his fingers spread open and hand flat on the ground, his head up or slightly raised, and on the flat of his feet. When he first tried to get about he crept on his hands and knees, this he did at about nine months, and continued till 11 months. This

. 360 .

method he quickly abandoned when he began to walk on all fours like a bear.

We have a record of his heredity on his paternal side six or seven generations back, and he is of English descent on that side, and of Scotch on the paternal side of his mother. We have been Americans since the Revolution.

We have no photo of the child in the four legged position, but could probably get one, as the child in walking out of doors on coming to any obstruction or rise in the ground always goes down on all fours until he clears the obstruction and then rises to an upright position.

He is an absolutely normal child, in perfect health, weight, 26½ pounds, is a decided blond and very active.

In return for our cooperation would appreciate being advised of any articles on the subject that have appeared in magazines and their name and dates.

> Sincerely yours,
> ROBERT G. WALKER,
> Passaic, N. J.

April 3, 1928

DEAR SIR:

I read in the March 10th issue of the *Literary Digest* of your interest in children who run on all fours instead of walking or creeping. Later I read about it in the *Denver Daily Post*.

My baby does this and I am going to tell you a few facts about him.

Born—June 19, 1927, at Anaconda, Montana.

Father—Joe W. Wallace, born April 27, 1907, parents—Hungarian.

Mother—Frances Bryson Wallace, born October 4, 1908, parents—maternal, English, but in America before Revolution; paternal—English.

Sex—male.

Weight when born—over twelve pounds.

Weight when 2 weeks old—twelve and one-half pounds.

Weight when started to walk on all fours—twenty-four pounds.

Age when he started to walk thus—eight months.

. 361 .

Joe does not put his feet flat on the floor but seems to use his toes and sometimes the balls of his feet. His hands are held flat. His head is held up a little but often very similar to that of a dog.

If I could, I would send you a picture of my baby doing this but I have tried in vain. You know it is hard to take a snapshot of a baby, particularly when it must be done inside.

I am deeply interested in this.

Sincerely yours,
Mrs. Joe W. Wallace,
Anaconda, Mont.

June 25, 1928

Dear Dr. Hrdlička:

I am especially interested in an article in the *Literary Digest* of June 23, about infants who walk on their all fours.

We have a baby daughter, born August 15, 1927, who walks some on her all fours. Sometimes it seems to be voluntarily and sometimes it seems to be when floor or grass are rough on her feet. When she began to crawl, she got to walk on her all fours so gradually that we did not notice it. Last week she began to try to walk. She took a step and sat down. Now she takes a step or two and then sits down. She is an average, normal baby; there is nothing unusual about her, except to her parents, of course.

We have a son, who will be three years old July 24, who did not crawl. He had a "Taylor Tot" or walker which may account for that. I might add that he walked on his tip-toes almost all of the time until he wore shoes in the winter, and even then tried to at times. Since the doctors advise high top shoes for children all of the year around, until three years of age, he does not go barefooted; but when allowed to he will "tip-toe" at times. He is unusually active and delights in climbing.

Details:

Child and family, American; ancestors way back—Scotch, Irish, English, Welsh, French.

Female, second child.

Average normal baby, and has never been ill.

No other walkers on all fours that I know of in the family or among relatives.

Began to move on fours about eighth month and continued until she began to walk at about ten months. She does once in a while even now.

She uses opposite hands and feet. Weight seems to be on inside of heel and toes slightly out.

Hands are fully open and head is up. She swings her right foot and leg back and outward. Sorry I am unable to get a picture.

She likes to climb and so does her brother, who is two years older than she. Her brother walked and ran on tip-toe when small, and still does when barefooted.

Very respectfully,
MRS. BARTON B. WALLACE,
Dallas, Tex.

March 12, 1928

DEAR SIR:

In the *Literary Digest* I read of your interest in children who ran on all fours at some time during babyhood.

As my small boy did just this and as it was most amusing to see him so, I took a snapshot which I am inclosing.

I am also tremendously interested in all progress and if in some small way I may help I shall be happy to do so.

Details:

Father; American since 1632.

Mother; American born of German parents.

Male, third child.

Has had pneumonia twice; chicken-pox. Rather high strung.

This peculiar way of walking has not been noticed in any other child in the family, to my knowledge.

He started to walk on all fours when about thirteen months old, continued this more or less until he walked upright, or until sixteen months.

His hands were open flat on the ground, head up or down according to what he wished to look at. He is precocious and sensitive, also extremely affectionate. (Plate XV*d*, p. 333.)

His older brother ate dirt until he was four or five years old.

His older sister died nine years ago at the age of five and a half of the flu.

Very sincerely,
MRS. C. WHEATON WALTER,
Brookhaven, L. I.,
N. Y.

August 7, 1928

MY DEAR DR. HRDLIČKA:

Needless to say, your articles have proven very interesting to me, as I have never heard of another child walking on all fours. I understand from your statements that the children who do this are usually stronger than the average. Mine is very strong now, but has had two very serious illnesses. She was born January 19th, 1927, at Walter Reed General Hospital, weight, 7 pounds ten ounces, height 20 inches. She was never able to nurse and nearly starved to death before the right food was found for her. At six weeks she regained her birth weight, and from then on gained steadily.

In September she was admitted to a Hospital with dysentery and nearly died at this time, but after about three weeks was back to normal. It was after we returned to the Post at El Paso that she began to walk on all fours. She became very proficient, and could cover the ground at a terrific rate of speed, thoroughly out-stripping her two contemporaries on the Post who crawled on hands and knees. As to her position, her knees were slightly bent when in action, as well as her elbows, but in repose she would stiffen up. Her hands were spread flat on the ground, and her head raised enough to see ahead of her.

In December she began pulling herself up to a standing position, but I would never let her remain standing more than a few seconds. On her first birthday she took her first step. Since then she has progressed rapidly.

Another curious thing she does that I have never observed in other babies is to try, whether she succeeds or not, to go either up or down stairs with one foot after the other, instead of taking a step with one foot and catching up to it with the other in usual baby fashion. She is now 35 inches tall and weighs 27 pounds. She has a very straight back and legs, and her shoulders are very broad and well developed. I am sure that her early method of running on all fours is responsible for her unusual physical development.

She never falls down, can climb up anything, and hangs on like a monkey. Although she is very alert and responsive she doesn't talk much yet, but that is the only thing she is backward in. As for her ancestry, her father's family is American back to pre-Revolution days, originally coming from England. Although my parents were both born in this country, their parents were not. My father's family is Swiss, and my mother's Swedish.

I know of no abnormalities in either my husband's family or my own.

I hope that this case will be of use to you in your very interesting research.

Sincerely yours,
Mrs. C. S. Ward,
Seattle, Wash.

January 24, 1928
Dear Sir:

In the current issue of the *Journal of the American Medical Association,* I note your request for reports of children who run on all fours.

My own son learned to do this spontaneously before he learned to walk in the erect position, and I therefore send you the following account.

The child is of English stock, his parents being native born Americans. He is the first child, a male, aged 19 months. He had congenital pyloric stenosis at birth which was relieved by operation. He is now in excellent health, weighs 25 pounds, and is more robust than the average baby of his age. When 15 months old he first began to run on all fours instead of creeping as is usual. This continued until he was eighteen months of age, when he began to walk in the erect position.

When running his hands were fully opened, his head was down (*i.e.,* towards the floor, and not in the direction in which he was travelling) and his legs were fully extended at the knees, being held rather stiffly.

I am unable to discover any other cases of children who run on all fours among either my own or my wife's people. My child has given up the habit almost completely. Occasionally, particularly after a fall, he will run a short distance on all fours, but almost immediately stands up and walks erect.

Yours very truly,
Dr. S. R. W.,
Calais, Me.

July 16, 1928

DEAR DOCTOR:

Lillian Nagle, daughter of Mr. and Mrs. H. Nagle, who live in Brooklyn, N. Y., was born November 13, 1923.

One day, when Lillian was about five months old, she undertook to crawl on her hands and knees. She then substituted her feet for the knees, and kept up this method of locomotion until she was eleven months old, at which time she learned to walk upright. She has always been a normal child in every way.

Unfortunately there are no photographs, but I feel that you will be glad to add the case to the data you are accumulating. The information has been given me by Mr. Nagle, a student at the Eastern Chiropractic Institute in New York, with which I am connected as professor of physiology. Articles concerning your researches were discussed recently in one of my classes with the result that the foregoing information was brought out.

Yours very truly,
C. W. WEIANT,
Eastern Chiropractic Institute,
New York, N. Y.

April 10, 1928

DEAR SIR:

The current number of the *Pathfinder* has an article entitled "The All-Four Habit." I have twin daughters, now six years old, one of whom has always very much preferred the all-four system of locomotion to any other. I have often wondered why. She seems to have an obsession to be a dog. When other children play with dolls and make mud pies, she can be depended upon to be around the corner running around on all fours, barking like her latest dog acquaintance. My mother has two dogs, a little old fox terrier, and a young Scotch or Sealyham terrier, just past the puppy stage. A neighbor has a collie, another a spitz, and still another a large bulldog. Naturally the bark of each differs from that of the others. This twin can imitate each bark perfectly, even getting in little shadings and gradations of sound which we notice in the old fox terrier, a peculiar wheeze which seems to come to dogs as they age. The bulldog's rumble comes as easily. I have sat concealed sometimes when she has played by herself and, although she refuses to discuss her antics, I have felt that she has acted out a complete "dog party." Dogs to her are real folk, with ways of communicating with each other like humans. Sometimes I almost think that she has acquired a knowledge of "dog language." She and her twin attend a school some nine blocks from our home. When the weather is fair, they ofttimes walk. Norma will have four or five dogs following her; they come from everywhere in our downtown neighborhood; Erma, her sister, hates dogs and they dislike her. When Norma was less than a year and a half old we had a Persian kitten given to us. After a day or two I found Norma in her play pen with a real "kitten" expression on her face, her eyes half closed, her hands and feet tucked under her in the manner a cat sleeps, and she was trying in her baby way to purr. It seemed rather cute at the time, but this animal imitation has reached a stage now where it is annoying. She is perfectly normal—a bit slower mentally than her sister, but we think that she learns things better, that she is more substantial, less "frothy" than Erma. Her dog obsession is her worst failing if such it may be called. When a friend of ours acquired two large police dogs recently, Norma, on saying her prayers afterwards, added this petition: "God, when you make me into a dog, please make me into a big brown police dog like Duke; not Pupsy, but the big one, Duke." She is perfectly certain that some day God will let her be a dog, and sometimes, when we drive through the streets, she points to some particularly fine dog and says, "See, Mother, there's me!"

This twin is lefthanded. We tried at the beginning to break her of the habit, but finding that she very definitely preferred to use her left hand we let it go. When she started to go to kindergarten her teacher found that she used the scissors only with the right hand and did her pasting with that hand, but for drawing lines with a piece of chalk she would always use the left. When she got into First Grade and commenced to write a bit, we found this peculiarity: She would write her name—amroN; cat was tac; dog was god; and she commenced to write from the right to the left always. I wondered if she "saw" things hind-side-to. She is being trained out of this now, but sometimes when she is tired I notice that she does it, then erases and does it right.

We have not worried about her peculiarities, feeling that she would in time outgrow the troublesome ones, and lefthandedness we face as a necessary evil. It was not until I read the *Path-*

finder article today that it occurred to me that there may be more behind this four-legged-dog gait of hers than I suspect. I am wondering if there is. I have no photographs of her running on all fours, but I shall get some later and will gladly mail them to you. She holds her hands open, puts them down just as a dog would in running, and she holds her head exactly like a dog, sometimes opening her mouth and attempting in the most ludicrous way to get her tongue to hang out as does a dog; on one occasion she lifted her leg and attempted to scratch her head as she had seen a dog do. It really has been very funny at times, but as I say, it is getting a bit beyond the humorous stage now that she is older. My mother is mortified to death about it, saying the neighbors will think we have a feeble-minded child. My husband says that no one without an unusual degree of intelligence could carry through some of this girl's stunts. Her imitations are too perfect.

If my experience with this infant is of any value, or if I can give you any other information which you may wish, I shall be pleased to know it.

Yours truly,
MRS. HOWARD H. WELKER,
Ashland, Wis.

First letter:

February 16, 1928

DEAR SIR:

My brother, Dr. E. Stanley Abbot, of Boston, recently called my attention to your request, in the Jan. 21 issue of the *Journal of the American Medical Association*, for data concerning children who have run on all fours. My three children all did so, but, as the youngest is now almost seventeen years old I may not be able to remember as much as you would like about the performance. However, I will do my best.

For race and nationality, the children are American—since pre-Revolutionary times—of English stock. There are traditions of other racial admixture, but they antedate 1700 at least.

The two oldest were girls, the youngest a boy, all of them rather exceptionally strong, healthy children. I remember that a mother of several boys speaking of my first baby said, "Such activity in a ten-months old child is new to me." The two pictures I enclose are of this child. She began to creep on hands and knees when about ten months. When she was about fourteen months we went to the sea-shore, and it is my impression that it was after we went there that she began sometimes to get up on hands and feet. I think she did it largely for amusement—she is laughing in the larger picture—or for a change, but she also did it when we came to a rough place in the ground, as in the smaller picture. Where the path was smooth she went on hands and knees; where it was rough she substituted feet for knees. Whether she kept up this practise till she began to walk at about eighteen months I do not remember. She was about sixteen months when these pictures were taken.

Of the second little girl I remember only that she did sometimes go on all fours. The picture that I have of her doing so is not very satisfactory.

I have only one mental picture of the boy going in the same way, and that was on the verandah. I fancy I remember that only because a caller commented on it. One remembers more details of the first child than of the later ones, I think. I have a snap-shot of the boy, however, going on hands and feet out on the grass, and intended to send you a copy, but I could not find the film to have it printed. It is very like that of his sister. His legs were a bit longer in proportion to his arms than hers, but they are just as straight and stiff in the picture. His hands are spread out in the same way. His head is raised a little more as if he were looking a little further in front of him than she is, but not enough to be looking entirely off the ground.

If the cousins or the aunts of these children ever went on all fours I never heard of it, nor did I ever hear that their father, my brothers or myself ever did so, though that is only negative evidence.

Mrs. Ralph G. Wells,
Needham, Mass.

Second letter:

March 6, 1928

My Dear Dr. Hrdlička:

If by "physical anomaly" you mean any physical malformation or peculiarity of that sort, no, none of the children had anything of the sort. If I may believe the testimony of doctors, nurses and other mothers, as well as my own less impartial judgment, they were above, rather than below, the average. Our old family physician told one of my friends that Winifred, our oldest child, was "the finest baby he had seen for a long time." The monthly nurse had been very enthusiastic about her (though *that* doesn't mean much) and one mother of grown children declared she was "born six months old." When a year old she had whooping cough badly enough to lose a good deal of her food and to cough ten or fifteen minutes (by the clock!) at a time, and in the worst four weeks of it she cut eight teeth,—the second eight, she had sixteen through by the time she was fourteen months and the only effect it all seemed to have on her was that she lost her rosy cheeks and failed to gain in weight. She neither lost weight nor grew languid or fretful. The doctor who saw her at that time called her "the finest baby he had ever seen." Her one physical weakness,—if it can be called that—was that in spite of her abounding vitality and store of reserve strength she was very susceptible to infection. She caught everything to which she was exposed, though she was seldom laid low thereby.

However, when she was eight and a half she got mumps at school and, though she did not seem to be made ill by them, when they were over we discovered that diabetes had developed. I suppose she had inherited the tendency from her grandmother, whom she resembled (at least the doctors seemed to think so) and, as it was before the discovery of insulin, only one outcome was possible. She died soon after her ninth birthday.

My second daughter is now in college, a strong, vigorous young woman, of whom I am sometimes asked, How does Katharine do so much?

My son, sixteen and a half, has been growing fast and does not seem to have quite the physical endurance his sister has. Still he looks on a ten-mile hike as a mere stroll.

None of the three "squirmed" when they were new-born. Katharine for a day or two had a suggestion of squirminess in her motions, but it was soon over, and I never saw any sign of it in the others. They kicked their legs and moved their arms in the fashion of a baby that has outgrown the squirming stage. I recall that a visitor to my three or four day old son said to the nurse, "Why, isn't he like a month-old child?" to which the nurse replied that he was. Perhaps running on all fours, if it is an indication of anything, is an indication of physical excellence.

As to your question regarding "any other striking peculiarity of behavior," Winifred, before she could creep, had one form of exercise which I never saw the other children employ. When on the floor, where she spent most of her waking hours after she was four or five months old (doctor's advice), she frequently flopped over on her stomach, threw up her head, raised her hands and feet off the ground and *bounced*. It was excellent exercise, surely tending to expand her chest and strengthen her abdominal muscles.

All the children slept most of the time on their stomachs. Katharine sometimes drew her knees up under her and slept that way, looking for all the world like a little rabbit.

The children were all sound sleepers. When Katharine's turn came to have whooping cough, when she was nine or ten years old, she slept through her coughing at night. To wake Dane, in case of necessity, it was necessary to drag him out of bed and wash his face with cold water. One exception to this—and perhaps this is a peculiarity—is that Winifred was subject to spells of waking up in the night and lying awake for a couple of hours or so. The first came when she was nine or ten months old and lasted about two months, if I remember aright. Every night about twelve o'clock she woke and laughed, peal after peal of laughter, till about two o'clock, when she grew fretful and hungry, was fed and went to sleep again. When she was about two, I think it was, she had another period of wakefulness at night. She did not laugh then, but kept up a kind of rythmical "mmm-mmm-mmm" until she went to sleep again. Still later she used to beat her head up and down on the pillow. These things lasted for a while, then stopped for a period, to begin again later and again stop.

Katharine at one time used to go about on the backs of her hands, instead of on the palms, when she did not wish to put down a toy she was holding, sometimes one hand, sometimes both, according to whether she wished to carry about one toy or two. That was a bit of ingenuity I never saw the others exhibit.

In disposition the three were very unlike, but all were good children and not mischievous. I never had to fear for the safety of the household belongings. All were intelligent—observing and reasoning. Winifred was always mature for her age, even as a baby. Dane was keen.

I do not think of anything else.

Yours very truly,
Mrs. R. G. Wells.

Third letter:

May 24, 1928

MY DEAR DR. HRDLIČKA:

Spring house-cleaning brought to light what my former search failed to reveal, and I am enclosing a (poor) snapshot of my boy on hands and feet.

My brother told me that when calling recently on an old aunt of ours he spoke of your interest in hands-and-feet creeping and of my writing you about my own children, and he said she exclaimed, "Why, Ned did that!" Ned is now a man between forty-five and fifty, and my brother considered that the length of time that has elapsed since his creeping days, and his mother's age, nearly ninety, would not make her recollections of scientific accuracy, but I do not think there is any reason to doubt my aunt's memory of the bare fact. Her mind seems entirely unclouded. This seems to indicate that the peculiarity has cropped up in at least two branches of the same family. "Ned" is my first cousin.

Yours very truly,
MRS. R. G. WELLS,
Needham, Mass.

Fourth letter:

February 16, 1928

DEAR DR. HRDLICKA:

This afternoon I saw a remarkable baby picture, that of a six months old boy standing upright on the palm of his father's hand. The mother's account of it was that the baby, who of course was too young to stand by himself, could keep his legs stiff and the father balanced him as he would a stick. It seemed incredible that a six months baby could do that, so incredible that I thought it might interest you to hear of it. The child evidently had enough comprehension of the situation to hold himself rigid, and that is what seems to me most noteworthy.

Hoping this little I have been able to tell you may be of some slight assistance, I am

Yours truly,
MRS. R. G. WELLS,
Needham, Mass.

July 2, 1928

Dr. Hrdlička:

My first two babies walked on all fours. The first, a dainty little girl, began this means of locomotion when she was about nine months old. She walked when a year old. The boy began about the same age to go on all fours but was walking good by the time he was ten months old. Neither one went back to this method of locomotion after they learned to walk. They both were very adept at getting around. They also climbed. I would often find them on the piano, table, or any piece of furniture in the house, even before they could walk. I did not think anything about their getting around on all fours, for I did not know it was an unusual thing for a child to do, although I can remember different people making remarks about their manner of getting around.

I have married again and have two children by my second husband and neither of these children got about on all fours, but crawled in the usual way. However they did not walk as soon nor were they as lively in getting around as my first two. The ones that walked on all fours are now eight and nine years old.

Sincerely,
Mrs. J. D. Whisler,
Tecumseh, Neb.

March 10, 1928

Dear Sir:

In the current issue of the *Literary Digest* I notice a short article regarding children who run on all fours. My oldest children are twins, a boy and a girl, born August 1, 1907. Neither of these children ever crept as do ordinary children but always ran on all fours until eventually, at about the age of twenty two months to two years, they began to walk like ordinary children. I enclose a kodak of the girl showing her in rompers walking across a quilt spread on the yard.

The twins are both juniors in college at the present time and are slightly above the normal average for size.

I have two other children, a boy past sixteen years of age and a girl twelve years of age, who crept in the manner of ordinary children.

If this information is of any value to you from a scientific standpoint, I am glad to furnish it.

Details:

Twins—oldest of four, boy and girl; next—boy; youngest—a girl; white; American.

Both twins ran on all fours, began that way—did not creep.

Kept up until they walked; the other two showed nothing of that sort.

All good and healthy, developed finely.

No other peculiarities; nothing like it known in family.

Yours very truly,
Milo A. White,
Fremont, Mich.

September 22, 1928

Dear Dr. Hrdlička:

I would like to tell you about my little girl who is now twenty-eight months old. When she was seven months old she started creeping on her hands and knees. In three or four weeks she got up on her hands and feet and finding that she could "scoot" faster that way, seldom went back to creeping. And she very seldom toppled over. Everybody who saw her said she had wonderful balance. When she was ten months old she would get out in the middle of the floor and stand up without any help or without holding on to anything. She would stand up for a few seconds and then sit down, she never fell down. The next months she would take a step or two before she sat down. But she was thirteen months old before she finally walked the length of the room, but the next day she was skipping and running. When she was fourteen months old she walked up and down stairs standing up not creeping or going down backwards. She had fewer falls and less help than any of my other children who crept and took longer to learn to walk. In fact she never did get any help in learning to walk because she refused it. And she is still independent, won't let me do anything for her that she can do herself. Not only feeds herself better than her five year old sister, but spreads her own bread and insists upon helping herself from the main dishes. She is also independent about dressing and undressing herself and does very well at it even to lacing her shoes and buttoning all the buttons she can reach . . .

I think children who walk on their hands and feet have better balance and are more independent than others. My mother had two children out of her eight who walked that way and they had better balance and were more independent than the other six.

Details:

She is descended from Puritans and Quakers; on her mother's side she is ten generations in direct descent from Jonathan Edwards; on her father's side she is eleven generations from Governor Bradford.

Female, second child.

Health, good now. She was born with bad tonsils and so had tonsillitis several times before they were removed but aside from that she was all right.

My other girl sat down to creep. My oldest brother walked on hands and feet instead of creeping. I (the youngest in a family of eight) moved that way part of the time.

I know that she was eight months old when she often stood on hands and feet and looked at us with her head on the floor directly between her feet. She never walked holding on to things and always refused help. She started standing up when she was ten and one-half months old. She would sit in the middle of the floor, rise to her hands and feet, give a push with her hands and stand up. When she got tired she would sit down (not fall). Our doctor saw her do this and said she had wonderful balance. At eleven and one-half months or maybe it was twelve she started taking a step or two but she did not walk across the room until thirteen months. The next day she was walking and running as well as her six year old sister. In about two weeks she was walking up and down stairs standing perfectly straight. I never saw her go down backwards or creep up and she never fell down stairs.

Held hands open with fingers spread and pointing toward the front.

Before she could creep or stand up she used to turn somersaults in her "Kiddee Koop." I don't know whether her good nature would come under the head of "peculiarity of behavior." But she was unusually good natured. She laughed aloud when she was five weeks old and she was a month old before I (her mother) heard her cry. She laughed where most babies cried. When she woke up she laughed; she laughed herself to sleep; she laughed if she was picked up; laughed when she was put down again. Our doctor who has had lots of experience with babies said she was the best natured baby he ever saw. She even laughed when she fell and hurt herself.

Yours very truly,
MRS. JAY WHITSON,
Des Moines, Ia.

July 9, 1928 ·

DEAR DOCTOR:

I am very glad to add two of my children to the list of baby cases who ran on all fours. My oldest boy never crept any other way and took his first steps alone just a few days before he was eleven months old. He was always very quick and could get about so much faster on all fours than his little cousin just six weeks younger who didn't walk till he was nearly two and who sat on his little bottom and hitched. The other boy, my youngest, now twenty months old, ran also on all fours and walked at ten months. He, too, moves very quickly and is a sturdy boy rather than a baby.

My little girl—three last March—never did creep on fours or in any other way. She was a strong little thing, too, and when she got ready she just formed a habit of sliding off our laps and standing by our knees or a chair, and soon commenced to take steps. She walked before she was ten months old too.

I feel as the other mothers have. It has been such a relief to have the two who ran on fours keep fairly clean. The other ways of creeping are dirty. They are a healthy bunch. We live on a farm and they have all the good clean milk they can drink and they like it which makes it so much easier.

Sincerely,
CHARLOTTE G. WILCOX,
Lagrange, O.

First letter:

February 17, 1928

DR. HRDLIČKA:

In reply to your request in the *Journal A. M. A.*, of January 21, 1928, I am sending you two small photographs and the following information.

Child of Anglo-Saxon parentage, female, health excellent, first child in family. At about eleven months began to travel on all fours. This continued until about thirteen months old when she started walking and immediately discontinued the former method of travel. She could travel across a floor or on the lawn in a run. The hands were open with fingers extended and the head well up as seen in the pictures.

These pictures were made from films taken in 1913. She is now almost 16 and is above average in health and general physical

FIG. 21.—Miss Williams.

condition. Since she is my daughter, of course I will say her mentality is far above the average.

The other child in the family, a boy, who is now eight years old, did not use this primitive method of locomotion.

Very truly yours,
E. G. C. WILLIAMS, M. D.,
Danville, Ill.

Second letter:

February 24, 1928

The child described to you in my previous letter and whose photographs were enclosed, is the only one in the entire family so far as we can find, who has gone on all fours.

She has never shown any other peculiarities of behavior or physical anomalies and at present, at the age of sixteen, is about as nearly perfect physically and mentally as any girl that we know of in this community.

She received Junior credits in High School after three semesters work and is carrying almost a double school program with no apparent effort. She is a good musician, has some dramatic ability and in all respects is apparently normal.

E. G. C. W.

June 6, 1928

DEAR SIR:

It is an old adage that we find that which we are looking for and I am constantly reminded that it must still hold true. Immediately after reading your recent article on quadrupedal progression in human children I was agreeably surprised to see a little fellow scamper across my path in such a manner, as I left one of the local hospitals.

Violet Croy, age 14 months, daughter of Mrs. Pauline Croy, Canton, Ga., is a white child of native stock and of normal birth and subsequent history until she reached the age of ten months. At this time she began to "crawl" but not in the usual manner. She places the palms of her hands and the soles of her feet flatly on the floor and progresses in such a manner that each foot falls slightly to the right of its corresponding hand. The head is held in hyperextension so that vision is focused well in front and in the direction to be traversed. She was remarkably swift in her progress from the first assumption of the peculiar gait and although she has walked erect since twelve months of age she resumes her quadrupedal progression when speed is demanded. On the occasion described she was "chasing" a playmate and quickly and gracefully arose to the erect position to grasp her "prey." Violet is one of four children, the eldest of which walked in a similar manner at about the same time. This child is at present eleven years of age and is normal in every respect.

The parents of the child have given me permission to photograph her on their next visit to the city and I will be glad to forward you any satisfactory prints.

Very sincerely yours,
DR. GEORGE A. WILLIAMS,
Atlanta, Ga.

April 15, 1928

DEAR SIR:

In reading the *Pathfinder*, I came across your article asking for any knowledge of children creeping or running on all fours.

I have a friend who has a very interesting child—a boy—of one year. He has used no other method of getting around but the all four. His movements are very rapid, using the hand flat or open—head up—has travelled in that manner since about seven months of age. He bears the uncommon name of Smith—a very bright, interesting child. We commented often upon this peculiar trait in relation to evolution. Will send pictures if desired.

Yours truly,
C. WILSON,
Waynesburg, Pa.

March 14, 1928

DEAR SIR:

In the issue of March 10th of the *Literary Digest*, I noted with interest your article on the children who run on all fours.

Our daughter who was born November 5, 1926, and who is now one year and four months old, has used this mode of locomotion for quite some time. She has never creeped but took up this method at about the age she normally would creep.

At the present time she is beginning to stand erect and taking a step or two, but if desirous of going somewhere quickly she still uses this method of locomotion because of the speed she can secure of the same.

We are taking some photos of her.

Very truly yours,
HAROLD P. WINTER,
John Hancock Mutual Life
Insurance Co.,
Boston, Mass.

January 27, 1928

DEAR DOCTOR:

The clipping about children running on all fours attracted my attention, as our son was just performing this feat at that time. He seems very responsive to the sense of touch—feels silks and satins, enjoys creeping on a deep turkish rug, etc., so we were not surprised when he walked on all fours like a bear when he got on the concrete floor of a neighbor's porch. May be he didn't like the feel of the concrete on his bare knees. Which may, of course, not be the whole story.

Sincerely,
F. E. WOLF,
Fort Thomas, Ky.

First letter:

June 29, 1928

DEAR SIR:

My three babies crept differently. The oldest crept on one knee and one foot and did so for exactly one calendar month. The second crept on her "sit-downer" as she called it for five months.

My third came nine years later. We have no near neighbors and living near the top of one of Berkeley's highest hills, our visitors during the rainy season were few and far between. Consequently my wee son seemed to imitate the only thing he saw, the dog. He ran on all fours and developed great speed.

My husband and I enjoy the psychological development of our youngsters, and as a kindergartner I have watched and analyzed each movement. Our cocker spaniel played with a ball, and our baby would take a ball and throw it over his head using a head motion just as the dog did. One day I found the baby with the dog's ball and immediately, mindful of germs, took it out of his mouth, and he growled at me just as the dog did in play!

MRS. CHARLES WOOD,
Berkeley, Calif.

Second letter:

April, 1930

Report by—Frances Jones Wood—mother of child.

People—Early Puritan on maternal side; Scotch-Irish on paternal.

Locality—Berkeley, Calif.

Sex of subject—Male.

Age of subject—Date of birth, March 18, 1924. Crept from approximately 7 months, walked at 14 months.

. 380 .

What child in family—Third.

Health, robustness and mentality of child—Lean but wiry and strong. Seldom fatigued. At 5 months "pat-a-caked" upon request. At 4 years had mentality of 7 year child (Terman test).

Nature of peculiar behavior—We owned a toy cocker spaniel. The child imitated every move of the dog. His first movements were in a flat swimming position with much arm movement. Gradually a more upright position until he moved about on palms of hands and soles of feet with legs upright and not bent at knees.

Peculiarities of behavior in other children or members of family— Oldest girl (June 21, 1914) crept on one knee and one foot for one month. Then walked. Second girl (Sept. 6, 1915) crept on buttocks from 7 to 17 months. She was very heavy. When she did walk, she walked sideways and would resort to creeping when tired or when she wanted to attain greater speed.

At the time I paid no attention to the child's going on all fours, I had seen a boy (since deceased) who crept in a "swimming" position using his arm for locomotion, so when my boy did this I felt it was nothing unusual; and I was not astonished when the more upright position on all fours followed in natural sequence the "flatter" position he assumed at first.

This may or may not interest you. Because I love old associations and am sentimental I saved the girls' dolls and doll carriages, etc. The boy was absolutely indifferent to them. He had every opportunity to play with "girl toys" but his first interest was a clock. His first word was "Bah" for "bow-wow," the imitation of dog sounds. The next was "Clah" for "clock." He used some old dolls to stand on to reach for a clock, and when he could walk he used a doll carriage to carry about his large collection of trucks, locomotives, etc. At two years he made three connections necessary to use an electric iron, and successfully burned the floor in my room, necessitating three new boards. He is mechanical and follows a line of paternal ancestors who owned a ship yard on the Clyde in Scotland. It interests me, for some friends (also kindergartners) say a boy will follow any line prepared for him, and that I have swayed him towards the masculine pursuits. I deliberately put them in his way—these left over girlish playthings—and found that he would have none of them.

Very sincerely yours,
Mrs. Charles Wood.

First letter:

February 3, 1928

DEAR DR. HRDLIČKA:

I have noted your request for reports of cases of children who, before learning to walk upright, have exhibited the phenomenon of "walking" on all fours. It may be of some interest to you to know that my youngest child, now $4\frac{1}{2}$ years old, began to move about in this way at the age of $8\frac{1}{2}$ months. She was a full term baby, weighing $10\frac{1}{4}$ lbs. at birth, in excellent health and quite robust. She was also of good mentality and is able at her present age to read simple words, print rapidly and accurately anything submitted to her, knows the alphabet thoroughly, can count to 100 without errors and make simple additions.

Other information which you requested is as follows: American parents of English stock; second child; the phenomenon was not noted in the first child; she continued this type of locomotion until able to walk normally, although I cannot give you the exact age, she was not unduly slow in learning to walk. She used this means of getting about in place of creeping—which she never did. She moved about rapidly, with knees fully extended, palms of hands open and head raised sufficiently to be able to see her course clearly.

It was apparently an easy means of locomotion. I am sorry I have no photograph of her in this position.

There is one other fact in regard to my child which may be of interest, and that is the presence of well defined "Darwinian tubercles" on the ears. There are no other known cases of either this type of locomotion or Darwinian tubercles, so far as my knowledge extends, on either side of her family.

Very truly yours,
DR. F. O. WOODWARD,
Jamestown, N. D.

Second letter:

February 11, 1928

I have been able to find another instance of a child running on all fours, and assuming that you wish to collect as many as possible, I am taking the liberty of reporting to you the details of this case:

Baby Spaulding: Female; age 16 mo. (at this writing). Started walking on all fours at age of 11 mo. The child had done some half hearted creeping using only one leg to propel herself for several weeks preceding. She had not been a very strong baby, suffering from infantile eczema, and difficult to feed. She was always slightly under weight. This perhaps accounts for the delayed attempt at locomotion. She is the fourth child of healthy parents. None others in the family or in the parents families used this type of locomotion so far as known. She is alert mentally and is now beginning to attempt walking upright. She talks but very little. She is a very light sleeper, good natured, but somewhat notional about her food.

I attempted to get some photographs of her in this position, but the kodak did not have a fast enough lens for satisfactory indoor work, so they are underexposed. I am enclosing them however as they give some idea of the posture she assumes and the position of her hands.

Very sincerely,
Dr. F. O. Woodward.

P. S. I am enclosing herewith some additional films, which I took Sunday of the Spaulding baby. They may be of some value to you, although they are underexposed. One of the good ones shows her as she is just starting out, and before she had raised her head.

December 18, 1928

Dear Dr. Hrdlička:

I was interested in your note in *Science* for March 9, 1928, concerning children who run on all fours.

You ask for information concerning children who run on all fours before walking upright. My own child does not quite meet these conditions, but nearly so. He started walking at about thirteen months, and between fifteen and sixteen months, after his walking habit was quite well developed, he took to running on all fours, more or less. We have observed this activity from its beginning. When getting up in the middle of the floor he, as do most children I think, puts his hands on the floor and then raises himself, rather completely doubled up. Some times at first he was a little unbalanced and the movement of his hands and feet caught him. The first time that we noticed him really walking in this manner came when he wanted some toy which was quite close to him and he moved towards it in this way, thereby apparently saving the process of straightening up and almost immediately doubling down again. Soon his older brother, ten years, noticed this and played with the child in this manner so that soon he adopted this method of locomotion in play. Usually the motion is semi-sideways, the hand and foot on the same side moving together, and his general course partially sideways, rather than directly forward. Sometimes, however, he pushes his two hands forward and then brings his feet up to them. His hands are always fully opened. His head is held sometimes vertically, and sometimes horizontally, depending on what he is doing. If he is really trying to go somewhere, his head is approximately horizontal, but if he is just moving a step or two towards a toy he does not raise it.

The child is of the white race, American of English descent, male, in perfect health, considerably taller and heavier than the average child of his age, the second child in the family. The older child did not exhibit this phenomenon.

> Very truly yours,
> D. A. WORCESTER,
> Professor, Educational Psychology,
> Lincoln, Neb.

March 15, 1928

DEAR SIR:

In the March 10th number of the *Literary Digest* I read a short article entitled "Children Who Run On All Fours."

My daughter, Esma Jean, now 2½ years old, when she was a little over a year old started to walk in this way and kept it up until she walked on two legs. Only once or twice did I ever see her try to actually creep, but this method of progression would always finish up like a quadruped. Of course we took pictures of her in these unusual poses, and I am enclosing the only one I can find at present.

She could get up a lot of speed. A grown-up would have to walk lively to keep up with her.

Details:

Esma Jean Wyant, born July 4, 1925.

White race—American—English, Scotch, Irish, way back.

Female, second child.

Extra healthy and robust, weighed twenty pounds eleven ounces at one year.

No other such case in families, to my knowledge.

Began to travel on all fours July 26, 1926 (was year old July 4, 1926) and continued to fifteen months, with occasionally afterwards.

A detailed description is hard to give at this late date. The picture that I sent you with my previous letter is descriptive. She could walk very rapidly on all fours. It hustled an adult to keep up with her. At that time I remember that she was particularly interested in the car in the garage and as many times as she was taken away she would quickly get on all fours and would soon be there.

Hands fully open, head up.

One thing we noticed about her at that time. In marked contrast to our son at her age, she was very slow at getting started to talk, only tried to say a very few words and when told to say a word, "Mama" for instance, it seemed to take a long time for the message to get to her brain and back to her tongue so that the word "Mama" in response to our request would come so long afterwards that it was very funny. Along about fifteen to sixteen months she started to jabber fast, long stories with all the intonations of conversation yet no intelligible word. This is very different from either Roger or Marjorie who just said and says a few (two to six perhaps) words at a time and actually say something. Shortly after Esma was one and one-half years old though, she began to talk and her progress was nothing short of remarkable. Right now she can converse nearly as well as Roger who is five and one-half, and has but few consonants that she has not mastered.

I have noticed that she is handy with her hands and clumsy with her feet. She is always falling down, *i.e.*, stumbling, or running into something. I am trying to have her learn to ride the tricycle so she will get better coordination.

We have a "Busy Kiddie" swing indoors and Esma has learned to pump, sitting down, this last week and can go the limit of height all by herself. Our little one and one-half year old Marjorie can swing as high when she is pushed and many times has gotten into the swing standing up, all by herself. Esma did that too, when very young. We did not have the swing when Roger was as small as they so I can not compare him with them.

I have noticed a tendency in Esma to stutter, but I have purposely not noticed it so that she will overcome it. This occurs only at times.

> Very truly yours,
> ZAE N. WYANT,
> Greenville, O.

March 8, 1928

DEAR SIR:

The Literary Digest states that you are interested in children who run on all fours.

I have a son who did that. He crept on his hands and knees when he was nine months. Later, before he learned to walk, he ran on all fours very rapidly. At eleven months he took a few steps alone. But he continued to run on all fours whenever he was in a hurry until after he was thirteen months old. He often started to walk on two feet and, finding that method too slow, went on all fours. He did this out of doors on the path from the door and, also, on the beach, as well as in the house. It seemed to me that he did not acquire skill in walking as rapidly as children who used the two-legged method entirely.

We lived in York Village, Maine, at that time, not in the city.

I had a chance to compare him with another child, as his cousin who is the same age, visited us for ten days.

The children were born June 9, 1920. On July 13, 1921, Keen's cousin, Ethel came to visit us. Keen was already walking alone, but Ethel walked only by holding on to things. In a few days she walked alone and never ceased to practise walking from that time. She never crept at all; not even before she walked. She stayed ten days. When she went home it seemed to me that she walked more steadily and kept her balance better than Keen. I thought it was because he went on all fours so much.

As I remember it he held his hands open and his head up. We took a picture of him, but it was not especially good and I am not sure that I can find it. I didn't know that the matter was of scientific interest but I thought it amusing to see him run like a little spider, or perhaps it was like a monkey.

His name is Keen Edward Wyllie. He was born in New York City, June 9, 1920. His mother was born in York, Maine, and his father in Waterbury, Conn. His grandfather Wyllie was born in England; his other grandparents in America.

He has other peculiarities which seem to me abnormal. They perplex and sometimes worry me. I never was a boy myself, so I don't know whether they are common to boys. I shall be grateful if you will tell me of any way to find out whether he is normal or abnormal or merely rather unusual. His mental twists worry me.

After hearing about "Pussy in the Well" he threw his kitten in the toilet. He said he wanted to put pussy in the well.

He was strictly forbidden to play in 80th St. where traffic was heavy. He went to kindergarten before he was five. The next time he went out to play, he played in 80th St. I scolded him. He said "I go to school. I am a big boy. Big boys play in the street."

When he was five he received a tricycle. He rode it several blocks away, although he was not allowed off our block.

He showed me a picture in a paper of a boy butting a man over. Foolishly, I told him the story of the boy Pickpocket of Paris. A few days later he took money from my pocket book and spent it.

I am worried as to whether he will always choose the bad. If he reads of a terrible murder when he is older, will he commit one? If he sees crimes in the movies, will he go out and commit them?

In school he spells words backward. He is now in 2 B¹. Yesterday he spelled "door" "rood." He can't tell "tell" from "let" or "was" from "saw." He confuses many other words in the same way.

When he started to read he had to be told over and over again not to begin at the right of the page.

I don't feel that I have any real control over him. Talking to him does very little good. Repeated whippings have kept him in the home neighborhood. I never believed in whipping children, but I can't have him running all over the city. And whipping him every time he went away has, so far, been the only way to keep him near home. He goes as far as he dares now.

His father is a bricklayer and he loses enough time so that it is hard to "make ends meet." I can't afford to spend money to have the child psycho-analyzed or anything of that sort. Books might help, if I knew which to choose.

He has a tendency to lie and steal and is rather cowardly when the boys hit him.

I seem to be able to guide him in his school work, so that he dosen't fail but is of average grade. The other things I don't know how to deal with, because I can't understand his feelings and motives.

I can't talk it over with his father with hope of help, because we can't understand each other either. He simply tells me it is all my fault and I ought to know what to do.

Perhaps it is, and perhaps I ought; but I am not wilfully doing wrong. I can't understand the mental makeup of either my husband or son.

My two girls have not puzzled me so much. One is four and a half and the other nineteen months. The older one can read as well as, or better than her brother. She always spoke plainly. The boys didn't talk plain. The baby seems bright but doesn't talk plain.

I taught school until thirteen days before my oldest girl was born. I am inclined to believe in pre-natal influence.

Details:

Race and nationality: White, American of English descent.
Sex: Male.
What child in numerical order: First.
Health and robustness: Very healthy appearance. Not much endurance. Nerves weak.

Has the phenomenon been observed in any other child of the same parents or among relatives? Third child—girl—traveled from one room to another on all fours on one occasion, not a habit of hers. She is 19 months old.

At what age has the child begun to run on all fours, and how long has it continued? Between creeping and walking; also, after walking. 11th to 13th months as I remember it.

Add description, etc.: My son from 11 to 13 months traveled on all fours when in a hurry both out of doors and in the house, both before and after he could walk. He would often start to walk and then go rapidly on all fours.

Position of hands, etc.: Hands open. Head straight in line with spine or raised to see where he was going.

Details as to any other peculiarity of behavior of the child, or any other children in the family: Great difficulty with speech. Tonsils and adenoids removed at four years. Daily drill on sound finally enabled him to speak to be understood. Difficulty with reading and spelling. Reads and spells backwards very frequently. Very hard to remove or change an idea which he gets. Objects to effort to improve.

Second child, a girl, unusually bright and speaks very distinctly.

Third child, 19 mos., difficulty with speech but willing to try.

Yours very truly,
Mrs. E. C. W.,
St. Albans, L. I., N. Y.

August 29, 1929

Dear Doctor Hrdlička:

Through Dr. E. L. Sevringhaus I heard that you are interested in babies who walk on all fours. So that when such a specimen was visiting in my home this summer, it occurred to me to gather what data I could in case you would care to add it to your collection. I am sorry the pictures are not better, but to make a more scientific exhibit would have required a faster lens and less amusement on the part of the photographer. Dr. Sevringhaus passed on the list of questions you sent him, and which the mother of the baby has helped me answer.

Race and nationality—White; American; one-fourth Jewish.

Sex—Female.

Apparently healthy, though delicately fashioned. "Hypertonic"; strenuously active, coordination and observation seem precociously developed (abt. 3 weeks premature).

First child of parents.

Similar style of locomotion not observed or recollected among relatives.

Began to run on all fours at about ten months, and at a year still does so, although she has walked with little assistance for a month or more.

She seems to prefer the "all four" method of travel, though occasionally uses her knees and is anxious to walk upright whenever somebody will loan her a finger. She often pounds along on all fours carrying a toy in one hand, but more often puts it in her mouth to carry.

Hands fully open unless carrying something. Head up, looking ahead or around. Sometimes alternates with crawling on hands and knees; in fact, does not stick to one method very long at a time.

. 389 .

Usually tries all fours first. If a slippery surface causes skidding, it annoys her, but she keeps trying.

No other evident peculiarities, but she seems a highly sensitive, nervous child, too active physically and alert mentally for her own best good health and development.

> MRS. KENNETH YOAKAM,
> mother,
> by MARION E. STARK,
> Madison, Wis.

April 19, 1928

DEAR SIR:

I read in the *Pathfinder* that you want reports of babies who crawled on all fours. My first baby did but my second son did not. I have had only two.

McDowell Young was born October 17, 1907.

He commenced sitting up and wriggling along on his stomach at the age of five months. He first crawled on his knees in the hot weather and ran on all fours by the time he was nine months old. He stood on his feet, without walking, alone until he was ten days less than a year old. He spent most of his time standing when he was nine months old.

He was always nervous, a poor sleeper. It was always a problem to feed him. He had a very big hemorrhage of the bowels when he was three days old. After this he grew but I could not nurse him after he was seven weeks old. In the spring he had intestinal indigestion which went into inflammation of the stomach and bowels. In the Fall he improved enough to hold his head up and sit up but by the first of January his appetite absolutely failed. He suffered until the eighteenth of January. You see he got no nourishment for 18 days, refused water 24 hours and had convulsive spasms for seven days before he died.

I can send a picture which shows a very fine head at six months. My race is American back to Colonial History, but I have one Scotch grandmother. Farther back they are English and one French grandfather.

His father's people are Americans from the mountains of the South for a few generations and go back to Scotland and France. My people have been professional people for several generations.

His father's people were farmers. They are very healthy, strong and muscular. I am not possessed with those three qualities.

McDowell was a blond, although his father is a dark brunette. His face and head were bruised by forceps. He could not cry for hours after birth and before he was a week old he was holding his head up when being bathed.

He had more unusual and interesting qualities than walking on all fours. I thought him very bright and the most unusual baby I ever saw, but I am

> His mother,
> MRS. N. E. YOUNG,
> La Plata, Mo.

DEAR DOCTOR:

You may add this to your collection of cases:

Child, American—long line on both sides—one paternal grandmother Norwegian.

Male, second child.

Very healthy, wiry and lean, nervous and high strung to a marked degree.

No other four-footer in families to my knowledge.

Began at ten months and still continues now at fourteen months.

The child runs with legs apart, feet straight out, hands likewise, fingers outspread, head up; sits back on his haunches like a frog. (Plate XVc, p. 333.)

He runs very fast with the left hand first, then right leg, right hand, left leg, almost "paces." To express anger or joy or tense excitement he hits his head on the floor or wall or whatever is handy. Shows a good deal of reasoning power for 14 months; knowing fire and hot things and obviously avoiding them, also avoiding repeating a fall.

> MASTER W. YOUNGER.

CHILDREN OTHER THAN WHITES

SERIES C (COLORED)

Huichol Indian, Sierra Madre of Mexico	Male
Washoe Indian, Sierras	Female
Zuñi	?
Kagaba Arhuaco, Colombia	?
Nicaraguan mestizo, Chontales, Nicaragua	?
Negro-Indian mestizo, Colombia	Male
Indian (Mexican), U. S. A.	Male
Indian, Peru	Female
Eskimo, Kiana, Kobuk River	Male
Eskimo—White (Peck)	Female
Australian, Arunta, Central Australia	?
Australian aboriginal	?
American Negro, U. S. A. (Davis)	Male
Congo, Africa	Male
Negro, Zambezi River	?
Negro, Belgian Congo	Female
Negro, Johannesburg	?
Negro, Central East Africa	?

Case 1c.—A Huichol child, fullblood, male,[1] well advanced in second year of life. Seen with Lumholtz in the Huichol country, Sierra Madre, Jalisco, Mexico, April, 1898.[2]

Child very well nourished, robust. Ran on the ground, easily, expeditiously. Hands and feet flat on the ground, knees slightly bent, body not far from horizontal, head nearly in line with body; fingers together.

A. HRDLIČKA.

[1] Erroneously reported originally as a female.

[2] Originally mentioned and pictured by Carl Lumholtz, in his "Unknown Mexico," chap. II, p. 90, New York, 1902.

Case 2c.—Zuñi. Lumholtz reported seeing a Zuñi infant at Gallup, N. M., running on all fours.[1] There are no details.

Case 3c.—This last summer in the Sierras I saw a Washoe Indian baby girl of about a year who ran around actively, and not ungrace-

FIG. 22.—Huichol child, "au naturel." (*Lumboltz, Hrdlička.*)

fully, on all fours. She was much more natural in her actions than was my baby during the period when he progressed on all fours. (No details noted at the time, and no photo.)

C. H. DANFORTH,
Stanford University, Calif.

FIG. 22a.—Indian mestizo, Colombia. (*Molloy.*)

October 29, 1928

Case 4c.—A photo of a Kagaba-Arhuaco Indian child, from the Sierra Nevada de Santa Marta, Colombia; taken by J. Alden Mason, on his expedition to Colombia for the Field Museum of Natural History, Chicago, 1923. Photo poor; no details.

[1] *Ibid.*

April 4, 1928

My dear Dr. Hrdlička:

I have read your communication to the *Journal of the American Medical Association* regarding children who run or walk on all fours and since I have seen two cases of this abnormality I am reporting them to you.

Case 5c.—One of these was a Nicaraguan mestizo child (with rather more of the native Indian stock) from the department of Chontales, Nicaragua. This child was about seven months old and

Fig. 23.—Indian mother and child (girl), Verrugas Canyon, central Peru. (*Photo by R. C. Shannon.*)

could walk on all fours with ease; although I did not see it *run* I am sure that it could run, so easily did it locomote on hands and feet, with the feet flat on the ground. I did not notice the position of the hands and can not say if the fingers were extended or not. I am sorry that I can give you no data regarding the child which will throw any light on its sex, heredity, etc.

Case 6c.—The other case was one I observed in Puerto Colombia, in the Republic of Colombia, S. A. I am sending you a picture of this child. I am sorry that I am unable to furnish you any specific information about the child. It was a male negro-Indian mestizo, I should say, with the Indian strain predominating. The child was crossing the narrow street when I first saw it and so rapid was its gait that I barely had time to adjust the focus of my Kodak before it entered the door, where it was "snapped." I tried to get more pictures but the mother resented the effort and refused to give any information about the child. I remember that the hands were clubbed while walking, the thumb being grasped in the palm of the hand. I think you can see this in the picture. The position shown in the picture is the one assumed in crossing the street and I presume is the one accustomed while walking on all fours.

> Very truly,
> Dr. D. M. MOLLOY,
> The Rockefeller Foundation,
> International Health Division,
> Managua, Nicaragua.

Case 18c.—Mr. R. C. Shannon furnished recently the two photographs shown in Fig. 23. The pictures show a young Indian mother with a little girl. On the left the girl is seen running on all fours, in a typical manner.

Case 7c.

July 31, 1929

DEAR DR. HRDLIČKA:

Here is another all-fours case.

In the waiting room of the C. B. & Q. station in Galesburg, Illinois, on the evening of May 17, I noticed a Mexican-Indian family, mother and four children. The youngest, fifteen or eighteen months old, but still nursed at the mother's breast, slipped off his mother's lap, crept a few feet, then raised up his legs and trotted on all fours across the room, forty or fifty feet, to where his father sat smoking. He seemed to go faster than he could have done creeping. In a few minutes he returned the same way. In the course of thirty or forty minutes he did this three times, always creeping a few feet first. He stood on his legs beside his mother munching crackers but I did not see him try to walk. The mother did not talk much English, but the older of the girls in the family, about ten years, said the boy always went that way, creeping first. The girl did not think any of the other children had gone on all fours. The father, a big fine-looking Indian type, said he was from Guatemala, had been in this country

· 395 ·

a number of years, worked in the railroad shops at Galesburg, and was being transferred to Denver. He seemed decidedly superior to the average Mexican laborer.

Yours for the all-fours,
EDWARD K. PUTNAM,
Director, Davenport Public
Museum,
Davenport, Ia.

Case 8c.—Eskimo child walking on all fours.

Dick, aged three years, son of Eli Machona (f.) and Kotuk (m.), both full blood Eskimos of Kiana, 90 miles up the Kobuk River. Mr. Southward reports that the child walks quadruped fashion as well as erect. Child is very energetic and impulsive. He has three brothers and sisters who crawled and walked normally.

Reported by J. W. SOUTHWARD,
U. S. Commissioner,
Noatak, Alaska,
through H. B. COLLINS, JR.

Case 9c.

June 4, 1928

DEAR DR. HRDLIČKA:

Rosie J. Peck, born July 6, 1921 at Kwiguk, Alaska, ran on all fours. Mother—Eskimo; Father—white American of English descent.

Child never crawled. Traveled on all fours at age of few months and with remarkable speed. Habit was not lost immediately upon learning to walk but gradually gave way. The pictures enclosed were taken without premeditation upon the appearance of the child approaching. Child turned to retreat whereupon another "snap" was made. The negatives are preserved but show deterioration.

The child is the daughter of the undersigned. Has recently completed the second grade. Health always excellent, intelligence normal, no eccentricities.

Details:

Half-breed, white-Eskimo, American.
Female; first child.

Healthy and robust.

No other case known.

Began at age of crawling and continued until learned to walk about 14 months of age.

Hands open. Extremely fond of raw meats, potatoes. Above the average half-breed.

The second and only other child is normal in all respects. The infant that went on "all fours" learns very well in school, likes to sew, has ability at music, amiable disposition, but cries loudly when a little injured at play. She is, I should say, thoroughly normal.

> Yours truly,
> ERNEST L. PECK, Teacher,
> Galena, Alaska.

FIG. 24.   FIG. 25.

Australian children going on all fours.

FIG. 24.—Arunta boy. (*After Spencer and Gillen; also in Hambly.*)

FIG. 25.—Australian child. (*Photo by Herbert Basedow.*)

Case 10c.—An Australian child. In "Across Australia," by Baldwin Spencer and F. J. Gillen[1] there is a picture of an aboriginal child, from "Arunta, Central Australia," "learning to walk," showing an infant of a little over one year of age progressing typically on all four.[2] The authors give no data concerning the

[1] Figure 71, facing p. 188, London, 1912.

[2] Figure 4, in first report.

condition. The only note relating to it being that the Australian infant, "At first it toddles about on all fours." The same picture is reproduced in W. D. Hambly's, "Origins of Education among Primitive Peoples."[1]

A. H.

Case 11c.—An Australian child. Dr. Herbert Basedow, the author of "The Australian Aboriginal,"[2] has kindly sent me a photo of an aboriginal Australian child between one and two years of age, progressing typically on all four. The photograph is here reproduced.

A. H.

Case 12c.

June 10, 1928

DEAR SIR:

Excuse pencil and pad, but I am writing while on duty and can not do otherwise. I saw the article in today's A. C. *Press* about babies walking on hands and feet and asking people writing you about it. We have a lusty he-boy born in the hospital here, the 25th of last August and now weighs 20 lbs. and 10 oz. When the baby was born the Doctors and nurses were amazed to find the hair on his body was white (not grey) while the hair on his head is black. When he was about 5½ months old he would lie flat on his back and place the soles of his feet on the bed and propel himself, moving backward like a crab (or lobster). About a month and a half later he began walking on hands and feet, raising his head every few seconds to see where he was going.

Now he goes on hands and knees, and tries desperately to stand alone, pulls himself up erect, and lets go and tries to balance himself alone. We are colored people, at least my wife was born colored, but about 15 years ago she began turning white and now cannot be told from any Caucasian in the land but the baby took her original complexion (light brown). Trusting these facts may be of some use to you and science, I remain

Yours very truly,
WALTER MAX DAVIS,
Atlantic City, N. J.

[1] Opp. p. 38, London, 1926.
[2] Adelaide, 1925.

Additional information:

Race and nationality—Afro-American.

Sex—Male.

What child in numerical order—Third.

Health and robustness—Very good.

Has the phenomenon been observed in any other child of the same parents or among relatives?—No, as far as we are aware.

At what age has the child begun to run on all fours, and how long has it continued?—5½ months, continued about 5 or 6 weeks.

Position of hands, etc.—Hands open, head down, looking up to see.

Details as to any other peculiarity of behavior of the child, or any other children in the family—Before 5½ months, used to propel himself with feet while lying flat on his back.

WALTER MAX DAVIS.

Fig. 26.—Negro boy, Congo.

Case 13c.—A negro boy, about fourteen months old, in Congo. Healthy and lively. No family data; photo sent to writer by a friend.

Has remarkably long and slender, though not emaciated, limbs.

Both the hands and the feet are applied flat to the ground, with the thumbs of the hands at wide angle (over 90°) from the hands. The head is held remarkably (and evidently easily) upright.

A second photograph, taken in same place, shows three negro children running on hands and knees, a mode of progression that in general is much more common, and one that has doubtless developed originally from the older quadruped progression; the two modes may show themselves in the same child.

A. H.

Case 14c.—A negro child, Zambezi River. In 1925, during my trip to South Africa, I had a chance to visit a village of one of the Bantu tribes near the Victoria Falls. Here I saw a child, not much over one year of age, moving on all fours, but the feet were bent so that it moved really on the upright hands and the knees. The walk was less free and less animal-like than that in both the preceding Indian and white child, nevertheless there was the impression of a quadruped. It was moving fast, not just trying, or crawling. This form of movement is considerably more common than that on all four limbs extended.

A. H.

Fig. 27.—"Child running on all fours without being told." (*Father v. d. Houdt*, Belgian Congo.)

Case 15c.—A Negro child, Belgian Congo. For some time now I have been corresponding with Father J. v. d. Houdt, of the Lulenga Mission, Rutshuru, Belgian Congo. In one of my letters I asked him about little children running on all fours, and in a few months received an interesting note in which the Father tells me that such occurrences are well known among the people whom he serves, and that they think nothing of it; and a little later he sent me a negative showing one of these cases, adding: "I send you one picture of a

child running on all fours of his own accord, without being told."
It will be seen from the picture that it is a case of a female child less
than two years old. The arms are upright, bent rather slightly outward, the knees moderately bending, the head but slightly raised,
the palms and soles applied flat and partly sideways to the ground.

A. H.

Case 16c.—Negro, fullblood, Johannesburg, So. Africa. A photograph of a group of native Asylum children, donated by the *Rand
Daily Mail*, shows a child of about one year of age in the act of
progressing on all fours. The sex of the child is indistinguishable.
The arms and lower limbs are straight (though the right leg is
invisible and may have been slightly bent), the body is slightly
inclined forward, the head is flexed back so that the child may well
see ahead; the hands are flat on the ground, fingers held fairly
together. (Plate I, frontispiece.)

A. H.

Case 17c.—A negro child, of apparently somewhat over a year of
age, of Central East Africa, has been seen by the author in the
recently shown Johnsons' "Safari" film of African game and scenes.

General:

May 18, 1928

Dear Sir:

This way of progressing among native children cannot be considered as being a very rare exception, because it rather frequently
occurs among male as well as female children.

The babies in question start by sliding on their seat pushing with
hands and feet. At the age of about one year they begin walking
on their hands and feet, with their knees off the ground. For
restive purposes they will have their knees on the ground. They
all have their hands fully open and their head slightly erected
when walking on all fours or as the natives here call it when walking
like cows. Now and then they try to erect themselves for a while.
They acquire in some cases a facility of progressing fast.

Some of them learn to walk erect after a month but others remain
in this state for a period of three or four months or even longer.

The natives consider it as a weakness of the sinews of the knee-cap and will daily rub that part of the body with a medicine which is made of the leaves of a small scrub called "indwasi" which leaves are pounded and boiled down with water; which same medicine they apply for sciatica. In the meantime they will support the child under the armpits and let it walk in front of them. If this does not help they dig a hole in the ground and put the child in while the arms are above ground and the hole being of a size that the child cannot sit down.

The health of the child is normal and this phenomenon has not necessarily been observed in any other child of the same parents or among relatives but occurs spasmodically like any other peculiarity in the bodily constitution.

Some of the children are "incurable" and one finds cases of adults where they have discontinued walking on all fours and proceed in a kind of sitting position while they have their hands on the top of their feet.

> Very truly yours,
> FATHER N. STAM,
> St. Peter's Catholic Mission,
> Mumias (via Mombasa),
> Kenya Colony, Central Africa.

General:

> June 10, 1928

DEAR DR. HRDLIČKA:

Your letter of April 9 has been received regarding an enclosed questionnaire. In reply I would say that my travels have taken me in nearly all parts of the Philippines, the interior of Borneo among the Dusuns, the Dyaks, etc., through the Celebes with its many tribes, through the Moluccas, Lambok, Bali, Java, crossing Malay states, Siam, through Cambodia and Annam; and I must say that I am a keen observer upon these points that you mention, and have run across a few of these cases. There is a certain time in the child's life, between the creeping and the beginning to walk, when I have observed them then at times trying to walk on all fours, but soon walk upright.

I have been much interested in this subject for some time and am giving careful thought and observation as I go around, and if I shall find anything that I think would be of special interest to you, I will be glad to forward it on.

Yours very truly,
L. V. Finster,
Singapore, S. S.

Special:

Dr. Hrdlička:

I read an article about the habit of children running on all fours saying you would be interested in unusual cases.

We have a very strange and interesting case of an old Indian man, known as "The Creeper." He is now about seventy and is an Indian medicine man. He is deformed, that is, his lower leg is very short. The distance between his knee and foot is about 6 or 8 inches. He runs around like a bear, his head upheld and walking on the palms of his hands. Sometimes the Indians call him "The Bear." I do not have any pictures of him, but might be able to secure some.

Sincerely,
Frances Frazer,
Chin Lee, Ariz.

ANALYTICAL INDEX

A

Abercrombie (L. L.), 53, 81, 99, 100
Abney (J. T.), 28, 31, 100
Abnormalities, 21, 55, 63
Abramowitz (M.), 26, 32, 53, 101
Activity (*see* Behavior).
Adornment, self-, passion for, 243
Affleck (B. F.), 36, 68, 102
Africa (*see* Negro).
Age, 17, 92
   (*See* also all individual records.)
Aggressiveness (*see* Disposition).
Ahlberg (E.), 53, 68, 103
Albers (F.), 54, 72, 103
Allen (Grant), 93
Allen (H. L.), 104
American Journal of Physical Anthro-pology, 169, 277
Anderson (A.), 19, 81, 105
Anderson (LeNore), 27, 43, 70, 82, 88, 106
Animal-like attitudes and manifesta-tions, 60, 78, 79, 82, 83, 91, 133, 143, 178, 190, 244–246, 286, 306, 345, 356
Animal-like sounds, 195
Animals, child identifying itself with, 367
   (*See also* Animals, imitation of.)
   children likened to, 9, 10, 28, 48, 56, 72, 80, 81, 99, 103, 106, 108, 116, 122, 128–130, 133, 137, 140, 141, 143, 146, 147, 153, 154, 160, 165, 168, 171, 172, 176, 179–181, 184, 185, 190, 191, 197, 198, 205, 207–209, 212, 215–217, 220, 224–226, 228–231, 233, 241, 244, 247, 250, 254, 257, 259, 262, 280, 281, 283, 292, 293, 299,

304–306, 311, 317, 321, 323, 324, 326, 328, 329, 339, 341, 342, 344–347, 351, 352, 355, 356, 358–360, 362, 364, 368, 380, 386, 391, 400, 403
   fondness of, 77, 102, 103, 203, 288, 306, 315, 320, 337, 350,
   imitation of, 60, 78, 90, 92, 124, 135, 186, 193, 198, 204, 256, 306, 314, 315, 366–368
   no fear of any, 103, 238, 242
Anomalies, 21
Apes, 31
   children likened to, 107, 172, 223, 229, 241, 249, 250, 290, 344, 352
   (*See also* Monkeys.)
Appliances, use of by the children, 58, 59, 138, 149, 315
Arabs, 7
Aristotle, 12
Arms, exceptional strength in, 20, 236–243, 247, 262, 282, 359
Armstrong (E. O.), 27, 107
Armstrong (J. W.), 27, 28, 43, 108
Asia, S. E., children running on all fours, 402
Atavism, 13, 76, 81, 90, 91
Attitude of parents and relatives, 99, 104, 123, 140, 159, 170, 194, 204, 209, 215, 216, 218–220, 222, 228, 229, 231, 234, 236, 253, 254, 258, 264, 273, 280, 282, 288, 292, 293, 296, 301, 302, 304, 305, 307, 311, 315, 321, 341–343, 346, 348, 355, 363, 364, 368, 369, 375, 376
Australians, 4, 5, 171
   children running on all fours, 392, 397, 398
   climbing, 68, 74, 249, 298